[■■■■] best regards and gratitude for all of your interest and support for my "psycho-legal" explorations.

Andy

Psychiatry for Lawyers

PSYCHIATRY
FOR
LAWYERS

Andrew S. Watson, M.D.

Professor of Psychiatry and Professor of Law
University of Michigan

International Universities Press, Inc.

NEW YORK

TO MY SONS

Contents

Foreword

Over seventy-five years ago, Justice Holmes pronounced that "the life of the law is not logic but experience." Since then the legal profession has become increasingly concerned with economic and political realities. Lawyers pride themselves on understanding how governments, corporations, and agencies really work. They also pride themselves on understanding how people work. But, in fact, their education rarely provides them with knowledge of developments in the behavioral sciences, even though such knowledge might greatly assist them in counseling clients, framing arguments, and drafting legislation.

Recently, lawyers and educators have come to recognize that a contemporary legal education must provide lawyers with a background in the behavioral sciences. Dr. Watson's new book provides such a background and also suggests specific areas where the insights of psychiatry are particularly relevant to the law and the practicing lawyer.

I have had little judicial experience with many of these areas—for example, adoption and divorce. But I have been deeply involved with one of Dr. Watson's major concerns—the nature of psychiatric testimony in criminal cases. And I believe Dr. Watson's analysis and his strictures are exceedingly valuable for courts, counsel, and psychiatrists. Dr. Watson reminds us that it is not the psychiatrist's role to determine whether or not a defendant is criminally responsible. The jury alone must make the difficult judgment. The psychiatrist's task is simply to enable the jury to understand the dynamics of the defendant's mental and emotional processes. He must describe the defendant's history and explain its psychiatric significance. Insofar as possible, he should avoid legal conclusions and medical jargon.

Happily, Dr. Watson practices what he preaches. He writes clearly, and carefully defines technical terms. Much more important, he does not leap from psychiatric explanations to legal conclusions. He suffers from no illusions that psychiatry can resolve age-old legal and moral questions. All Dr. Watson asks is that lawyers begin to explore the contributions behavioral science may be able to make to our legal system. His book is an excellent starting point for that exploration.

David L. Bazelon
Chief Judge, United States
Court of Appeals
District of Columbia Circuit

Preface

In initially planning this book, it was decided that, instead of dealing with psychiatry from the standpoint of specific mental problems in relation to law (the traditional approach of most forensic psychiatry texts), an attempt would be made to present an outline of human behavior and development, and to relate this to some of the problems of law. This descriptive system and its insights into human behavior, a matter which previously had been dealt with by intuition and common sense, is the principal contribution which modern dynamic psychiatry can bring to the law. While this science of the mind is still young, its knowledge and skills can shed light on the social and emotional interactions in the practice of law.

In the past, there have been several systematic efforts to relate materials and knowledge from other disciplines, including psychology, to the law (2). At the beginning of those efforts, high hopes were entertained for "solving" various legal problems by bringing more rational and scientific concepts into the framework of legal procedure. Although the outcome was regarded as a failure by most critics of the day, one would gather from the reports of those efforts that there was a desire on the part of lawyers—or more accurately, law professors—to be presented with scientific data which prove certain assumptions conclusively which could then, and only then, be incorporated into the law.[1] This degree of validation is quite

[1] That such controversy still exists may be seen in Hazard's article (3).

unrealistic. Many of the "facts" being sought are so complex in nature that to deal scientifically with all of the variables is virtually impossible without fantastic expenditure of time and energy. While ultimately we may wish to rest our theories of behavior on such studies, at present such intellectual security is not to be had. It is hoped that a greater understanding of dynamic psychiatric theory will forestall such false hopes, and hasten a more realistic approach to resolving mutual problems of law and psychiatry. Perhaps this volume may assist this process.

Does the present state of knowledge in psychiatry justify its use in the law? While there are many obvious gaps in knowledge, behavioral scientists can legitimately state that their theories have much greater reliability than many of the intuitive hunches which were used in the past to explain human motivation and human behavior. On this basis alone, their use by legislative and judicial bodies seems justified. It is not for the scientist to make such ethical decisions and judgments for the law as defining crimes or deciding punishments. What he can do is apply his understanding of human behavior to some of the questions which courts and lawyers seek to settle in order to assist in predicting the advantages versus the disadvantages of a proposed piece of legislation or a particular legal assumption.

During the past fifty years, scientific observations of human behavior have been accumulating rapidly. Most of these observations have been empirical in nature and various hypotheses have been presented to account for them. Slowly, a well-integrated theory has been evolved which attempts to account for all human behavior. This theory has been subjected to constant revision as observation continues. Recently, it has become possible occasionally to subject these theories to experimental study and, happily, some theories are beginning to approach fact. This text has been written to present what is currently the most widely held psychiatric theory of human behavior. It draws heavily from the concepts of psychoanalysis, but by no means leans exclusively on any particular "school" or theory. One problem for the beginning reader is the technical psychiatric jargon which is often used inconsistently in the scientific literature. The author uses such technical nomenclature only when necessary, and after it has been defined. The aim is to provide a solid introduction to psychiatric theory which, in addition to being immediately useful, will provide a bridge to the technical literature.

It might be well to make a few comments on this author's conception of how the book may be utilized in law-school teaching. The Socratic method commonly utilized by law teachers is also used by teaching psychiatrists. It is therefore anticipated that the contents of this volume will become the focus of vigorous classroom or seminar discussion. The best utilization of these materials categorically includes such discussion, which permits and indeed forces, the student to actively identify himself with the subject matter presented (1, 4). Such a method provides the best classroom technique to help each student clear away some of the barriers to understanding in his own psychic apparatus, which block access to a fuller understanding of "what makes people tick" both inside and outside the social process of the law.

Finally, let me acknowledge the background and support which has been so important to the development of this book. It was begun while I was a member of the faculty of the University of Pennsylvania Law School between 1955-1959. My colleagues there were crucial to my development as a teacher and in my learning about the law. Although they bear no responsibility for the views which I hold, they helped me understand some of the basic principles and values of our legal system. They made law a source of intellectual and philosophical excitement for me. Also, they became the prototypes for my image of lawyer capacity and brilliance. I wish to express my special thanks to Professors Louis B. Schwartz, Caleb Foote, James C. N. Paul, and Dean Jefferson B. Fordham for the many personal things they did to assist me in my legal education. Also, I owe much to Chief Judge David L. Bazelon, of the United States Court of Appeals for the District of Columbia who, as a colleague, taught a seminar with me for two years in which we used these materials.

I am grateful to the National Institute of Mental Health for the fact that they subsidized the experiment which brought me to the Pennsylvania law faculty and launched my career as a Social Psychiatrist working in the world of law schools and legal affairs. It has become a most satisfying career.

Joining the law faculty of the University of Michigan in 1959 incurred indebtedness to new colleagues, especially Professor B. J. George. Working with him for these past nine years has greatly clarified my ideas about the law and put much patina on my teaching techniques. Many other friends and colleagues have read this book in manuscript at various stages of its development and have made many valuable suggestions.

As is always the case, I owe thanks to my editor, Mrs. Irene Azarian, for smoothing the way through the final polishing and preparation of this volume. What could have been a painful task was made easy through her skillful and understanding assistance.

Last, I want to acknowledge indebtedness to my most important teachers—my patients past and present. They, more than anyone else, have taught me of the beautiful, the beastly, and the wonderful which are to be found in everyone.

A.S.W.
May, 1968

REFERENCES

1. American Psychiatric Association, *Psychiatry and Medical Education.* Washington, D. C., 1952.
2. Currie, B., The Materials of Law Study: Part Three. *J. Legal Ed.,* 8:1-78, 1955.
3. Hazard, G. C., Jr., Limitations on the Uses of Behavioral Science in the Law. *Case Western Reserve Law Rev.,* 19:71-77, 1967.
4. Watson, A. S., The Quest for Professional Competence: Psychological Aspects of Legal Education. *Univ. Cincinnati Law Rev.,* 37:91-166, 1968.

Psychiatry for Lawyers

I

The Lawyer and His Client: The Process of Emotional Involvement

It is often suggested that only the trial lawyer, or attorneys specializing in Criminal or Domestic Relations Law need know anything of formal psychological theory. Nothing could be further from fact. Lawyers, as practitioners of a profession, are driven irrevocably into some sort of working relationship with people. They must either interview them to ascertain "facts," cross-examine them in court to decide if they are telling the truth, or just plain talk to them in order to figure out what they wish to accomplish. All of this *can* be done blindly and intuitively, and if a lawyer is lucky enough to have "good" intuition he will fare well. If he is like most, he will stumble and grope along, hoping to catch a glimpse of what the client seeks, trusting to luck that not too many intentionally hidden or unwillingly obscured facts will escape the net of his interviewing technique.

Lawyers, it appears, are constantly caught up in the powerful, emotional undercurrents and ambitions of their clients—this notwithstanding the fact that as law students they are taught "to take either side of an argument without becoming emotionally involved." The principal effect of this teaching concept seems to be that many lawyers lose *awareness* of their involvement, to the detriment of their professional work.[1] It seems appropriate to initiate our ex-

---

[1] Cozzens in his novel, *By Love Possessed* (3), provides us with several excellent examples of such problems, in which the lawyer (the author) demonstrated unusual skill in handling them.

ploration of contemporary psychiatric theory in the context of the lawyer-client relationship. The elucidation of this relationship should clearly demonstrate, not only an important professional problem, but give us a frame of reference to which we may relate a theory of human behavior. As everyone knows but many forget, to understand the man you must know the child. After we have demonstrated the kinds of problems raised in interviews with adult clients, we will proceed to describe their genesis.

The era in which we live is characterized by great popular interest in such topics as "how to win friends and influence people," and "the power of positive thinking." We should not be surprised, therefore, when it is suggested that understanding the nature of the emotional reactions between lawyer and client when they talk together is vitally important to any successful communication. Our everyday experience informs us that this sort of transaction, at best, is not free of clearly irrational elements which complicate and confound our efforts at understanding each other.

THE TOOL OF TRANSFERENCE

One of these irrational elements is designated as *transference* by psychiatrists, and the understanding of this ubiquitous phenomenon is one of the major contributions which psychoanalytic psychiatry has made to our knowledge of human behavior. Lawyers, whose work nearly always involves either the elicitation or the analysis of information which is transmitted verbally, can profit immensely from any knowledge of this subject which they might gain.

Transference has been defined variously, as the concept developed. Simply put, it is the unreal attributes which the observer believes he sees or feels to be present in the observed, and which are drawn from some superficial likeness to an important person from the past, such as a parent. This tendency to make a whole from a part represents projection[2] on the part of the observer.

What is the importance of the concept of transference to the law? Fortas states that, "Lawyers have been increasingly aware of the fact that their interrelationships with clients, witnesses, judges and jurors are at least as important as their mastering of the statutes in

[2] See Chapter IV for a description of projection.

precedence" (6). The concepts of transference and countertransference describe the nature of these interrelationships. While we will begin by discussing these concepts within the framework of psychiatry, the parallel will become apparent. The sociologist, Talcott Parsons, in his essay, "A Sociologist Views the Legal Profession" (17) has said, ". . . A pattern of analysis, worked out in an entirely different context—the psycho-therapeutic aspect of the role of the physician—turns out to be applicable in this field as well. This is something of which I myself was not aware until I attempted to put together some thoughts about the legal profession. . . ."

Before we further explore the phenomenon of transference, let us briefly survey the development of this concept in order to clarify its nature and significance.

Psychoanalytic therapy developed as an offshoot of Sigmund Freud's early exploration of the hypnotic technique.[3] Hypnotic phenomena were recognized as psychological relationships between the hypnotist and his subject, but some time elapsed before the full implications were understood. From the time of Freud's collaboration with Breuer in the "Case of Anna," he had been aware of the importance of the relationship of patient to doctor as a therapeutic tool (13). By 1909, there had been much discussion of this topic, and in that year Ferenczi published a paper in which he used the word "transfer" to describe some specific aspects of this emotional axis (4). By 1912, the concept had been quite clearly formulated and Freud wrote a detailed paper, describing "The Dynamics of the Transference" (11). Ferenczi said, "These transferences are re-impressions and reproductions of the emotions and phantasies that have to be awakened and brought into consciousness during the progress of the analysis, and are characterized by the replacement of a former person by the physician" (5). Freud, in his 1910 lecture at Clark University, said, "In every psycho-analytic treatment of a neurotic patient the strange phenomenon that is known as 'transference' makes its appearance. The patient, that is to say, directs towards the physician a degree of affectionate feeling (mingled, often enough, with hostility) which is based on no real relation between them and which—as is shown by every detail of its emergence—can only be traced back to old wishful fantasies of the patient's . . ."

[3] See Chapter II.

(10). From these early beginnings, stems the present concept of transference.

Today, the term transference has been broadened to include all of the reactions which the patient has to the physician—not only the unconscious projected images from the past, but also reactions related to the physician's personality as it is correctly and appropriately perceived by the patient. It is just those irrational, projected, elements in the relationship which provide the physician with the most potentially beneficial means for understanding his patient, for here he has the opportunity to compare the real with the unreal, provided he has some awareness of his own personality attributes. What could be a major barrier to therapy is turned to enormous therapeutic advantage.

Whenever one makes an acquaintance, there is an immediate flood of perceptions about the newly encountered person. This includes such things as physical characteristics, interests, estimates of various personality traits, and other impressions about his nature (1). These new, mainly unconscious impressions are associated with many past personal encounters, especially those with the members of one's immediate family. There is a powerful unconscious tendency to generalize the nature of the new acquaintance so that instead of seeing a face which is reminiscent of father's face, or a manner of speech which is like brother's, there is the feeling that this new person is *like* father or *like* brother. In other words, from the similarity of a part, the new person is given the whole characteristic of the past figure. Thus, at best, part of the reaction to the new person is inappropriate. While this distortion may be helpful in establishing a close relationship with great rapidity, it can just as likely cause coolness and withdrawal, depending on the nature of the past relationships from which the transference is made. At any rate, the reaction is *not* based on a realistic appraisal of the nature of the new person, and the way is laid open for future difficulties which can be formidable and difficult to untangle. We must regard this kind of projection as universal, and hold it responsible for at least some difficulty in all interpersonal relationships.

Let us consider a simple illustration of this phenomenon in a legal setting. A young lawyer starts to work for a law firm shortly after his graduation from law school. His superior is a forceful, direct, and forthright person who makes judgments swiftly and tends to stick to them. In reality, this man is remarkably skillful in making good decisions rapidly. However, the young lawyer, whose father had been dogmatic and impulsive in his judgments, immediately and unconsciously identifies this new person with his father. He "transfers" his attitudes toward his father into this new relationship; he reacts to his superior in terms of his earlier relation to his father. Father had been autocratic and belittling and had never shown respect for his son's capacity for independent thinking and good judgment. The young lawyer projected this expectation onto his new boss.

Unfortunately, he was wrong, since his superior desired and encouraged independent thought and action from his subordinates. The "transference" inhibited the young lawyer's ability to act decisively and, in this way, to gain the respect which he so strongly desired. Instead of taking appropriate action, he was made hesitant and defensive by his expectations. His superior could hardly be expected to be impressed favorably and, after a few efforts at encouragement or challenge, he wrote off the younger man as hopelessly lacking in initiative. This is not an unusual example. Irrational reactions such as this one occur in everyone.

The concept of *countertransference* was somewhat later to be discovered, formulated, and understood. In the early psychoanalytic literature, there are many allusions to the reactions of the physician to his patient, but it was not until recently that many papers were written about this specific reaction (16). Originally, countertransference was defined as the doctor's transference to the patient. In other words, those irrational projections which the patient's character precipitated in the doctor were called countertransference. However, this term has also been broadened and is widely used to include all of the doctor's reactions and feelings toward his patient and toward all his work with that patient. We might utilize the definition of Rene Spitz, who says, "We will define countertransference as one part of the analyst's relation to his patient; it is one of the determinants of the emotional climate of a given analytic relationship; it usually originates in the analyst; its manifestations of his transference act on, and are responded to, by the given analyst's personality. The response will begin with a dynamic process in the analyst's unconscious. This will translate itself into derivatives expressed in the attitude of the analyst. When the patient becomes aware of the analyst's attitude, changes in the nature of the patient's transference take place. Thus a circular process between analyst and patient is set in motion, which determines the analytic climate" (26). Transference and countertransference are the halves in a circle of dynamic interaction between the personalities of the two individuals in the relationship. Although these reactions are at first unconscious, they are brought into consciousness later in therapy.

It is important for professional persons engaged in close personal relationships with clients or patients to understand the nature of this dynamic interaction. In the illustration above, transference caused the young lawyer difficulty in fulfilling his professional role. Since transference is unconscious, the question arises whether one can do anything about it. The answer is something of a paradox. The mere acknowledgment of the possibility of such unconscious reactions permits the participants to look more objectively at relationships and to question causes. The capacity to accept the possibility that one's feelings about another may be due to unconscious and unrealistic coloring rather than to the other's reality traits, is a major step toward understanding. Without awareness of transference phenomena, people are over- or under-convinced by their own emotional responses and have no opportunity to work out any understanding of them.

Once the idea is accepted that the emotions which are aroused in a relationship always have specific unconscious meanings for the participants, these very emotions can become useful. It is this fact which permits the analyst to penetrate unconscious aspects of his relationship to his patients. The young man already mentioned obviously has problems with authority figures. In the analytic situation, he would have the same reactions to the analyst as to his superior in the law office. This would be seen as hesitancy to express himself, reluctance to take issue with anything which the analyst said, and other evidences that authority, in this case the analyst, causes him to withdraw. The patient would be all too ready to agree with everything that was said, and yet it would be clear that there was no real acceptance. Persons who need to acquiesce in this manner generally resent intensely having to do so. Sooner or later this resentment would be manifested in subtle ways which the analyst would feel, even before they became viable. Against the relatively neutral ground of the analytic situation, the patient demonstrates the way he deals with authority, and his feelings and methods of dealing with anger. Through interpreting this behavior and demonstrating it over and over again, the psychiatrist slowly helps the patient toward an understanding of himself (2).

While the lawyer will never use the transference phenomenon in this same way, he can at least learn that emotional responses to his client may be due to hidden provocations of which his client is unaware. With practice, this insight will help him immensely in dealing with his clients. For example, he will encounter clients who come into the office, ask for advice, and then progressively provoke him to anger until he is inclined to drop his contact with the client altogether. Early in the game, it would be well for the lawyer to ask himself, "Why should a person ask me for help and then make me want to withdraw?" While answers to such questions are not always forthcoming, especially in the lawyer-client relationship, such questioning lends a perspective to the relationship which was previously absent, and raises the possibility that some of the transactions between the lawyer and his client are based on irrationality, and not on logic. The lawyer who can learn to do this (many do this intuitively anyway) is in a better position to help his clients and accomplish his legal goals.

THE ATMOSPHERE FOR COUNSELING

So far we have described nothing of the atmosphere which permits full emergence of transference in the psychotherapeutic situation. This is important to understand, since by reproducing such a climate the lawyer may gain his goals more readily. The analyst, in relation to his patient, takes a more or less "neutral" position. This means that, at least in the initial phases of the relationship, he very carefully avoids injecting anything which might show directly his feelings and attitudes about either the problem at hand or life in general. This allows him to assume (providing he has actually achieved such a neutral position) that whatever the patient brings forth in relation to the doctor can only represent the inner attitudes and reactions of the patient, and thus is a reflection of the patient's personality. This behavior is an approximately pure sample of the patient's method of relating to people, since the relationship was not created or directed to any major degree by the actions or comments of the analyst. The method of asking questions and directing queries to the patient is always as neutral as the analyst can achieve, in order that the patient may not take the analyst's views into account when he presents his answers. Once more this presents reflections of the patient's own attitudes and not reactions to those of the analyst. Such a technique can be used by lawyers in interviewing, in order not only to provide answers to specific questions, but also to elicit inner feelings and attitudes which would not ordinarily be evoked. To quote Emily Mudd, a well-known authority on marriage counseling, "There is some evidence to support the view that the setting of a permissive, encouraging atmosphere and relationship is the principally helpful function of the counsellor." The mere willingness to listen and be friendly, encouraging, and nonjudgmental will help many individuals through their emotional blocks to expression, especially when the listener is a respected authority (15).

In the interview situation, the analyst takes no judgmental position, clearly telling his patient that he may say anything he chooses in any manner he chooses, and it will not lead to criticism. The analyst must be an accepting, noncritical listener in order that the patient may feel free to express his true feelings. This is of utmost importance, if any adequate information is to be elicited from the patient. Perhaps this sounds like nothing more than the description of a tactful, friendly relationship. Yet, all too often, such an atmosphere is *not* created by doctors, lawyers, or other professional persons. It is very easy to let judgments slip into one's relationships, where they form road-blocks to free communication.

One aspect of creating such a free atmosphere rests in the interviewer knowing as much as possible about his own ideas and attitudes, and accepting them comfortably. We will note later that what lies in our unconscious is largely inaccessible to change. However, there is another rule of thumb which is useful in increasing one's self-understanding. Whenever we react with emotion, more strongly than the situation would seem to warrant, we may be sure there is some underlying unconscious attitude toward the problem. For these reasons, it behooves the lawyer to understand himself and his attitudes just as thoroughly as he can, so that he may work as freely as possible in his professional relationships, many of which are heavily charged with emotions. Although his professional role calls for objectivity, this is not achieved by blocking emotions. True objectivity requires direct dealing with one's emotional responses. If they are handled by ignoring them as if they did not exist, the superficial appearance of objectivity is without emotional reality. Hidden emotions direct decisions, and only the person himself is deceived.

If counsel senses such an inappropriate response in himself, he may find this an excellent time to seek assistance from another. Perhaps a colleague's view will help him clarify the basis for his strong response. If not, this may be the point at which to seek psychiatric or psychological consultation. Sometimes such a blind response provides the stimulus for a new and fruitful avenue of exploration in the case. In that event, the "feeling" of counsel becomes a crucial piece of datum to the case.

THE NATURE OF PROFESSIONALISM

There are other aspects of emotional behavior which affect the practice of law. Lawyers, doctors, and other professional persons often have deep conflicts about the ethical responsibilities of their professions. Let us begin by examining the word "professional." To quote Talcott Parsons, "The professional man is not thought of as engaged in the pursuit of his personal profit, but in performing services to his patients or clients, or to impersonal values like the advancement of science" (20). He goes on to say that "The dominance of a business economy has seemed to justify the view that ours was an 'acquisitive society' in which every one was an 'economic man' who cared little for the interests of others. Professional men, on the other hand, have been thought of as standing above these sordid considerations, devoting their lives to the 'service' of their fellow men" (21). The professional practitioner's self-image in his professional role may contain potential difficulties, for in addition to the goal of service, each individual has many other goals, often in conflict with this one. Some of the motivations which may lead to gratification in the profession of psychiatry may well apply to the practice of law (29). Although these motives may cause trouble when unconscious, there is nothing intrinsically inappropriate about them. Discussion of countertransference in the literature makes this point (28). The analyst's satisfactions are: "(1) The pleasure derived from listening to the unclear complaints of patients because of the ability to interpret and thus make sense out of what is at first confusing. (2) Mastery of the dreads of one's own infancy. (3) Sublimated sexual curiosity. (4) Enrichment of the ego by contact with many diverse personalities. (5) The pleasure derived from doing *'useful work.'* (6) The pleasure derived from *being needed.* (7) The pleasure derived from the mastery of *conflicts in human relationships* through verbalization and mutual understanding. (8) The pleasure derived from the contact with the patient as a *protection from loneliness"* (27). Szasz points out that these sources of gratification accrue to the working analyst. We may see that some of them tend to reinforce one's sense of security through gaining a sense of ability in achieving goals and solving problems. Others come by way of vicarious identification with patients (clients), thus broadening one's own experience. We might add that there is also the pleasure derived from a secure source of income, and the status gained in being a professional person. We see in examining these factors that they have no direct bearing on the "service" aspects of one's professional goals (33). In other words, they appear to be separate from the altruistic implication of professionalism. It is probably just for these reasons that there has been some reluctance, at least in the medical field, to come forward with discussion of these important emotional aspects of the treatment process.

The sources of gratification noted above would seem to apply directly to the practice of law. ". . . The professional practitioner in our society exercises authority. . . . A lawyer generally gives 'advice,' but if the client knew just as well what to do it would be unnecessary for him to consult a lawyer" (22). It is this position of authority and competence which gratifies one's sense of control and mastery (8). When the lawyer is able to come forward with a clear explanation of the legal situation and formulate it in precise legal terms, surely he must derive some sense of personal adequacy and importance from this act. We could speculate that this might be one unconscious, or perhaps conscious, motivation for an individual to select law as a field of professional endeavor. It is interesting to note that the famous Harvard law professor, "Bull" Warren, was aware of this motive. One of his contemporaries has said, "At first his aim was to study and teach sociology and economics, but what may fairly be termed his veritable passion for exactitude and certainty led him to seek in the law more precise definition of doctrines than he found in the subjects of his earlier choice" (34). Certainly, the lawyer shares with the analyst the opportunity to come into contact with a wide variety of persons in a wide variety of life situations, and to gratify curiosity.

The basic importance of understanding these sources of gratification and making them as conscious as possible rests in the fact that, if they enter into the process unconsciously, they may result in what Parsons calls "tendencies to various types of 'deviate' behavior . . ." He lists the principal deviant tendencies:

> One of these may be probably *yielding to expediency,* above all through financial temptations and pressures from clients. Ideological trends in our society are such that there is almost certainly serious exaggeration in the views of many circles about lawyers on this point, but that there is the tendency to abdicate responsibilities in the service of financial "self-interest," or merely "peace" in the face of severe pressure can scarcely be doubted.
>
> A second type of deviation consists in *exaggerated legal "formalism,"* the tendency to insist on what is conceived to be the "letter" of the law without due regard to a "reasonable" balance of considerations. Legal "technicalities" may, of course, be and often are, invoked . . . but, apart from their instrumental use, undoubtedly there is a tendency in many legal quarters to exaggerate the importance of being formally "correct" down to the last detail. In psychological terms, the legal profession probably has at least its share, if not more, of "compulsive personalities" as compared with other occupations. The essential present point is that this tendency in the profession is not simply a result of certain types of people "happening" to be lawyers, but has grown out of a situation in which lawyers as a group are placed.
>
> The third type of deviant tendency in the law may be said to be the *"sentimental" exaggeration of the substantive claims of clients or other "interests,"* represented by the lawyer. Thus corporation lawyers may often become more lyrical about the rights of "property" than the main tradition of law warrants, or labor lawyers about "human rights" and the like [18].[4]

Parsons goes on to describe the lawyer's role as involving a confidential relationship in which the client may "get things off his chest." He emphasizes the fact that lawyers, by their role function, are to be "tolerant" and helpful to their clients rather than judge them morally. Then he mentions the fact that the lawyer, as a mem-

---

[4] Italics are the author's.

ber of the bar, must represent his client regardless of his own position on the issue. In this way he is both "permissive and supportive" while following the difficult line of giving his clients what they want, as well as remaining within the limits of the law. This is an arduous but gratifying function to perform. Last, ". . . like the medical profession, payment for the services of lawyers is not on an ordinary 'commercial' basis but on a 'sliding scale' with a presumption that the lawyer will be willing to help this client relatively independently of whether it is financially worth his while" (19).

We may see in these comments by a psychoanalyst and a sociologist, that there are many emotional gratifications available to the lawyer within his "professional role." Though they are available as gratification, they are also possible sources of conflict. The degree to which they arouse conflict is the measure of their interference with efficient accomplishment of the professional job. Within the traditional form of legal education, it does not appear likely that any degree of self-awareness in regard to multiple motivation will be fostered. Some broadening of the legal curriculum to include such learning, would be highly desirable (30, 31).

SOME TACTICAL SUGGESTIONS

Now let us turn to some of the specific places in which lawyers might, through a broader understanding of the interview and counseling process, achieve their professional goals more effectively. Lawyers, because of their professional relationship to their community, frequently come in contact with individuals whose problems originate from their internal emotional conflicts. Awareness of these facts and some basic understanding of how they might be approached would greatly increase professional skill and effectiveness. The question may well be raised as to whether or not it is appropriate or even legitimate for lawyers to embark on the treacherous ground of counseling (9). However, this is a purely academic question since, for better or for worse, the very nature of a lawyer's activities forces him into this role. Every psychiatrist has encountered individuals whose family life was greatly complicated as a result of inappropriate legal intervention. Once the legal wheels begin to turn, it may be difficult to stop them (24).

There are also many instances of families who swear by their lawyer as the best friend they have. A lawyer can be a wise guide in maintaining intelligent and amiable family functioning. That he can do the same in many areas of family law seems to be supported by investigations from the field of counseling. For example, a lawyer may decide to help a client obtain a divorce. Since divorce has far-reaching social reverberations, especially when children are involved, it certainly is in the service of the public good for him to make whatever efforts he can to insure that the decision to obtain a divorce is an appropriate one. He need not make it his mission to help his clients arrive at the "right" decision, but he can help them inquire into the adequacy of their thinking about marriage and into their reasons for wishing divorce. For the lawyer to attempt such a function raises several problems in regard to his potential role as counsel for one of the adversaries. However, it is sheer fiction that he plays a neutral role, only implementing the wishes of one of the contesting parties. While a spouse may "wish" a divorce, this is but rarely the whole story. For him to act on this wish may tip the scales in a direction which may, in fact, run counter to the main desires of the parties involved, and can hardly be seen as the best solution in regard to social issues. For these reasons, it seems clearly indicated that public policy is best served by the lawyer who makes an attempt to help the parties arrive at a solution which reflects *all* of their feelings and attitudes—not just the tempest of the moment.

To follow this approach, the lawyer will need extensive data about the marriage relationship, in order to form an opinion as to whether the impending divorce is based on solid grounds or neurotic ones. Neurotic factors quite generally enter into the selection of a marriage partner. If neurotic bases become apparent to the lawyer (and obvious inconsistencies in the description of the problem make such a likelihood apparent), he may refer his client to an agency set up to deal skillfully with the problem—such as Marriage Councils, or The Family Service, a nation-wide organization. Such agencies have skilled counselors who understand problems of marital discord and can help to disentangle them. In the event a client's problems are deeply neurotic, he may be referred for psychiatric assistance. While psychiatrists do not necessarily have the special training needed to deal with a "double problem" involving the treatment of both partners simultaneously, they can at least assist their patients as individuals (32). The most important factor in making a referral is to be sure that the counselor has a solid, dynamic understanding of human behavior and knows how to deal with "transference phenomena."

The family's religious advisor is another source of assistance in such problems. Traditionally religious counselors do much of the marriage counseling for the community. The more skillful and wise among them are very effective, although most take a moral position regarding divorce which strongly biases the counseling, and limits the possibility for working out problems. On the positive side, however, the religious counselor is usually dedicated to being a friend, and tends to create a receptive and encouraging atmosphere which helps considerably in talking out these problems. Some emotional disturbances are "cured" by this type of friendly relationship (7). Technically, these are "transference cures," predicated upon and limited by the degree of dependency gratification involved. Some early psychotherapeutic efforts which initially seemed to be effective, but later appeared to be failures, were due to this phenomenon. This resulted in closer study of the dependency aspects of transference. From these failures, analysts obtained greater understanding of the transference relationship. Lawyers, somewhat inclined toward an authoritative stand with their clients, can logically anticipate that they will "cure" some problems merely by virtue of their authority role. This may have advantages in some circumstances, but subsequent difficulties must be anticipated from many such solutions.

Knowledge of the interview-transference relationship may be put to excellent use in the general area of data-gathering. Throughout a lawyer's career, regardless of what specialization he may develop, he is always in search of facts with which to work. Frequently, he feels frustrated and angry with the distortions and errors which crop up in his data accumulation. Occasionally, his client wishes to deceive him, but more frequently, inaccuracies are due to unconscious distortions resulting from the emotional interaction between lawyer and client. When this source of distortion is better understood by the interviewer, instead of causing frustration and error, it becomes an additional source of information which can be used to illuminate areas which were virtually inaccessible previously.

By acknowledging the emotional interplay between himself and his client, the lawyer will better understand his client's relations with others. Take, for example, legal transactions relating to a partnership. Not infrequently, partners get into tangles with each other which they try to solve by legal means. Frequently, these difficulties arise from emotional relationships and from the blind spots that the partners have for each other. Legal intervention may easily place serious obstacles in the way of continuing the partnership. However, a perceptive lawyer might help these partners unscramble their emotional difficulties merely by pointing them out. We do not expect the lawyer to do intensive psychotherapeutic work with his clients, but he can point out the realities of the way clients are relating to each other—perhaps too demanding, or too suspicious, too submissive, and then resentful. Any of these observations may help such people work more positively toward solving their difficulties.[5]

Let us consider the specific ways in which clients' conscious and unconscious attitudes toward lawyers may impinge upon the professional relationship.[6] First of all, when a client seeks help from a lawyer, he is generally ignorant of the technical aspects of law. His ordinary techniques for judging persons or situations must be suspended, for he has no way of adequately testing the competency of the lawyer he chooses. He may make inquiries about him, and he may be able to investigate past successes and failures; but, generally, he is unable to make any realistic appraisal of skill and trustworthiness. Of necessity, then, he must place himself under the authority and assistance of the lawyer, essentially in blind trust. By virtue of this fact, all the client's previous attitudes about authority and dependency will be stirred up. This will elicit, usually, a certain amount of irrational fear and concern, which the client will be helpless to deal with. He will feel impotent to broach these fears, and will conceive of the relationship to his attorney as one of helplessness although, in reality, he is free to procure a new lawyer any time he wishes.

With such an attitude, the client may harbor certain magical expectations, for instance, that the lawyer is able to accomplish any

[5] Information has come to the attention of the author about a law firm engaged in corporation practice, which worked out an arrangement with psychiatrists whereby they may call them into consultation in appropriate cases. When a situation arises where the lawyers believe that emotional problems are the cause of the legal difficulty, it is suggested to the client that a psychiatric colleague be called into consultation. It is reported that results have been excellent in terms of salvaging clients' business relationships, and that all participants in the arrangement have regarded this procedure most favorably.

[6] For a discussion of the theory regarding levels of consciousness see Chapter III.

manipulation or transaction which the client desires. Failure to achieve such omnipotence generally provokes anger which, since it is irrational and generally unconscious, may only be expressed in distorted ways. A lawyer can deal with this source of trouble more easily by knowing in advance that he is going to be assigned this authority role, with all of its imagined power and omnipotence. Early in the relationship, he can recognize the evidences of resentment which may come with his failure or imagined failure to live up to the pedestaled position. Often clients can be helped through their emotional conflicts if the lawyer comfortably alludes to their sense of frustration and offers to let them talk about their feelings. Anyone occupying an authority role will often be seen as a person with godlike powers. This is very flattering to most of us, since childhood weaknesses and feelings of inadequacy always stir fantasies of gaining the upper hand in some kind of authoritative relationship. In addition to being aware of the anger which will follow failure to live up to the god-role, one should also be wary of believing it oneself. Unconscious readiness to become the "big daddy" may result in self-deception about one's real capabilities and lead to trouble.

Another conflict, referred to previously, revolves around one's self-image as a professional person. There may be conflict between the motive of service and the economic motive. Such conflict can cause impetuous and inappropriate decisions, as well as various vague tensions in professional relationships. In the world of adult reality, success, economic security, and a sense of individual worth and well-being, relate to the capacity for accomplishing productive, creative, and valuable work for others. Financial and emotional rewards generally relate directly to reality value for the community. The professional man in our society has a unique opportunity to gain a deep sense of value and creativity. He is in a position to carry out difficult and highly technical jobs which permit a maximum of self-expression and self-direction, rewarding in themselves. He deserves an appropriate reward for his efforts. In the emotional sphere, this reward is evidenced in terms of prestige and status in the community. On the economic scale, the reward is substantial financial success. To accept these rewards for solid reality accomplishments should not cause emotional conflict. Unfortunately, it frequently does. A confused sense of guilt causes some professional people to feel that it is vaguely immoral to make money. Parsons describes this phenomenon and its sociological implications and points out that there is a common feeling among professionals that, when a person performs a task which is socially valuable, he should not be rewarded as greatly as if he were a "businessman." A "businessman" is assumed to have no particular stake in the social goals of his community, at least insofar as they relate to his business activities (23). It is highly desirable for a professional man to achieve a clear, well-integrated self-image, which includes considerations of economic worth as well as ethical values, and which fits the social patterns within which he functions. "Man may not live by bread alone," but it is also true that he may not live without it. Arriving at a realistic, individual self-appraisal should cause no loss of professional stature.

In most law schools there is little opportunity for students to deal directly and consciously with these problems. Though it is felt that they are best dealt with in the context of practice experience, it is likely that failure to approach these problems is a reflection of the emotional conflict which surrounds them. It would be wise to provide opportunities for exploration of these issues before the young practitioner comes face to face with them, when he must decide almost instantaneously. Decisions made under these circumstances are often wildly inappropriate. This is a neglected area of education, although there have been some recent and excellent efforts to evolve techniques for teaching about some of these pressing reality problems (25).

The law practitioner who spends the time to help his clients disentangle what are primarily psychological problems is performing just as valuable a service as if he were giving legal advice. This being true, he may, with a clear conscience, charge an appropriate fee for his time and help. It would seem that the social goal is served quite as well when a client decides he does *not* need to take legal action, as when he takes some action with legal advice. In the absolute, both types of advice relate to legal process, both are valuable, and both may be appropriately compensated.

Lawyers must deal frequently with problems arising from variations in cultural background, and the American cultural scene is anything but homogeneous. "American culture" is really a multitude of smaller subcultures easily distinguishable from each other. There may be an Irish-Catholic community, an Italian-Catholic community, a Negro community, a Jewish community, the "Blue-stocking," and many others, all functioning more or less in cultural independence. Each of these groups has its own cultural attitudes, and children reared in them grow up with many conscious and unconscious identifications with their own specific backgrounds. Those reared in such subcultures often grow up with conflict between old patterns of cultural identification and the new "American" cultural identity which they seek to achieve, even though it may not exist in reality. Each is saddled with his cultural heritage, though he may evolve elaborate unconscious and conscious techniques for circumventing or camouflaging it. The lawyer, coming in contact with clients, not only sees them as parts of a cultural background, but also through his own cultural preconceptions. This creates serious problems in communication, and a multitude of difficulties arise about which lawyers frequently are remarkably naïve. Expert at verbalization within their own framework of assumptions, they may be almost wholly innocent of the self-awareness necessary to communicate across cultural barriers. Research has demonstrated ways and means for minimizing the blind biases we all have, and this information will be a useful addition to legal education.

Lawyers, like doctors, meet people with a wide range of personality patterns, and meet them on very intimate terms. The last group of problems we shall mention are those which derive from basic differences in personality characteristics. As we shall see, each person during his years of growth and development must solve emotional problems which are common to all human beings. In doing so, he attains his own unique character. This background of common emotional experience is the means by which one person may understand and "feel for" another, while at the same time, the individualized "character traits" involved may block this means of rapport. Psychoanalysis has made major contributions to our knowledge about dealing with variant personality types with specific therapeutic techniques.

The therapeutic relationship has often been described as an "emphatic identification" with the patient (14). For purposes of therapy, the therapist can identify with the patient in a noncritical, understanding way, in order to get inside of his problem. Using this identification to understand what is going on with the patient, he is in a better position to help him modify his manner of living. Emphatic identification must also be part of the practicing lawyer's professional skill, if he is to approach the professional goal of being able to represent either side of an issue. He must be able to identify himself truly with his client, to understand the problem with which he is dealing. Whatever tendency exists to react *unconsciously* to the client will impede and hinder the lawyer-client relationship. For example, sexual crimes which run strongly counter to our social mores might well arouse a strong reaction in a lawyer. If this is due to unconscious conflicts about his own sexual impulses, the lawyer's effectiveness will be impaired. One can do little about one's own unconscious impulses, but at least intellectual comprehension of the problem is possible. If reaction is very strong and there is too marked an emotional response, the lawyer should realize that it would be in the interest of his client to refer him to someone else. It is possible for the lawyer to recognize that his reaction indicates the presence of emotional conflict in himself. Often mere acceptance of this fact reduces tension in a relationship and facilitates freer communication. If communication between the lawyer and his client is impeded to any considerable extent, it would appear that he has an obligation to bring another lawyer into the case, in order to guarantee maximum professional efficiency. There are many instances of similar identification problems. However, they all have essentially the same dynamic significance, and all should be met in approximately the same way.

Most of the dynamics of the relationship between the professional person and his client have always been understood intuitively by the skillful and efficient practitioner. Tactfulness, skill, and a real interest in one's clients or patients are required. All are not so fortunate as to be blessed with such skill and tactfulness on an intuitive level. Dynamic psychiatric insights and modern sociological knowledge have clarified and specified the nature of some of these professional and emotional transactions. In the interest of professional efficiency, it is wise to strive consciously and conscientiously for awareness and competence in professional relationships. Also, we must make what maturing steps we can in regard to our own personalities to enable us better to perform our professional mission.

PROBLEMS

A section entitled "Problems" will be found at the end of each chapter. Its purpose is to provide some "clinical experience" in applying the psychodynamic material set forth in the chapters, to everyday problems of the law. Within each of these sections, one such problem will be elaborated and an illustrative "solution" presented. While the solution will never deal with all aspects of the problem, hopefully it will demonstrate a methodology for approach.

Since the goal of this volume is to develop sensitivity and skill in this applicatory process, the measure of success will not only be the reader's comprehension and mastery of the concepts but his ability to carry out such a process as well.

Example

A young woman (Jane) accompanied by her father and mother, arrived for an appointment with a lawyer, one which the father had set up through the firm which handles his company's legal business. When the lawyer opened the interview by asking what it was they wished him to do, the young woman appeared hesitant and on the verge of tears. At that point the father moved in to answer the question, stating that his daughter wanted to obtain a divorce from her husband. Without prompting he went on to angrily describe the "grounds," which appeared to be that the husband had beaten her "till she was black and blue," was "shacking up" with another woman, and on many occasions had treated her in very undignified and insulting ways. The father's voice was loud, angry, and rather overpowering throughout the discussion, while Jane sat with lowered head, fighting tears. Jane's mother sat passively throughout, merely nodding agreement with her husband on those few occasions when he turned to her.

The young lawyer who handled this difficult assignment was struck at once with the aggressive presentation of the father, and the near silence of Jane. Wisely sensing that there might be a side to the story which he wasn't getting, he moved to separate Jane from her parents and had her re-tell the story. At first she described the same picture as her father, expressing the same indignant feelings. As she continued, he became aware that the events leading up to her return home did not seem to make sense. Wondering out loud if she had ever felt upset by her husband's behavior before the last year or two, she replied to his surprise that, as a matter of fact, she had been seeing a psychiatrist about this for some time. At this point the lawyer decided that "perhaps it would be a good idea to get a psychiatric opinion, to see whether or not we should proceed with the divorce action." He then made a psychiatric referral.

This case well illustrates the psychological undercurrents which exist, even when the "facts" seem to point clearly to what "ought to be done." Here, the husband had beaten up his wife, he was having an affair with another woman, and he had used abusive language with her. The wife had run home to her parents and told them she wanted to divorce her husband because he had been so terrible to her. Even so, the lawyer's hunch that something was missing proved to be dead right. Why had he chosen to look for further information before moving toward a divorce action? What were the countertransference reactions that helped him decide to refer his client to a psychiatrist?

First, we recall that Jane's father called his company's lawyer to help with the divorce. Often this kind of legal problem is brought to a law firm which deals mainly with corporation law, and they feel an obligation to handle it in order to maintain proper relations with their clients. Such cases are correctly viewed as being "loaded," because if they do not turn out to the satisfaction of the client, it will be held against the firm. The client must be pleased with the outcome, which means that unconscious as well as conscious goals must be dealt with. The lawyer in this case had some awareness of the potential trap, for when he called the psychiatrist to make the referral, he remarked that, "this case is a mess and will surely end in a divorce, but I just want to make sure this comes out all right, because the father is a good client of our firm." He was *not* aware of the fact that he "sensed" Jane's underlying wish to stay married. In this situation it would have been appropriate for the lawyer to "read" his misgivings as evidence to challenge the basic premise that a divorce was indicated. If he had done so, he might have ferreted out the details which later helped the psychiatrist to understand the problem.

Another piece of "data" which could have helped him to consciously seek the crucial information was the fact that the father obviously was deeply involved in pressing the divorce action. While it is true that a good father *will* be concerned about his daughter's marriage, in fact this man had some hidden feelings which did not emerge until they were deliberately sought out by the examiner. The lawyer again "sensed" this fact, but was not able to make the intellectual leap of trusting his feelings about the father and using them to understand what was going on. In the referral conversation, he expressed his feeling and his perception when he remarked, "The old man is all excited about this matter and it isn't helping me work with his daughter. I hope you will be able to help get him off my back." The meaning of this observation will be made clear below.

Another countertransference reaction which was overlooked but felt, related to the daughter's reluctance to speak in front of her father. While the lawyer did notice and feel this, he did not carry it a step further and wonder what this might have meant to the daughter in terms of her relationship to her father as well as to her husband. The significance of this observation was very important to the proper resolution of the problem.

Now let us turn to what was "really going on." When the psychiatric interviews were begun, the woman (now a "patient") reiterated the story outlined above. While she was relating it, the interviewer had a feeling that he had to tease the information out of his informant, and very little was given freely. Once the appropriate questions were asked, answers were promptly forthcoming. This led the interviewer to feel that he had to drag the woman after him in the interview, and he was mildly irritated. Once this perception was made (i.e., once the countertransference sensation was noted by means of deliberate introspection), it became possible for the psychiatrist to ask himself, "What does this wish to be led mean? Why does she want me to do all of the work?" When these questions are stated, there is an immediate corollary question: "If she wants a divorce, why doesn't she proceed with the arrangements herself, and why is her father doing all of the pressing?" (We have not yet studied sufficient theory to deal fully with the dynamics of this complex interaction. Because of this, our description will be limited to those factors which are related to the curious way in which this case was unfolding.) Now let us see what additional facts emerged in the psychiatric interview and note some of the cues which led to their exposure.

It has been stated that this woman presented her initial story to the psychiatrist in much the same way as to the lawyer. He was aware at once of the time gap between the beating described and the arrival of the woman at her family's home. When he asked about this, he learned that she had gone to see her first psychiatrist and had told him, too, of the beating. He had urged her to leave her husband at once, offered to take her to the train, which he did, and saw her off for home. With all of this help one wonders why she was so unhappy and why she could not come forth with a more persuasive statement about her wish for a divorce. It is just this last clue which causes one to develop a vague feeling that she did not in fact *want* a divorce. We become aware that, so far, we know nothing of how *she* feels about her husband. The psychiatrist also became aware that the "chief complaints" clearly "seemed" to be victim-provoked. (The psychological significance of these factors will also have to await clarification later in this volume.) It is enough to say that Jane did *not* view them as terribly serious, nor did her further description make them seem so.

We now move to the next logical question to ask Jane. "Tell me more about your husband, where you met him, about your engagement and courtship, what kind of a fellow he is, etc." If all was well settled in Jane's mind about a divorce, we would anticipate at least some kind of negative response regarding the husband. Instead, Jane began to cry profusely and expressed an obvious desire to remain married to her husband *if*. . . . There unfolded a long story about the marital relationship and the *real* problems began to come to light. It was soon revealed that this young woman had spent her whole married life supporting her husband (John) while he obtained professional training. Needless to say, in addition to supporting the family, she had to abandon temporarily all of her own immediate goals as a wife and a woman. Also, she received very little attention from her chronically exhausted husband, who devoted nearly all of his energies and interest to the job of learning his profession. His behavior made good sense and was highly logical, but it *was* the source of much frustration and deprivation to Jane. Did she protest? Did she argue about this with her husband and demand that he pay more attention to her? In fact, she did not, and this leads to the next line of exploration.

How did this intelligent, apparently normal woman get herself into this mess? She quickly revealed that after going steady through most of their undergraduate years, the couple had decided to marry before John went to graduate school. It was a half-shaped hope that Jane's father would offer them financial help, which he could easily afford to do. The announcement of their intention to marry shattered all such hopes and, in fact, brought down a tirade of furious protest from father. While mother supported Jane when they were alone, in father's presence she always openly agreed with him. The description given of Jane up to now makes her appear weak and submissive, but her response to her father's fury was to defy him to stop her. Although he did not try, his acceptance of the forthcoming marriage was reluctant and openly skeptical. He always doubted that it would work and he never failed to say so.

These facts shed more light on the nature of the problem. Among other things, we see that one significance of this marriage was that it represented Jane's powerful urge to assert her independence from a rather dominating father. For years she had observed her mother's submission and had vowed inwardly that she would acquiesce to no man as her mother had. Such vows, unfortunately, do not provide the means to withstand pressures, and there is always lingering doubt that one can be truly independent and the equal of others. This latter fact was responsible for Jane's need to somehow get others to help her achieve her goals. Must we conclude, then, that her wish was to get her father to help her obtain a divorce? Had this been true, she would have gone along more easily and unequivocally with the decision, and the sensation of doubt would not have crept into the lawyer's feelings. What then was she trying to get others to help her achieve? Oddly, she wanted them to help her *make* her husband love her and take care of her in a way more in keeping with her hidden wishes. She said this very explicitly once she was helped to feel that such wishes were appropriate and that she could talk about them. Most of her behavior during this episode represented unconscious efforts to achieve this goal, but since these efforts were unspoken and shrouded in camouflage, she very nearly missed her mark. Behind this façade (which obviously involves neurotic behavior) was a very mature and healthy wish to remain married and to work out a better way to relate to her husband. A divorce for this couple would have been a tragic mistake.

How did the lawyer fare in this case? In the first place, he did not need to pursue the divorce action, for Jane went back to her husband. (After four years, they are still getting along well and happily.) He probably had to take some *initial* recrimination from her father, because the father still wished to prove that he had been right all along about his daughter's marriage. However, it is always safe to assume that, in the end, parents want their children to be happy—even if they are forced to admit (openly or not) that they have been wrong. This positive desire will usually bring ultimate awareness that the lawyer *did* do a good job, and therefore his judgment can be safely followed in future. At any rate, the best odds ride with this presumption, and in the end one's professional status is safest with such a decision.

This example illustrates how misleading surface "facts" may be. Although one rarely will have the time or inclination to find out all of the factors involved in such complex situations, understanding the possibilities, coupled with good interview technique, will help improve the likelihood of wise professional decisions.

1. How may transference be manifested in:
    (a) lawyer-judge relationships?
    (b) witness-judge relationships?

2. Relate the concept of countertransference to the above situations.

3. (a) Physicians are cautioned against providing medical care for members of their own family. What do you think about a lawyer acting as counsel for his family?

(b) What would be the psychological factors involved in such a relationship?

4. An attractive woman in her mid-forties came to a lawyer's office and asked him to represent her in a divorce action, charging that her husband had been carrying on an affair for the past one and a half years. She informed him that she had been the client of Mr. Smith, a lawyer in a nearby town, but left after three interviews during which he made "several propositions," and attempted "to ply her with drink."
  (a) What are your reactions to this story?
  (b) How would you proceed, after hearing such a story?
  (c) What are your speculations in regard to the psychological situation of the other lawyer, the client, yourself, and the husband?
  (d) What do your speculations lead to regarding the interrelationships between these parties?

REFERENCES

1. Birdwhistell, R. L., Background to Kinesics. *Etc.*, 13:10-18, 1955.
2. Bromberg, W., An Analysis of Therapeutic Artfulness. *Amer. J. Psychiat.*, 114:719-725, 1958.
3. Cozzens, J. G., *By Love Possessed.* New York: Harcourt, Brace, 1957.
4. Ferenczi, S., Introjection and Transference. In: *Sex and Psychoanalysis.* New York: Basic Books, 1950.
5. *Ibid.*, p. 35.
6. Fortas, A., The Legal Interview. *Psychiat.*, 15:91, 1952.
7. Frank J., *Persuasion and Healing.* Baltimore: Johns Hopkins Press, 1961, pp. 65-74.
8. Freedman, A. L., On Advocacy. *Villanova Law Rev.*, 1:293-294, 1956.
9. Freeman, H., *Legal Interviewing and Counseling.* St. Paul: West Publishing, 1964.
10. Freud, S., Five Lectures on Psychoanalysis (1910). *Standard Edition*, 11:55. London: Hogarth Press, 1957.
11. Freud, S., The Dynamics of the Transference (1912). *Standard Edition*, 12:99-208. London: Hogarth Press, 1958.
12. Freud, S., An Outline of Psychoanalysis (1940). *Standard Edition*, 23:141-207. London: Hogarth Press, 1964.
13. Freud, S., & Breuer, J., Studies on Hysteria (1843-1895). *Standard Edition*, 2. London: Hogarth Press, 1955.
14. Katz, R. L., *Empathy.* Glencoe, Ill.: Free Press, 1963.
15. Mudd, E. H., Psychiatry and Marital Problems: Mental Health Implications. *Eugen. Quart.*, 2:116, 1955.
16. Orr, D. W. (1954), Transference and Countertransference: A Historical Survey. *J. Amer. Psychoanal. Assn.* 2:621-670, 1954.

17. Parsons, T., A Sociologist Views the Legal Profession. *Conference Series,* 11:62. The Law School, University of Chicago, 1952.
18. *Ibid.,* p. 55.
19. *Ibid.,* pp. 60-61.
20. Parsons, T., *Essays in Sociological Theory,* Glencoe, Ill.: Free Press, 1954, p. 35.
21. *Ibid.,* p. 43.
22. *Ibid.,* p. 38.
23. *Ibid.,* pp. 43-44.
24. Redmount, R., Attorney Personalities and Some Psychological Aspects of Legal Consultation. *Univ. Pa. Law Rev.,* 109:972-990, 1961.
25. Schwartz, M. L., *Cases and Materials on Professional Responsibility and the Administration of Criminal Justice.* Chicago: National Council on Legal Education, 1961.
26. Spitz, R., Countertransference: Comments on Its Varying Role in the Analytic Situation. *J. Amer. Psychoanal. Assn.,* 4:256-257, 1956.
27. Szasz, T., On the Experiences of the Analyst in the Psychoanalytic Situation. *J. Amer. Psychoanal. Assn.,* 4:204-208, 1956.
28. Tower, L. E., Countertransference. *J. Amer. Psychoanal. Assn.,* 4:226-227, 1956.
29. Watson, A. S., The Psychology of the Professional Self-Image. *Chem. & Engineer. News,* 38(12):84-88, 1960.
30. Watson, A. S., Reflections on the Teaching of Criminal Law. *Univ. Detroit Law J.* 37:701-717, 1960.
31. Watson, A. S., Some Psychological Aspects of Teaching Professional Responsibility. *J. Leg. Ed.,* 16:1-23, 1963.
32. Watson, A. S., The Conjoint Psychotherapy of Marriage Partners. *Amer. J. Orthopsychiat.,* 33:912, 1963.
33. Wheelis, A., The Vocational Hazards of Psychoanalysis. *Internat. J. Psychoanal.,* 36:171-184, 1956.
34. Williston, S., Edward Henry Warren. *Harvard Law Rev.,* 58:1122, 1945.

II

Freud, Psychiatry and Science: Origins of a Medical Psychology

There are urgent reasons for lawyers and psychiatrists to learn about and understand some of the goals and concepts of each other's disciplines. Both are seeking through their own specialized methods, means for making society more secure, fruitful, and gratifying to individuals. The law seeks to arrive at this goal through effective regulations and procedures. The psychiatrist strives for the same goal through helping individuals to deal with their self-centered impulses in ways which do not conflict inappropriately with external social standards and practices. Each profession is dedicated to studying and perfecting its techniques in order to achieve this mutually held objective.

The professional training of lawyers enables them to analyze skillfully and systematically and to integrate the enormously complex legal relationships which are essential to the efficient functioning of a modern society. The professional skill of psychiatrists lies in their ability to analyze and relate the subtle nuances of motivation and behavior which underlie *all* human relationships, including the individual's relationship to the law. To effect an optimally rational system of social regulation, it should be quite clear that the skills and knowledge of these two important social disciplines must be joined.

SCIENCE AND THE SCIENTIFIC METHOD

Both lawyers and psychiatrists face the same public attitude, which is that neither of them is concerned with ethical values. Often the lawyer is judged to be a hypocrite and the psychiatrist an anarchist. In fact, both have specialized consciences and their own standards, which are unlike the standards of society at large. It does not seem practical for them to attack one another. As Sir James Stephen said while discussing the subject of mental illness, "I think that in dealing with matters so obscure and difficult, the two great professions of law and medicine ought rather to feel for each other's difficulties than to speak harshly of each other's shortcomings" (61).

For the most part, in the past, the discoveries of science have not found their way directly into law. Mainly, acceptance has occurred only after these discoveries have become a part of the general culture. This cultural lag has elements of safety in it, but it also means that some law will always appear ignorant and unreasonable to the ill-informed. Though this state of the law may be necessary, there is no reason why the individual lawyer cannot know and understand the best relevant knowledge which the psychiatrist has to offer.

In the following pages, the findings of dynamic psychiatry will be discussed in regard to human development, behavior, and the principles which apparently govern the psychic apparatus. Let us consider the background of these studies before we attack the particular.

Man's efforts to understand and cope with his environment are older than the 6,000 years of recorded history. Anthropologists and geologists believe that man has existed for 600,000 to 700,000 years (67). The discovered remains of his cultural efforts, which go back even further in time, show evidence of this struggle to understand and control the forces of nature. The human animal, by virtue of his highly developed brain and nervous system, acquired the ability to turn experience into memories in the form of abstract symbols, and thus to develop and pass on to his children highly elaborated "cultures." This single developmental attainment makes possible the accumulation of vast amounts of experience in the form of culture, and removes the necessity for each person to learn everything by first-hand experience. "Instinctual behavior" seems less important as learning and education loom larger (36).

Scientific knowledge is a part of our accumulated cultural heritage and the *scientific method* is the slowly evolved technique we have perfected for investigating and establishing "the facts." Discovering "facts" always involves the observer and the observed. While we assume that what is observed is governed by discernible and stable "laws," the observer is influenced by many variables which are difficult to follow and impossible to eliminate. These variables in the observer make accurate observation difficult, especially in the behavioral sciences. The scientific method is designed to resolve these observational problems in so far as possible.

Even scientists themselves occasionally misapprehend the nature of science. If we look at two of the dictionary definitions, we may see how some of the confusion arises. First, *science* is defined as "knowledge, or any department of systematized knowledge." The second important definition says that it is "a branch of study concerned with the observation and classification of facts, especially with the establishment of verifiable general laws chiefly by induction and hypothesis."

We can see that, in one form of the definition, science is a more or less static accumulation of knowledge, and in the other, it is a *process*, by means of which knowledge may be obtained (49). As Ashley Montagu has said, "It is not its subject matter which makes a science, but the scientific application of efficient methods to the analysis and organization of the subject matter" (39).

"Science is not any particular method or set of techniques. It is a way of reasoning. The standards are intellectual rather than procedural. The method of observation, formalization, and testing may vary with the nature of the problem" (38). Leslie White says, "Science is sciencing," and he emphasizes the methodological aspects of scientific observation (68).

The first step of the scientific method is that of *collecting data*. The scientist, either from motives of curiosity or in an attempt to answer some specific question, begins by collecting observational data. After a series of observations have been made, the second step of *classification* is made. In this step, the data are sorted and organized according to some concept of similarity. In the third step, a *hypothesis* to account for the data is formulated. Here the goal is to arrive at some theory of cause and effect, which would explain the observations which have been made. The next step is to *test the hypothesis*. Carefully controlled experimental procedures are set up, and new observations are made in order to corroborate or disprove the hypothesis. If the hypothesis has validity,[1] the experimentor reproduces the events which were originally observed. The testing phase of the process is multiform, and as many test variations as possible are used to ascertain the correctness of the hypothesis. If the hypothesis repeatedly accounts for the events observed, then it is considered a *law*. Let us illustrate how this process may be used in practice.

Let us assume that a legislative or judicial agency wishes to know what factors cause individuals to commit "auto larceny." Let us further assume that this piece of research will be conducted by psychiatrists. They would begin by locating a group of persons convicted of auto larceny. Strict standards of sampling would be followed so that it could be shown that a representative group of auto larcenists had been selected. Then a "control group" of nonlarcenists would be selected. All of these persons would be studied psychiatrically. Specialized data on personality, motivational factors, and background would be carefully collected. Information on age, sex, sibling relationships, family relationships, family patterns and status, attitudes about auto larceny, health factors, environmental factors, and educational information would be collected. After an adequate series of observations had been made, an analysis of the results would determine if there were any significant patterns in the data. Next, an attempt would be made to discover and formulate an explanation for the larcenous behavior, using these data, and comparing it with the "control series" data. There might now appear some explanation for the specific behavior (or there might not, in which case the study would yield a negative result, but a result nonetheless). Such an explanation would be the hypothesis. There are several strategies for testing this hypothesis. One would be to select and examine a subsequent series of auto larcenists and to compare the results with the first series. Another would be to examine an appro-

---

[1] . . . in a special sense, in statistics, of the extent to which a test measures what it is intended or purports to measure, which is determined by the correlation between its results, and some other criterion of what it was devised to measure; e.g., the validity of an *aptitude test* would be determined by correlation with subsequent performance (18).

priate population sample and to attempt to predict which individuals will commit auto larceny in the future. The prediction technique is more difficult, is more conclusive, and is the test of choice whenever possible. If the hypothesis is correct, these procedures confirm it (i.e., validate it).

To summarize, the scientific method of study may take many shapes and forms. The crucial point is that it is a *method* for controlling observations, analyzing results, and predicting future "experimental" events through applying the knowledge derived from prior observational data. Technique may involve narrowly limited and mechanically or electronically controlled procedures, or it may be the careful observation of "clinical" situations where it is virtually impossible to regulate all of the variables and where the "control" must be applied by deductive means (34, 64). This latter method is naturally subject to greater and more frequent error, but it is often the only way in which any information may be obtained. Full awareness of the limitations of this kind of data and careful analysis of observations can lead to formulation of further and more exact experimentation. Many major discoveries have come about in this way. From any viewpoint, the experimental and scientific "set" of mind is the surest way to facilitate serendipity.

THE BEHAVIORAL SCIENCE SPECIALTIES

As the law progressively concerns itself with the question of how to treat those who are found guilty or liable, (for example, the auto larcenists above) a shift of interest becomes apparent. In addition to the task of defining the nature of the crime, or the character of the inappropriate action, the problem of deciding what to *do* with the individual offender arises. It is just at this point that there is ground for close and fruitful interdisciplinary cooperation. Here the well-trained psychiatrist has technique and experience for rendering an expert opinion on what kind of disposition will be best suited to the individual defendant, and at the same time protect the best interests of society.

The answers to these questions are not simple, and no perfect method exists for achieving this goal. However, a thorough understanding of techniques for dealing with problems of behavior and motivation would clear up some of the problems of working together. The law cannot function as an adequate social instrument if it runs counter to the laws of human behavior.[2] Neither can the psychiatrist make his appropriate contribution if he is oblivious of the problems and concepts of the law.

As the lawyer and the psychiatrist attempt to find answers regarding motivation or behavior in a given case, we see a pressing problem which is common to both. Different from many social scientists, lawyers and psychiatrists are frequently pressed in their work by the need for immediate decision. The court, in dealing with cases, must arrive at a decision of guilt or innocence, liability or nonliability, responsibility or nonresponsibility. Likewise, when a psychiatrist is confronted with a patient for diagnosis and treatment, he must act at once—he cannot wait for further evolution and verification of his etiological and therapeutic concepts. While this pressure to decide carries with it possible errors, it is a fact of everyday practice.

Whether the psychiatrist functions as a diagnostician during the trial, or as a therapist while formulating the sentence recommendations, he must clearly see what his role is to be.[3] His proper function under the present legal system is not to render a verdict, but rather to present an expert *opinion*.[4] For cooperation to be effective, the lawyer and the psychiatrist must comprehend and respect each other's conceptual system (27).

Modern dynamic psychiatry has made great strides in understanding the powerful unconscious factors in human behavior. Earlier descriptions of behavior have been displaced by better substantiated concepts, and scientific testing, refining, and elaboration continue.

Although each scientific specialty uses a basically similar procedure, each field has its own problems. In the study of human behavior, the problem of controlled observation was, until Freud, ex-

[2] Justice Cardozo states that "Courts know today that statutes are to be viewed, not in isolation or *in vacuo*, as pronouncements of abstract principles for the guidance of an ideal community, but in the setting and the framework of present-day conditions, as revealed by the labors of economists and students of the social sciences in our own country and abroad" (12).

[3] For a recent judicial opinion on this point, see *Washington v. U.S.* 390 F.2d 444(1967).

[4] A point often overlooked by Szasz (62). One must distinguish between failure to perform roles appropriately and defects in concept. One is remedied by education, while the other may necessitate revamping.

tremely problematical. It is still most remarkably difficult. In the chemical laboratory, it is relatively easy to set up a controlled experiment, since all scientists can use it with equal results. Observing human behavior, however, permits us no such felicitous solution. We may not turn a spectroscope or a microscope on mental functioning. It must be viewed through the eyes of an observer and go through his processes of attention, selection, memory and recording. For better or worse, he reacts to the observations. It is for this reason that the physical scientists so long denied recognition to the behavioral sciences, as sciences.

It was Freud who attempted by means of new and heretical techniques to turn the observer into a scientific tool. According to Zilboorg:

> Freud . . . was destined to stand alone because he announced to the scientific world that the forbidden realm of the psyche was going to be his object of scientific scrutiny, even though he possessed no psychological microtome, no psychological oil-immersion lens, nor any scale for psychological measurements. To the philosophic and religious world, he announced that he cared little about the alleged untouchability of the soul, and that he was going to proceed into the unknown, not in order to wander in awe, but in order to learn and to understand [69].

One of the major contributions which Freud and his co-workers made to the science of human behavior was to define and formulate the psychological events which take place when two people relate to each other in any situation.[5] They developed techniques whereby the observer, through understanding his own emotional reactions to the observed, may have some "control" for his observations. Though this technique is difficult, it is not impossible. Psychoanalytic science recognizes this by including a personal psychoanalysis in the training of all analysts. When the analyst has completed his training, he will have been thoroughly analyzed, which means that he should be able, for the most part, to differentiate his own reactions as the observer from the reactions of the observed (25). There is now a large body of evidence to support this as an appropriate scientific method.

Practicing lawyers commonly accept that behavior, manner of

[5] See Chapter I.

speaking, and similar expressions of personality are meaningful clues to understanding what is going on in a person's mind. The great literary artists of all time have reacted sensitively to human behavior and have accurately described it in all of its subtlety. Their descriptions vividly communicate to the reader what is going on in the mind of the person described, and this is one of the hallmarks of all great writing.

The psychiatrist uses similar materials. He takes an elaborate and detailed history of background and early life. He utilizes early memories (53), dreams (21), gestures, expressions, jokes (15, 16). These materials provide him with historical evidence and, even more important, with the patient's own deepest feelings about himself and the world. The psychiatrist may, by luck, be an "artist." Whether he is or not (and most often he is not), he brings something new to intuitive ways of understanding behavior. He is able to define, describe, and work out testable psychological meanings of manifest and unconscious behavior. He has been able to do what the scientist always aims to do, which is to formulate general rules to describe why events have occurred as they have. From these rules he then hopes to be able to predict what will happen in any given situation.

The term *psychiatry* always denotes medicine. It is defined as "The medical science which deals with the origin, diagnosis, prevention and treatment of emotional illness and asocial behavior. It also includes such special fields as mental retardation, the emotional components of physical disorders, mental hospital administration, and the legal aspects of psychiatric disorders" (1). By law, in the United States, only physicians may "practice," and treat disease, and this explains why all psychiatrists in this country are doctors of medicine. We should note, in passing, that any person holding a license to practice medicine *may* call himself a psychiatrist, so this designation gives no indication whatever of his level of training and experience. Within the medical profession itself, however, there are standards of training which bear importantly on the medical qualifications and prestige of the psychiatrist.

In order to be regarded as "trained" in this field today, the physician, in addition to his medical degree, will have taken a year of general medical internship, followed by three years of "residency training" in psychiatry. This is specialized training in the diagnosis and treatment of mental illness. It includes experience in treating the "insane" who are hospitalized, as well as prolonged and closely supervised treatment of outpatients. He also receives some training in neurology—the purely organic neurologic disabilities. This supervised training is followed by a minimum of two years' specialized practice—experience in the field, followed by an examination. Psychiatrists who have this training and have passed the qualifying examination are said to be "board-certified."

The next term we shall discuss is *psychoanalysis,* which is a system of psychological theory as well as a treatment technique which results in conscious acknowledgment of what is repressed in mental life (22). Drever defines psychoanalysis as a "system of psychology and a method of treatment of mental and nervous disorders, developed by Sigmund Freud, characterized by a dynamic view of all aspects of mental life, conscious and unconscious, with special emphasis upon the phenomena of the *unconscious,* and by an elaborate technique of investigation and treatment, based on the employment of *continuous free association*" (17). Munroe states that, "psychoanalytic treatment consists in the intervention of the doctor *at the level of understanding the patient can truly assimilate,* finally taking the patient back to the deepest strata of his personality. The interpretive comment is the major device employed by the psychoanalyst" (40). Gitelson says, "The chief qualitative distinction of psychoanalysis from all other mental therapies is its effort to destroy the suggestive influence of the authority of the therapist. It aims to set the patient free" (26).[6]

Freud's theory of psychoanalysis stirs profound emotional reactions (usually negative) in many people who come into contact with it. This is quite different from reactions to theories in the physical sciences. However, time and the force of evidence have mitigated these reactions. While there is still marked disparity of opinion, almost no psychiatrist uses a theory of treatment which does not involve many of Freud's concepts. Although many antagonists speak loudly against Freud and his analytic technique, they unwittingly use his concepts. The sheer necessity of logic and utility has brought the techniques and approaches of analytic, dynamic psychiatry to the fore.

[6] For a description of how to deal with transference, see Chapter I.

In recent years, there has been an increasing awareness that in order to treat a patient effectively one must be able to integrate an understanding of his intrapsychic functioning with his capacity to perform in the external world. The term *psychodynamics* is used to describe this integrated understanding. *Dynamic psychology* is "a psychology emphasizing motives and drives used specially by representatives of the analytic schools" (19). This term has been used extensively by Rado (44), Saul (51, 52), and others (14), to indicate the use of biology, psychology, physiology, and analytic concepts in a unified theory of human behavior.

Since early dynamic psychiatry developed in an atmosphere charged with emotion, it quite inevitably brought with it much feeling and activity which were nonscientific in character. These are in themselves a fascinating subject for study. While it is obvious that there was a solid scientific basis for some of these early debates, it is equally clear that there was much dogma, mysticism, and almost magical ritual adapted into theory along with the more solid observations developed from analytic technique (54). Since those early days, much of this original emotionalism has been stripped away, and though there is still lively debate in psychiatric circles, more techniques are evolving for objective evaluation of this very subjective area.[7] Progress has been made and, as Bertrand Russell has said, "Science, whatever unpleasant consequences it may have by the way, is in its very nature, a liberator, a liberator of bondage to physical nature and, in time to come, a liberator from the weight of destructive passions" (50).

Recent years have not only brought great advances from the science of psychiatry, but from the other behavioral sciences as well. Although these materials do not have easy applicability to the law, they illuminate the goals of law and those timeless riddles which law struggles to resolve.

The science of *psychology* had its roots in philosophy and began to separate itself from the parent trunk during the late 18th century.[8] It now has several major subspecialties, and to assay the com-

[7] See, for example, the work of Shakow (57, 58).

[8] *Psychology* is "The branch of biological science which studies the phenomena of conscious life in their origin, development, and manifestations, and employing such methods as are available and applicable to the particular field of study or particular problem with which the individual scientist is engaged" (20). This term embraces both medical and nonmedical psychologies.

petence of a particular psychologist, just as with a physician, one must know his specialty. Traditionally, psychology was a laboratory science and much of its early work related to experiments with animal behavior. Efforts were made to arrive at general theories to explain the observations from such experiments. Awareness that rats are not people led many psychologists to study human behavior directly in order to avoid the pitfalls of overgeneralization. Thus developed a large group of *experimental psychologists* who work exclusively with human behavior, and their research has contributed enormously to our knowledge about human activity. These scientists have made large contributions to our knowledge of memory, perception, and other areas of mental functioning (46, 47, 48). Their work will ultimately be applied directly to a multitude of legal problem areas such as evidence, judicial procedure, and jury function.

Another psychological subspecialty is *clinical psychology*. The work of this group is well known to lawyers because of the psychological testing which they carry out. They have studied and perfected means for assaying intelligence, personality structure, and various aptitudes. The Rorschach, thematic apperception (TAT), draw-a-person, and other "projective tests" are some of the instruments they commonly use and which lawyers will encounter when they seek help from clinical psychologists. These tests help to objectify observation of a person's behavior.

Clinical psychologists at this juncture of time are also doing "therapy." Although they still tend to use the word "client" to designate their subject, this is more related to problems of their legally defined prerogatives than of their clinical operations. What they *do* is psychotherapy of the same type as that carried out by the physician-therapist. Whether or not they do it well is a function of their training and skill, just as with the physician. The crucial social concern focuses on whether or not this group of professionals carries out its work in a way which protects the patient and the therapist against inappropriate behavior by either party. To this end, clinical psychologists have progressively evolved professional standards and certification boards, and society has moved toward a licensing or registration procedure which legally regulates those who may practice. Much remains to be clarified in this area, and the

medical profession shares the responsibility for developing new attitudes toward this group of therapists.

There are other specialized groups of psychologists which should
be mentioned. The *social psychologist* studies and works with social
and institutional processes. We may anticipate that such things as
judicial decision-making, operation of correctional institutions, and
jury functioning will be explored by this group. They have, in fact,
already produced interesting work in some of these areas (6, 59).

Also deserving of mention is the group of psychologists trained in
group dynamics. Kurt Lewin and his students have evolved excellent techniques for training groups of people toward better self-
understanding (13). Their "T-groups" have been widely used in
work with trial judges, juvenile court staffs, and various groups
of lawyers.[9]

Sociology and its subspecialty *criminology* have made major contributions to the law, especially criminal law. They are well adapted
for studying the impact of particular statutes on populations, trends
in public attitudes (11), or the function of public institutions (63).
Their methods are statistical and thus readily adapted to the broad
social policy questions of the law.

The last behavioral science we shall mention is *anthropology*. Anthropologists study man and his institutions, his biological evolution
and his culture. It is the latter area—*cultural anthropology*—which is
of direct interest to lawyers. Cultural anthropologists (in a similar
way to social psychologists and sociologists) have developed tools
for studying social institutions. Their special skill lies in discovering
the operational utility of specific institutional behavior which may
or may not be identical with its manifest or stated purpose. Law
and legal institutions are replete with areas of potential interest to
this group of scientists. Some studies have already been made in
relatively "simple" societies to assay the impact of laws and legal
behavior (9).

There have been "scientific observers" since the dawn of civilization, but before observational methods were clearly formulated,
natural fact and supernatural philosophical concepts were regarded

[9] For example, the National Council of Juvenile Court Judges has for several years
held five-day-long conferences in which T-groups were a central feature of the program. These conferences have been held in all geographic regions of the country so
that a representative sample of juvenile judges have had an opportunity to participate
in them (60).

as equally reliable. Men have never felt easy with unresolved questions, and our need for the security of order and comprehension compels us to make up answers when we do not have facts. Early man, like primitive people and children today, tended to humanize the forces of nature. He projected his own feelings onto his natural surroundings and conceived of natural law as something which functioned as he himself did. This form of thinking (which is also a form of primitive religion) is called animism. It is an effort to gain control of the incomprehensible in nature and oneself, to avert the feeling of helplessness.[10]

THE HISTORY OF PSYCHIATRY AS A SCIENCE

The early Egyptian culture achieved much technical knowledge and made the early beginnings in developing science. However, it was not until the time of the Greeks that a sophisticated and systematic approach to the universe was made. The Egyptians, for instance, looked on mental illness as spiritual transgressions. However, the Greek physicians believed mental illness to be a physiological phenomenon and, although they did not understand much of its cause, they did conceive a theory based on a biological concept. They diligently studied all illness including mental illness, and evolved an advanced system of medicine.

The fall of the Roman Empire ended all organized scientific effort for several centuries. Medicine as well as theories about mental disease once more came under the influence of the religious doctrines of the time. Mental illness was seen as a punishment for sin, much as the Egyptians had believed. Treatment and diagnostic methods were largely theological, and the mentally ill of the fifteenth century were treated as witches. As Zilboorg pointed out in his discussion of the blood-chilling *Malleus Maleficarum*, "Not all accused of being witches and sorcerers were mentally sick, but almost all mentally sick were considered witches, or sorcerers, or bewitched. As such their treatment was generally to be burned. The problem of mental illness in that day was solved by the Inquisitor. Though the *Malleus* provides good clinical descriptions of various

[10] Today we may be driven to similar reactions as our industrial processes become more and more automated (43). Who controls one's mechanized destiny is a conspicuous aspect of most labor-management contract discussions.

forms of mental disease, since they were regarded as religious problems, little was accomplished in terms of learning about the nature of this illness" (70).

During the Dark Ages, fortunately for civilization, many of the concepts and observations of early Greek medicine were recorded and saved in the libraries of the monasteries, as well as in Mohammedan cultural centers. The economic and social changes effected by the Renaissance sent travellers into the Middle East who brought back some of this knowledge with them. Slowly, science and scientists began to appear in the Western World. New theories about the nature of the natural world began to appear. Such theories were rigorously opposed by the Church, and many early scientists such as Galileo were punished for witchcraft or forced to recant.

With the gradual increase in the scientific exploration of mental ills, the important first step to understanding was the classification of observations. By the sixteenth century some doctors had begun to accumulate series of case records from which they attempted to categorize the various types of mental disorders.

One interesting practitioner who should be mentioned because of his subsequent impact on psychiatry is Anton Mesmer (71). In the latter part of the eighteenth century, Mesmer was fascinating court society and disturbing scientific circles by "curing" various forms of physical disability. Though he was something of a charlatan, by using his concept of "animal magnetism" (this was at first called Mesmerism and, later on, hypnotism), he succeeded in penetrating man's unconscious and influencing it (temporarily). The French Faculty of Medicine, attempting to debunk Mesmer, investigated him and wrote a report which denounced his observations. Erroneously and perhaps speciously presented, it had the effect of obscuring some of the accurate observations made by Mesmer.

During approximately the same period, Phillipe Pinel was practicing in Paris. He developed the first "modern" mental hospital (72). After he was appointed physician-in-chief for the *Bicêtre* and the *Salpêtrière,* two famous Parisian hospitals, he made the momentous decision to strike the chains from the insane and treat them humanely. Pinel's methods were to shape the pattern of treatment for all mentally ill patients, and marked the beginning of the end to fear and ignorance surrounding the "bewitched" insane.

By the beginning of the nineteenth century, much of the superstitious and supernatural aura which had previously surrounded mental illness had been stripped away. In several medical centers of Europe, doctors were actively studying mental disease and were applying the scientific method to their work. The phenomenon of "Mesmerism" had been redescribed as hypnotism. By 1860, Liebeault, working in Nancy, had begun systematically to study hypnosis and to use it for treatment and research (73). In 1882, Bernheim joined Liebeault. Their work is important to the development of psychiatry. They contributed to Freud's early concepts of neuroses. The famous French neurologist, Charcot, director of the Salpêtrière, also had a profound influence on Freud, who visited and worked with Charcot in 1885. In 1882, Charcot had once more presented a detailed description of the phenomena of hypnosis to the French Academy of Science. This time, in contrast to three previous occasions when it had approached the subject of "animal magnetism," the Academy accepted the study with great interest. This officially established the phenomenon of the hypnotic state as a subject for legitimate scientific study and opened the way for much new research in the field of mental illness, and what was later to be known as "the unconscious."

Charcot, with his training in organic medicine, had difficulty in accepting the implications of some of his observations of mental phenomena observed in hypnotized patients. However, Hippolyte Bernheim, utilizing his voluminous observations of hypnotized patients, made "the first (known) attempt to evolve a general understanding of human behavior and its motivation on the basis of the study of psychopathology, rather than on the basis of philosophical systems" (74). Lawyers should note with interest that Bernheim, in 1897, read a paper entitled *L'Hypnotisme et la Suggestion dans leurs Rapports avec la Médecine Légale et les Maladies Mentales* before the International Congress of Medicine in Moscow.

Using as a point of departure his views on suggestion and autosuggestion, Bernheim was the very first to absolve the will, the allegedly great free agent and author of all evil, from the tarnished, old-fashioned stigma of being the origin of mental disease and crime. His was a momentous attempt to destroy the tradition responsible for the mistakes, the cruelty, the complacent sadism, and the just as complacent ignorance which had reigned in theology, law, and medicine for almost two thousand years. Bernheim recognized the existence of involuntary "psychisms," of psychological "automatisms," that is, acts devoid of conscious intent or even conscious origin which impose themselves upon us, and through us upon the world through the multiplicity of obvious and obscure ways in which our imitativeness and suggestibility, or as Bernheim said, our *crédivité naturelle*, works and manifests itself. "In truth," he insisted, "we are all potentially or actually hallucinating people during the greatest part of our lives." He thought that suggestion, to be effective, does not need the induction of hypnotic sleep. Even in the waking states, suggestion works. Persuasion is a form of suggestion: "Suggestion, that is, the idea, no matter where it comes from, imposes itself on our brain and plays a role in almost all crimes. The criminal therefore is no more responsible, legally, than 'a weak tree.' "

Bernheim was thus the first scientific psychologist to advance the principle of the "irresistible impulse," a principle disregarded even now by the majority of the penal codes of the world. No matter how convincing Bernheim's clinical demonstration, the Law . . . persisted for the most part in the attitude that "Bernheim was just a doctor and not a lawyer" [75].

Another French psychiatrist who greatly influenced Freud's thinking was Pierre Janet, a very careful observer who compiled voluminous studies of his neurotic patients. Although he described something of the automatic functioning of the neurotic, and although he used the word "unconscious," he later vehemently denied any similarity to Freud's meaning when he described his theory of the unconscious. This is supported by the fact that Janet looked upon neuroses as being due to neurological degeneration. His is an interesting example of the scientist who, although he describes phenomena accurately and with great insight, is not able to leave the conceptual frame of reference of his own era and advance to newer insights and generalizations (76).

We might roughly summarize the psychiatric activity of Western Europe and America as follows: In France, after the death of Charcot and his group of collaborators, there was a tendency to center investigation on physical causes of mental disease. Voluminous studies appeared which described the various changes attributed to mental degeneration. Typical of these was the work of Morel, who studied the effects of alcohol, narcotics, and other organic etiological factors (77). After his death, the center of psychiatric influence in Europe shifted from France to Germany (78). In the meantime, in England, emphasis tended to center on the care of the mentally ill, without much effort at understanding etiology. One of the more famous English psychiatrists, who shares recognition with Pinel for humanizing the treatment of the mentally ill, was Daniel Hack Tuke (79). Tuke was the leader of British psychiatry until his death in 1785. (The unchaining of patients in England was accomplished by William Tuke, the great-grandfather of Daniel Hack Tuke [80]). In the United States, the major emphasis of psychiatry was on hospital administration. A leader in this activity was Isaac Ray, who wrote one of the first treatises on the legal defense of insanity in a criminal trial (45).

After leadership in psychiatry passed from France to Germany, except for the work of Freud and his followers, the goal of study was to arrive at a system of classification for mental illness. The most prominent of those working in this area was Emil Kraepelin (1855-1926). Kraepelin approached the problem of mental illness in a detached and scientific way (10). He collected thousands of case histories which he analyzed closely in order to discover the factors which they had in common. He was able to produce a classification system which gave a general picture of mental illness as a whole, but "he seems to have been almost unaware that in his careful study he lost the individual" (82). Kraepelin's work epitomized the scientific attitude of his day (33).

Let us now return to the work which Freud was doing.[11] Before Freud began to investigate the function of the mental apparatus, he had worked for many years as a neuroanatomist and a clinical neurologist. He had the best possible training in these fields and was regarded as one of the brilliant young neurologists of his day. He made several contributions to our knowledge of clinical neurology, as well as several fundamental discoveries on the nature of the nervous system (4). Only as clinical experience forced him to face several unexplained manifestations of hysteria did he turn toward the study of unconscious mental functioning in his research. This ran counter to inclination because of his deep distrust for that which could not be subjected to objective experimental evaluation.

[11] For those who are interested, a full description of his life and work is now available in an excellent biographical study by the eminent British psychoanalyst, Ernest Jones (29, 31, 32). This three-volume work is the definitive study. A clear picture of the unfolding of Freud's theories may be gained from it.

However, after Freud returned from his Paris studies with Charcot, he was drawn further and further away from the laboratory approach. His later work became the major source of theoretical formulations in present-day psychiatry. He stands as a monumental figure among behavioral scientists because of his willingness to look where generations had feared to look. He gave his successors not only an example of tenaciousness but also a vast and inspiring framework of speculation based on keen observation coupled with a brilliant intellect, rigorously and creatively applied. Not only was his writing scientifically brilliant, but it is in many instances beautiful from a literary standpoint.[12]

Before Freud left for Paris and Charcot's clinic, he had discussed with Josef Breuer the now famous case of hysteria, Anna O. Breuer had treated her symptoms of hysterical paralysis by what was to be called "the cathartic method." "It was so far outside his experience that it made a deep impression on him, and he would discuss the details of it with Breuer over and over again. When he got to Paris and had an opportunity of talking with Charcot, he told him about the remarkable discovery; but . . . 'Charcot's thoughts seemed to be elsewhere,' and he quite failed to arouse his interest. This seems for a time to have damped his own enthusiasm about the discovery" (30).

Freud returned to Vienna with the firm conviction that hysteria was psychogenic, even though he had learned nothing about the nature of such an origin. During the late 1880's, Freud worked closely with Breuer and, in 1895, he published with Breuer the *Studies in Hysteria* (24), which aroused extensive criticism from the medical world. Also, Breuer was made very uneasy by his female patients' erotic interest in him (a phenomenon now well understood). These two events caused Breuer's interest in hysteria to wane, and he progressively withdrew his support from Freud. The publication of *Studies in Hysteria* marks the beginning of what has become known as *psychoanalysis*. In the course of treating patients, Freud discovered that it was not possible to effect change in them simply by admonition. He discovered the technique of free association at this time, and how the interpretation of these associations could effect more successful treatment. From these early in-

[12] In recognition of these "creative efforts," Freud won the annual Goethe award in 1930 (5).

vestigations, Freud went on to make four major contributions which constitute his discovery—psychoanalysis.

The first of these contributions, and the one which was of utmost importance to the future of psychiatry, was his demonstration of the existence of the *unconscious*. Although the existence of the unconscious had been postulated previously, especially by philosophers such as Jeremy Bentham (8) and Sir William Hamilton (28), Freud was the first to demonstrate and describe this phenomenon clinically.[13] This is one of the most important theoretical concepts of modern psychiatry.

The second important contribution is his *theory of infantile sexuality*. Probably no other subject associated with Freud has stirred up such antagonism and controversy as this one. Freud stated this theory in the early years of the twentieth century, at a time when even to acknowledge that sex existed was largely taboo. His thesis that children have sexual feelings was shocking and revolting to a whole world of "respectable" people. Many scientific periodicals and those lay publications which acknowledged his theories at all (56), joined in denying and mocking them. However, Freud persisted, and stated that in the end the evidence would speak for itself (as it has [10a]).

Freud's third contribution was his attempt to unify all psychic activity under one theoretical explanation. This he called the *libido theory*. The central point of this theory is that there is a basic psychic energy, libido, which stems from the stimulation of the psyche by all of the physiological forces. This energy is capable of being shifted to (invested in) various organ sites or persons (objects), under the control of the ego (the "management" portion of the psyche). These shifts (cathexes) are motivated by considerations of internal physiological drives, external (reality) limitations, and learned (internalized) value systems (conscience or "superego"). He visualized this as being analogous to other energy systems and behavior; hysterical symptom formation and character structure were manifestations of accumulated libido.

For many years Freud attempted to categorize all instincts as subordinate to the libido. Later in his career, after heated debates with several of his close associates (especially Adler and Jung),

[13] There are some interesting connections between philosophy and Freud's work (65).

he adopted a dual instinct theory. While there is still some controversy among analysts as to whether there is one instinct or
whether there are two, most present-day analytic theory does not
follow Freud's initial libido concept (7). Much of its significance
has been incorporated, however, into subsequent conceptualizations.
This concept is important as one of the first attempts to place all
clinical observations of emotional disability under a single theoretical explanation (41).

The fourth of Freud's contributions is the psychoanalytic method
of psychotherapy. Most present-day treatment methods incorporate
to some degree the techniques of free association and interpretation
which Freud discovered and perfected. He found that individuals,
if encouraged to verbalize everything which came into their minds,
would inevitably, with the interpretive help of the analyst, discover
the directions and nature of their unconscious emotional attitudes.
Some changes have been made in this technique from its classical
beginnings, but the basic idea is present in most contemporary
techniques.

Unlike the development of psychiatry and psychoanalytic thought
in Europe, the analytic movement in the United States has always
been associated with medicine. This has been fortunate in that it
brought the friendly introduction of dynamic psychological theory
into the practice and teaching of medicine. Prior to the introduction
of Freud's works in the United States, there were several brilliant
psychiatrists working here who, themselves, were aiming at dynamic
concepts of human behavior (81).[14] One of the major figures in the
development of contemporaneous American psychiatry was Adolph
Meyer. He arrived in the United States from Zurich in 1892. After
working in several mental hospitals, he was appointed Professor of
Psychiatry at Johns Hopkins University. Early in his career, he had
abandoned the widely accepted systems of nomenclature elaborated
by Kahlbaum, Hecker, and Kraepelin, and defined what he called
"reaction types." These were detailed descriptions of total personality reactions, with attempts to define why they functioned as they
did. Although he never accepted psychoanalytic theory and remained aloof from the important work of Bleuler, he did view
patients' reactions as a summation of the organic, sociocultural, and

[14] For a history of American psychiatry and psychoanalysis see Oberndorf's treatise
(42).

psychological influences on their development. Meyer wrote very little, but his personal leadership had a profound effect on American psychiatrists (35, 37).

> In this respect he was one of the very last representatives of a great age which required that a psychiatrist be acquainted not only with the routine of managing mental patients, but with the history of medicine and science, with the theories one accepts and imposes, with the sum total of the cultural heritage which a current civilization represents. It is within this current civilization that man stays healthy or becomes ill, depending on the interaction of his total personality with the world he is called upon to meet [83].

Although Freud visited the United States in 1909 to give a series of lectures at Clark University (23), there was no immediate response to this visit. Stanley Hall and James J. Putnam of Harvard were familiar with Freud, but it was not until A. A. Brill began to publish translations of Freud's articles in 1909 that analytic work became known in the United States. Brill is regarded as the original disseminator of psychoanalysis in the United States, and in 1911 he founded the first American psychoanalytic society. From these early beginnings, and after Hitler's rise to power in Germany, the United States came to the forefront of leadership in the field of psychoanalytic medicine (55). Today there is a growing trend in all medical centers and medical schools in the United States to use a theory of psychiatry which is dynamic in character, although they often draw on an eclectic background for their theoretical constructs. This is a healthy trend, and shows not only the growing awareness of the importance of personality in health and disease, but also stands to bring psychological theory into closer proximity with laboratory medicine (3).

PROBLEMS

Example

One day, while walking through the corridor of the courthouse, you encounter the judge who is sitting in the criminal court. Instead of merely exchanging good-mornings, you find yourself appointed counsel for an

indigent defendant charged with first-degree homicide. After accepting
the good wishes of the judge, you proceed to the prosecutor's office
where you obtain the particulars of the charge against your client. The
allegations are as follows:

Defendant, a Spanish-speaking farm laborer, has signed a confession
stating that he strangled the victim and then buried the body in the floor
of the chicken coop. Seven months later, he dug up the body, decapi-
tated it, cleaned the skull, and then used it to perform a voodoo ritual.
When the ritual did not work, he became worried, engineered his own
apprehension, and then confessed. The prosecutor comments to you in
passing that your client "certainly is a strange fellow." After a brief
visit with him in his cell, you're ready to concur with the observation.
The problem is what to do. What legal tack should be taken?

The first issue to clarify in this case is why the defendant became involved in such a bizarre crime. Since the details of the confession coincide
completely with the coroner's autopsy report, there is little reason (or
hope?) to find the confession inaccurate. Why did he commit the crime,
and how can you find the answer to that question?

The weird details of this case should lead counsel to seek immediate
consultation with a psychiatrist. The psychiatrist should carry out a
thorough examination in order to ascertain the motivational basis for the
homicide. He (the psychiatrist) will undoubtedly engage the services of
a clinical psychologist in order to administer a projective test battery and
pin down the motivational matrix of defendant's behavior, and to objectify such concepts as far as possible.

Perhaps consultation with a sociologist or an anthropologist would
cast light on the cultural background (Puerto Rican) of the man, in
order that sharper differentiation between cultural patterns and psychic
status may be drawn. (This "differential diagnosis" will be crucial to
subsequent decision-making for the client.)

After all of these examinations and consultations have been carried
out, and after all available information and evidence has been placed in
the hands of the psychiatrist, he should be able to set forth a full dynamic
formulation of the defendant's behavior before, during, and after the
act of homicide. Then counsel can intelligently answer such questions
as whether or not his client is competent to stand trial, whether he
should plead insanity, whether he should plead mitigation because of
incapacity to have the appropriate *mens rea* for first degree murder, and
how to handle a multitude of strategic and tactical details of the trial.[15]

[15] Because we have not yet dealt sufficiently with dynamic theory, the actual
formulation of this case will not be set forth.

The psychiatric consultant, if he knows or if counsel teaches him about the trial issues, may be able to give useful assistance with these complicated questions.[16]

Another problem exists in this case which raises several intriguing questions: the defendant speaks Spanish, which will necessitate the use of an interpreter. What effect does the use of an interpreter have on a psychiatric examination? Should the testimony of a Spanish-speaking psychiatrist have greater evidencial weight during a trial? What if the interpreter does not understand the nuances of a psychiatric examination? These and other *behavioral* problems would be raised by the fact of defendant's foreign tongue.

In summary, counsel, when confronted by a situation such as this, should move to engage the services of a qualified, dynamically trained psychiatrist who will help him to conceptualize a theory of the case which can account for every known detail about defendant and his behavior (66). The psychiatrist should engage a clinical psychologist, whose test observations would be utilized to cross-check, correlate, or invalidate the clinical conclusions arrived at by the psychiatrist during his examination. At that point, additional information about defendant's background may also be sought through consultation with an anthropologist or sociologist.

All of these data must be fitted finally into the *context* of the case before decisions can be made wisely. All should be handled with the assistance of the expert so that his evidence will be made comprehensible to the fact-finders. When such a procedure is followed, a lucid description of the crime will ensue and the fact-finders will have all the data possible in order to reach a decision with maximum rationality. Without such a thorough presentation, they can only mobilize their most atavistic impulses in order to gain a sense of security, and a punitive verdict would more probably be rendered.

1. There is much discussion in the press and in legal literature about the "deterrent effect" of various kinds of punishment. Describe how you would set up a study of the deterrent effects of incarceration on those found guilty of "drunken driving," using the "scientific method" and using the tools of dynamic psychiatry.

2. What do you consider to be the barriers to the scientific study of the judicial process?

[16] The details of this problem are drawn from a real case encounter. Although not all of these procedures were carried out, most were, and the "formulation" of the case was well accomplished (2).

3. From your reading on the methodology of psychiatric investigation, what do you consider to be its limitations of usefulness to law? Its values?

4. (a) The possibility of using behavioral science experts to assist in the preparation and/or trial of a law case often arises. When should one retain the services of (1) a psychologist, (2) a psychiatrist, (3) a psychoanalyst to help prepare the defense in a murder trial? What would be their respective roles in the trial?

(b) When a psychiatrist testifies as an expert witness for the defense in a murder trial, how may you test his competence? His credibility? What kinds of special problems are likely to arise in the course of his testimony regarding his opinion as to the facts in the case? See *Briscoe v. U. S.* (248 F. 2d 640 [1957]).

(c) What are your reactions to the views of the reviewing courts in regard to the psychiatric testimony in *Commonwealth v. Moon* (125 A2d 594), and *Douglas v. U. S.* (239 F. 2d 52).

REFERENCES

1. American Psychiatric Association, Committee on Public Information, *A Psychiatric Glossary*. Washington, D. C.: American Psychiatric Association, 1957, p. 36.
2. *Aponte v. State of New Jersey*, 30 N. J. 441, 1959.
3. Appel, K. E., Psychoanalysis: Reflections of Varying Concepts. *Amer. J. Psychiat.*, 112:712, 1956.
4. Arlow, J. A., *The Legacy of Sigmund Freud*. New York: International Universities Press, 1956, pp. 12-16.
5. *Ibid.*, pp. 95-96.
6. Asch, S. E., *Social Psychology*. New York: Prentice-Hall, 1952.
7. Bellak, L., Ostow, M., Pumpian-Mindlin, E., Stanton, A. H., & Szasz, T., Conceptual and Methodological Problems in Psychoanalysis. *Ann. N. Y. Acad. Sci.*, 76:971-1134, 1959.
8. Bentham, J., *Works*. Edinburgh: W. Tait, 1843.
9. Bohannan, P., *African Homicide and Suicide*. Princeton: Princeton University Press, 1960.
10. Braceland, F. J., Kraepelin, His System and His Influence. *Amer. J. Psychiat.*, 113:871-876, 1957.
10a. Broderick, C., Preadolescent Sexual Behavior. *Med. Aspects Human Sexuality*, 2(1):20-29, 1968.
11. Campbell, A., Converse, P., Miller, W. E., & Stokes, D. E., *The American Voter*. New York: John Wiley, 1960.
12. Cardozo, B. N., *The Nature of the Judicial Process*. New Haven: Yale University Press, 1921, p. 81.

13. Cartwright, D. & Zander, A., Eds., *Group Dynamics*. Evanston, Ill.: Row, Peterson, 1953.
14. Cobb, S., One Hundred Years of Progress in Neurology, Psychiatry and Neurosurgery. *Arch. Neurol. & Psychiat.*, 59:63-98, 1949.
15. Deutsch, F., Analysis of Postural Behavior. *Psychoanal. Quart.*, 16:195-213, 1947.
16. Deutsch, F., Correlations of Verbal and Nonverbal Communication in Interviews Elicited by The Associative Anamnesis. *Psychosom. Med.*, 21:123-130, 1959.
17. Drever, J., *A Dictionary of Psychology*. Harmondsworth, Eng.: Penguin Books, 1952, p. 304.
18. *Ibid.*, p. 226.
19. *Ibid.*, p. 74.
20. *Ibid.*, p. 227.
21. Freud, S., On Dreams (1901). *Standard Edition*, 5:629-686. London: Hogarth Press, 1953.
22. Freud, S., An Outline of Psychoanalysis (1910). *Standard Edition*, 23:141-207. London: Hogarth Press, 1964.
23. *Ibid.*
24. Freud, S. & Breuer, J., Studies on Hysteria (1843-1895). *Standard Edition*, 2. London: Hogarth Press, 1955.
25. Gitelson, M., Psychoanalyst, U. S. A. 1955. *Amer. J. Psychiat.*, 9:704, 1956.
26. *Ibid.*, p. 700.
27. Group for the Advancement of Psychiatry, Report No. 25: Collaborative Research in Psychopathology. Topeka, Kansas, 1954, pp. 6-7.
28. Hamilton, W., *The Metaphysics of Sir William Hamilton*, Cambridge: Sever & Francis, 1862.
29. Jones, E., *The Life and Work of Sigmund Freud: 1856-1900; The Formative Years and The Great Discoveries*, Vol. 1. New York: Basic Books, 1955.
30. *Ibid.*, p. 226.
31. Jones, E., *The Life and Work of Sigmund Freud: 1901-1919; Years of Maturity*, Vol. 2. New York: Basic Books, 1955.
32. Jones, E., *The Life and Work of Sigmund Freud: 1919-1934; The Last Phase*, Vol. 3. New York: Basic Books, 1957.
33. Kraepelin, E., *Lectures on Clinical Psychiatry*. New York: W. Wood, 1917.
34. Kubie, L., Problems and Techniques of Psychoanalytic Validation and Progress. In: *Psychoanalysis as a Science*. New York: Basic Books, p. 46-124.
35. Lewis, N. D. C., American Psychiatry from Its Beginnings to World War II. In: *American Handbook of Psychiatry*, Ed. S. Arieti. New York: Basic Books, 1959, pp. 10-11.
36. Lorenz, K. Z., The Evolution of Behavior. *Scient. Amer.*, 199:67-78, 1958.
37. Meyer, A., Objective Psychology or Psychobiology with Subordination of the Medically Useless Contrast of Mental and Physical. *J. Amer. Med. Assn.*, 65:860-862, 1915.
38. Miller, E. G., Jr., Scientific Method and Social Problems. *Science*, 109:290-291, 1949.

39. Montagu, A., *The Direction of Human Development*. New York: Harper Bros., 1955, pp. 7-8.
40. Munroe, R. L., *Schools of Psychoanalytic Thought*. New York: Dryden Press, 1955, p. 308.
41. *Ibid.*, pp. 238-241.
42. Oberndorf, C. P., *A History of Psychoanalysis in America*. New York: Grune & Stratton, 1953.
43. Pederson-Krag, G., A Psychoanalytic Approach to Mass Production. *Psychoanal. Quart.*, 20:434-451, 1951.
44. Rado, S., Psychodynamics as a Basic Science. *Amer. J. Orthopsychiat.*, 33:405, 1946
45. Ray, I., *A Treatise on the Medical Jurisprudence of Insanity*. Boston: Little Brown, 1860.
46. Redmount, R. S., Psychological Tests for Selecting Jurors. *Univ. Kansas Law Rev.*, 5:391-403, 1957.
47. Redmount, R. S., The Psychological Basis of Evidence Practices: Intelligence. *Minn. Law Rev.*, 42:559-597, 1958.
48. Redmount, R. S., The Psychological Basis of Evidence Practices: Memory. *J. Crim. Law, Criminol. & Poli. Sci.*, 50:249-264, 1959.
49. Richfield, J., On the Scientific Status of Psychoanalysis. *Sci. Monthly*, 79:306-309, 1954.
50. Russell, B., Science and Human Life. In: *What Is Science?* Ed. J. R. Newman. New York: Simon & Schuster, 1955, p. 17.
51. Saul, L. J., Preventive Psychiatry. *Proc. Amer. Philosoph. Soc.*, 93:330, 1949.
52. Saul, L. J., *The Bases of Human Behavior*. Philadelphia: J. B. Lippincott, 1951, pp. 3-5.
53. Saul, L. J., Snyder, T. R., & Sheppard, E., On Earliest Memories. *Psychoanal. Quart.*, 25:228-237, 1956.
54. Saul, L. J. & Watson, A. S., Milestones in Psychoanalysis. In: *Present-Day Psychology*, Ed. A. A. Roback, New York: Philosophical Library, 1955, pp. 563-590.
55. *Ibid.*, pp. 567-570.
56. Seldes, G., The Wreckage of Psycho-Analysis. *Redbook*, 50(4):86-90, 1928.
57. Shakow, D., Research in Child Development: A Case Illustration of the Psychologist's Dilemma. *Amer. J. Orthopsychiat.*, 29:45-59, 1959.
58. Shakow, D., The Recorded Psychoanalytic Interview as an Objective Approach to Research in Psychoanalysis. *Psychoanal. Quart.*, 29:82-97, 1960.
59. Sherif, M. & Sherif, C., *An Outline of Social Psychology*, New York: Harper & Row, 1956.
60. Skoler, D. L., A Program Is Launched. *Juvenile Court Judges J.*, 14:12-17, 1963.
61. Stephen, J., *History of Criminal Law in England*, Vol. 2. London: Macmillan & Co., 1883, p. 128.
62. Szasz, T. S. X., *Law, Liberty and Psychiatry*. New York: Macmillan, 1963.
63. Vintner, R. & Janowitz, M., Effective Institutions for Juvenile Delinquents: A Research Statement. *Soc. Serv. Rev.*, 33:118-130, 1959.
64. Waelder, R., *Basic Theory of Psychoanalysis*. New York: International Universities Press, 1960, pp. 3-31.

65. Watson, A. S., Freud the Translator; Some Contacts with Philosophy. *Internat. J. Psychoanal.*, 39:326-327, 1958.
66. Watson, A. S., Communication between Psychiatrists and Lawyers. In: *International Psychiatry Clinics*, Vol. 1. Boston: Little, Brown, 1964, pp. 185-198.
67. Washburn, S. L., Human Evolution. In: *What Is Science?* Ed. J. R. Newman: Simon & Schuster, 1955.
68. White, L. A., *The Science of Culture*. New York: Farrar, Straus, 1949, pp. 3-21.
69. Zilboorg, G., Psychoanalytic Borderlines. *Amer. J. Psychiat.*, 112:708, 1956.
70. Zilboorg, G. & Henry, G., *A History of Medical Psychology*. New York: W. W. Norton, 1941, pp. 144-174.
71. *Ibid.*, pp. 342-350.
72. *Ibid.*, pp. 319-328.
73. *Ibid.*, p. 357.
74. *Ibid.*, p. 368.
75. *Ibid.*, pp. 368-369.
76. *Ibid.*, pp. 375-377.
77. *Ibid.*, pp. 400-404.
78. *Ibid.*, p. 403.
79. *Ibid.*, pp. 422-431.
80. *Ibid.*, pp. 315-317.
81. *Ibid.*, p. 419.
82. *Ibid.*, p. 452.
83. *Ibid.*, pp. 503-504.

III

Concepts of Structure, Function and Development of the Personality

The strongest objection raised against the acceptance of much psychiatric theory is the fact that it is built largely on hypotheses which do not readily lend themselves to "proof." This is indeed cause for suspicion, and yet men of intelligence and scientific integrity *do* accept these hypotheses and employ them in their work. We do not possess the necessary physiological facts nor suitable experimental animals to explore human thought, feeling, and behavior through the usual experimental manipulations. The complexity of the variables in each human situation is such that no statistical design yet devised can handle them adequately.[1] The need to deal with human problems and to treat patients has been present in all civilizations. In this century, however, that pressure has been enormously intensified by the breakdown of traditional systems of belief, and enormously magnified by shrinking space which formerly isolated and quarantined many human problems. The only tool available has been intellectual manipulation. It has been necessary to erect various theoretical abstractions to account for the observable phenomena of mental life. After Freud, it remains for experimental procedures, clinical evidence, and statistical analysis to correct,

---

[1] Statistical analysis provides us with results either so basic or so superficial as to be virtually useless in helping us to *understand* behavior, although it is extremely useful for checking isolated facts.

modify, and amplify that body of fact, theory, and speculation which is the stuff of contemporary "dynamic psychiatry."

Freud, at the time of his early investigations and speculations into the mental life of his patients, stated clearly that even though he was forced to resort to abstractions to account for what he saw, in the last analysis, all mental function was subject to the governing mechanisms of physiology. Although a great deal has been learned in the fields of neurophysiology and neuroanatomy since Freud's day, the gaps in our knowledge are still so large that any practical effort to understand human behavior must still rest on metapsychological abstraction (63).

"Economic" Abstractions

In his initial theoretical speculations about mental functioning, Freud was concerned primarily with what might be called the energy sources of the psyche. His abstractions were similar to some of the concepts of energy mechanics of that era, and he attempted to subsume all mental activity under a unitary concept—*libido theory*. This theory postulated that "libido," the basic psychic energy, could be likened to the amoeba which "can stretch out pseudopodia, originally concentrated within its own body substance, toward the outside world, and then draw them back again [27]." While libido has often been paraphrased as "sexual energy," this usage bears no similarity to the usual meaning of the word sex. Rather, libido signifies sensual pleasure in the very broadest sense, and includes any form of pleasurable tension release, connected with any part of the physical organism.

Libido was conceived as having an "aim"—the specific discharge action which dispels physical excitement (i.e., tension) and thus achieves satisfaction. It has an "object," defined as that instrument (i.e., person, activity, or body structure) by which or through which the aim may be achieved. And last, libido has a source—the chemico-physical stimulus which produces the excitement or tension state (28). Here we see, then, a concept of psychological energy, with generator, power lines, and machinery to produce a specific result.

For many years psychoanalysts attempted to view all psychic energy as libido. However, in time, the influence of Alfred Adler

forced awareness of the importance of social striving and competi-
tiveness as a source of psychic energy (80). This resulted in a dual
instinct theory wherein libido and aggression were viewed as opposing forces in psychic life. Adler also seemed to point the way toward the contemporary view that, in the end, all psychic energy
serves the purpose of adapting the person to his internal and external
environments, and the patterns utilized in such adaptation are a
function of past experience as well as the innate biophysiologic
apparatus with which a person is born.

Much early psychoanalytic writing attempts to understand all
human behavior by referring it back to a single drive—sex. This
aspect of analytic theory, which has the smallest claim to fame
among practitioners, is the best known to the public, as a wealth
of jokes testify. The greatest practical importance these theories
had was to insist on recognition of the importance of sexual drives,
which society had succeeded in ignoring. Thus, in a Victorian society, the force of the sexual drive was held to the light. In our
era, which makes such a fetish of superficial good will, the strength
and impact of hostility has moved to the fore.

"Anatomical" Abstractions

The next set of abstractions to be considered are utilized to conceptualize *structural* relationships in the psyche.[2] These "structures"
are termed the *id,* the *ego,* and the *superego.* It must be re-emphasized that these designations have never borne relationship to any
anatomical correlates but were defined, rather, in terms of functions
attributed to them (64). Although there is some evidence now
available about the approximate location of some of these psychophysiological functions, such locations are still very general in
character. Walter has said, "The Freudian analysts named, but
never dared to identify, the hierarchy of id and ego, superego and
censor. An Explorer searching the whereabouts of these locations
might rough out a map: id—mid-brain?; ego—sensory cortex?; censor
—K-complex spindles" (103). Let us examine each of these "structures" separately.

---

[2] These abstractions have also been designated as "geographic" or "topographical,"
and contrast with the economic abstractions which imply *physiological* relationships.

The Id

Id is the biological force of the organism which provides the psychic energies utilized to solve the problems of survival and social living. It is made up of the instinctual, inborn, unlearned aspects of personality, which the individual brings into the world with him. It is the "drives." In a sense, it represents the biological needs to which the individual must respond. Saul has stated, "The term 'id' expresses the impersonal nature of the biologic forces which power the organism, some of which power the mind. The regulation of the body temperature, the subtle chemistry of digestion, the outpouring of cells and anti-bodies to attack infectious bacteria, and the myriad mechanisms of regulation and defense all take place, for the most part, automatically and impersonally. Some of these forces well up into the mind; self-preservation and hunger; love, mating, reproduction and rearing of young; the fight-flight reaction; impulses to cooperate and to make societies.

"The id quite naturally generates mature drives, as well as those which are immature, and those which are of a basic nature, not properly classifiable as mature or immature. By 'immature' is meant the drives and the responses of the organism before it reaches its full growth and full adult powers. . . . When it reaches adulthood it is driven by desires for independence, for mating, home, and offspring, as is seen throughout the animal kingdom. . . . Not uncommonly the id is spoken of as though it generated only the infantile urges, whereas obviously the mature drives of the adult also well up from the id [91]." It presses implacably toward maturity. To use a homely illustration, no matter how much a child may wish to continue being rocked to sleep on his mother's breast, and regardless of how strong is the mother's desire to continue to do it, soonor or later his mere increase in size makes it impossible.

Current research has begun to elucidate the physiological and biochemical bases of the instincts. Future gains in these areas of investigation will no doubt give us far more precise knowledge, but, for the foreseeable future, we shall need to conceptualize the effects of culture and conditioning on these biological substrates in abstract terms.

In summary, the id is the powerhouse of the personality—the biological energy of human life and its instinctual channels. Although we have no way of measuring differences, each individual is born with a specific id or instinct potential. There may be a wide variation of potential from one person to another, but the manner in which each learns to channel this energy and relate it to the highly variable external world accounts for individuality.

The Ego

In considering the problem of "relating to the external world," we enter the domain of the *ego*. This part of the psyche effects adaptation between the inner world of the self and the outer world of reality. Obviously, this must be a complicated and elaborate set of functions.

The study of ego is relatively new in the field of clinical psychiatry. Once the tabooed subjects of sex and instincts were fairly well understood, it became apparent that the specific ways in which each individual handled his instinctual life and the way he related his instinctual life to his surroundings was of major importance.

The concept of the ego evolved very slowly and, as with all such concepts, underwent a series of modifications. It was first described as consciousness, but then unconscious ego aspects were discovered to be of at least equal importance. The first extensive description of the ego is to be found in Freud's book, *The Ego and the Id*. This was a rather static treatment of the subject, and it was some time before dynamic descriptions of the ego began to appear in the psychiatric literature. The first systematic study of ego functioning and its influence on "character" was made by Wilhelm Reich (88) in *Character Analysis* (1933). In 1936, Anna Freud published a landmark study of ego, *The Ego and Mechanisms of Defense* (48). Although these and other studies of the communicating and coordinating center of the personality are relatively new, we understand enough about this aspect of mental behavior to make major use of it in all aspects of psychiatric work.[3]

To describe the ego in more contemporary terms, we may say that it has the function of maintaining what has been called *homeostasis*. This is the condition in which the biophysiological processes of the organism are in optimum balance to fulfill adaptive needs. For example, if blood is lost through hemorrhage, fluid will promptly be

[3] For another classic treatise, see Hartmann (61).

shifted into the bloodstream to make up for lost blood volume. At the same time, the organs which produce blood cells are stimulated to manufacture enough cells to make up for those lost. When the "normal" blood volume and blood-cell count is restored, the *state* of homeostasis is achieved and the "homeostatic process" is successful. While the term was used initially to describe physiological processes, it is now equally useful for understanding psychological adaptation. By this view, *all* acts, thoughts, feelings, and attitudes are related to the person's total adjustment process and therefore are of *positive* value. Seen in this light, they are *needed* until some more effective means can be "learned." This is a crucial concept when such problems as prediction of future behavior, treatment, and reconstruction of past actions are contemplated. It is a vital foundation stone in modern dynamic theory, and nearly all legal questions turn on such a consideration.

As suggested above, the structure of the ego is defined mainly by the study of its functions. Perhaps this is comparable to the philosophical approach of Voltaire's Dr. Pangloss who said, "Observe: our noses were made to carry spectacles, so we have spectacles" (100). However, in our present stage of knowledge, this technique affords us our best means of understanding. It is possible to categorize the functions of the ego in various ways, but we shall divide these activities into nine principal areas.[4]

Functions of the Ego

Perception. As the new-born comes into contact with the multiple stimuli of its surroundings, one of the first activities of the ego is that of perception.[5] Perception is "the process of becoming immediately aware of something" (22). The ego "has two perceptive surfaces, one directed inwardly toward the instinctive impulses and needs, the other directed toward external reality through sense per-

[4] For a more detailed breakdown of the ego's functioning, especially as it relates to the control of aggression, see the excellent work of Redl and Wineman, *Children Who Hate* (86). This study is of special interest to lawyers since it deals with a group of young children who were well on the road toward totally delinquent and criminal behavior. It is an excellent description of the dynamics of their behavior as well as techniques for altering it. For another fine description of ego functioning see Heinz Hartmann, *Comments on the Psychoanalytic Theory of Ego* (62).

[5] In fact, it is clear that a child *in utero* can perceive, since conditioned reflexes may be set up (86). Do we need to re-examine the old wives' tales about prenatal influences?

ception" (1). External perception is the most familiar. It is effected through the five senses (sight, hearing, taste, touch, smell) with their specialized end organs which are adapted to the reception of specific stimuli (i.e., eye-light, skin-touch, ear-sound).

Internal perception is less familiar. The more obvious examples relate to such physiological reactions as hunger, sensations of full bladder or bowel, and an awareness of sexual tension. There is evidence that we are more highly aware of the physiological activities of our viscera than was believed earlier. "Silent" physical ailments and disabilities may be reflected in a person's dream activity which *must* reflect awareness on an unconscious level.

Intellect. The next ego function is intellectual and logical activity, commonly called "thinking." This involves the ego's ability to sort out its perceptions, call forth appropriate memory associations, and bring them into relationship with new perceptions from the person's past experience. These logical thought processes are extremely elaborate. In spite of the complexity of this function, it is the one most generally understood (i.e., accepted) as part of the personality.

Memory. Memory is an ego activity of great importance and special human uniqueness. There are two types of memory: feeling or emotional memory, and the "idea" memory of abstract symbols. While Freud speculated that the brain was capable of splitting off emotion from idea and storing the memories separately, he had no experimental or anatomical evidence to support this speculation. Recent experiments by Penfield show decisively that this splitting does occur. He has located abstract symbol memory in the frontal lobes, and the "interpretive" memory of emotion in the temporal lobe (83). The coordination of these two components of memory occurs in some of the nuclei of the hypothalamus or "brain stem," the most primitive part of the brain.

More is known about symbolic memory than about memory of feelings. Symbolic memory must be carried out in code through the use of symbol images. When a person has an experience, he reduces it to a series of symbolic representations of that experience. For example, if one remembers "I rode a horse," he will have a highly complex set of symbols which he can draw forth to describe that experience at a later date. However, the description will be comprehensible to another person only to the extent in which they have had shared experiences surrounding the coded symbols. In other words, memory and its coding are a highly personal process, and to communicate memories to another, much mutual exploration of the code is necessary.

Several theories have been generated recently to account for the mental process of memory. Probably, memories are stored by means of a "reverberating circuit." This is a chain of neurons (nerve cells) which tend to keep themselves active by a closed cycle of stimulation, and are not unlike the elements of electronic computors. In fact, the function of memory and association of memories are thought by some to be analogous to the behavior of these electronic brains (77).

Memory and the symbol-forming capability are capacities peculiar to the human mind which make possible man's elaborate functioning and his accumulation of experience in the form of culture.[6] "Very early in the human story the brain must have acquired the mechanism of what we recognize in action as imagination, calculation, prediction. Later came the processes of abstract reason and the control of what we call violence. The operation of these mental controls . . . can be recorded as electrical eddies swirling in subtle patterns through the brain. But our most sensitive instruments, amplifying the electrical changes ten million times or more, detect only isolated and intermittent elements of these higher functions in the brains of other animals" (104).

Integration. Next is the synthetic and integrative function of the ego. Accumulating memories and reacting perceptively to one's surroundings have little value if they cannot be organized into usable patterns. The ego is capable of pulling together or associating meaningful memories, experiences, and feelings from the past with the immediate problem under consideration. The new experiences are tied in with the old, and become part of the ego's data for use in future similar situations. It is only through the efficient use of this ego function that a person is able to face and solve problems.

Judgment. Once present perceptions have been compared with past experiences and related to them, the next function of the ego to be called into action is judgment. Since any new experience is not

---

[6] Perhaps this peculiarity is merely a matter of degree, since it is now amply clear that many lower animals do develop cultures and pass these data on to their offspring. The scientific data on this subject is to be found in the literature of the new biological science of ethology (70).

likely to be exactly identical with the past, the ego is called upon to make new decisions and choices in reaction to the current problem. It must balance past, present, and future demands with the demands of reality. "Good judgment" means that the ego is capable of sorting out all aspects of a problem, and of coming up with an algebraic sum of its parts.[7]

Executive. Good decisions and good judgments are relatively useless without some form of action. Once they are achieved, the ego utilizes its executive function. An absence of action may also be a form of activity—an inhibiting action. A man in the desert who encounters a rattlesnake at close range feels a strong impulse to jump away. However, a well-functioning ego might produce the recall that when a rattlesnake is encountered, it is better to stand still or "freeze" and allow the rattler to retreat. In this instance, the ego acts to immobilize and counter all impulses to move. Such an executive act is the mark of a well-functioning, experienced ego, capable of overcoming primitive action impulses and of giving the individual maximum opportunity for survival.

Reality Testing. A healthy person's ego constantly evaluates all of his actions and tests them for efficiency. This is called the reality-testing function. In relation to the rattlesnake illustration above, the decision to freeze would be observed as an effective way to deal with rattlesnakes. It would be "remembered" as a tested and successful solution. This capacity to test is the most important of all of the ego's activities, and effective learning is anchored in reality testing. Ideally, a person should be capable of examining every aspect of his activity and his thoughts about his activity, and to relate this introspection to the results achieved if he is to make skillful and fruitful decisions in the future. Failure of this function is manifested as progressive loss of contact with the environment and is the primary symptom of mental illness.

Defense. Very often reality has a way of creating pain and anxiety. The ego is capable of drastic measures to keep the organism in a state of comfort. When reality creates more discomfort than the person can bear, and there is no immediate solace or relief in sight, the ego may utilize its function of defense. The ego's defense mechanisms are the means by which it wards off painful feelings. Since

[7] Example of "algebraic sum": $-2 - 4 + 7 - 3 = -2$

they always involve some distortion of reality, they must be unconscious in order to succeed. If we are to avoid facing something painful, we must not know that we are ignoring the threat or this would itself create more anxiety. In order to escape the surveillance of the ego's reality-testing function, the defenses are kept beneath the surface of awareness and are unknown to the individual who employs them. Each person's defenses tend to evolve in specialized patterns, according to the nature of their prior experience. While the presence of some defenses is "normal" (and in fact to the growing child they are essential), if they occur to any excessive degree, they must be regarded as pathological. This does not mean that they are ineffective or that they do not solve the individual's homeostatic needs, but the very nature of the solution exacts a toll on the ego's efficiency.

Although defenses will be discussed more fully later, let us demonstrate the manner in which they work by returning to the example of the encounter with a rattlesnake. Anyone encountering a rattlesnake (that is, anyone who knows what a rattlesnake is) would be startled and frightened. This reaction is appropriate since rattlesnakes are dangerous. An immature or inexperienced ego might well be overwhelmed by the threat and the fear. To avoid stark panic, something would have to be done to master the sensation of great danger. One possible defense would be to look at the rattlesnake and "not see it," and thereby not "know" that there was any danger. While this technique has some psychological efficiency and permits the conscious "sensation" of comfort, in fact, the individual is in much greater danger than before. This illustrates the pathological and self-defeating way in which defenses may function, as well as the immediate "gain" they provide.

Dream Censorship. The last ego function which we will discuss is really not separate from those already described. However, since we shall use it as one of our special means of investigating the characteristics of a person's psyche, we shall place it in a separate category of significance. One of the main purposes of dreaming is to keep the dreamer comfortable enough so that he may maintain sleep (20). The ego tends to take the left-over problems of the day and, by symbolizing, disguising, and "censoring" them, produce dreams which allow sleep to continue and physiological and psychological equilibrium to be restored. Censorship is revealed largely by the way in which the dream content is symbolized, and this is a part of "the dream work" of the ego. We shall later discuss the manner in which this dream work is carried on.

These brief descriptions can only suggest the elaborate activity of the ego. Every instant of the day and night all of these activities are going on simultaneously, with some shift of importance from one to another, according to the situation of the moment. It is because of this complexity and because so much ego activity is unconscious that it is so difficult to use standard experimental techniques to elucidate the nature of human mental activity. One cannot isolate a single aspect of the ego by any experimental technique without grossly altering other activities by the doing. We have ample evidence to demonstrate that the most simple intervention in an interpersonal relationship stirs up specific reactions to that intervention which are of a highly personal nature (73). We may bemoan the fact that this difficulty makes our scientific investigations so complex. However, there is little we can do about it except to recognize our involvement in the experiments and attempt to understand them at the same time. One of the best ways we know for doing this is through the use of "analytic technique" which is designed to deal with multiple variables simultaneously.

The Superego

The *superego* is the part of the psyche which deals with ethical and moral value judgments, and contains a mind's-eye picture of an ideal way to behave and to be. (The latter is called the *ego ideal*.) Alexander has defined the superego as ". . . the mind's latest development, which embodies the code of society. This code is dependent upon the social environment and varies in different cultural milieus. Through identification with adults this code is gradually incorporated into the personality and becomes a part of it" (2). Fenichel calls the superego the "part which has the function (among others) of deciding which impulses are acceptable and which are not . . ."(29). Part of the superego is conscious and rational, part is unconscious and irrational.

Lawyers have a particular interest in this part of the personality since much of the behavior which falls under the purview of the law emanates from the immature or inappropriate superegos of the persons involved. "The law," in fact, represents at least part of the individual superego, and is a part of the social conscience (other parts are morals, ethics, mores, and religious ideals). Law will be effective only insofar as it correlates closely with the superegos of the members of society. Questions of "deterrence," "rehabilitation," and "retribution" all relate to the problems of *how* the conscience functions and *how* it is formed. What does retribution do to an offender's conscience to modify his subsequent behavior? Does retribution have any impact of consequence upon the conscience of society, so that conformity to socially acceptable patterns of behavior is more possible? What is deterrence in psychological terms, and how does it actually work, if it does? While precise answers to these questions must still await scientific exploration, from our clinical knowledge we can presently formulate some tentative hypotheses of how the conscience operates to control behavior.

Freud stated that a major part of the superego is not accessible to conscious awareness and represents the earliest contacts of the child's instincts (id) with the outer world. From these contacts some judgments are formed about *how* one can best relate to the outer world. In other words, the superego stems partially from the rudimentary perceptions of the effects of the id (instinctual self) upon the environment (54). Since the early formations of the superego are based on "forgotten," unconscious, memories of childhood, they are not readily accessible to conscious alteration.

One of the implications these observations have for the Law is that there can be little *direct* or conscious alteration of basic attitudes through many of the *corrective* techniques utilized. The criminal with a faulty superego has a primitive, built-in misconception of the world around him, and can only continue to follow the direction of his antisocial leanings, because to him they *are* "reality."[8]

Throughout the individual's growth and development, culture imposes many value judgments which are built into the superego with the help of the *ego ideal*. The latter may be defined as "the patterns of what one would like to be" (22), that is, values and characteristics which are perceived in other people, especially those upon whom love and respect are focused. These concepts are not only intrinsically important, but provide a vital motive force for learning and mastering other ideas and attitudes which will be utilized in the

8 A discussion of the "repetition-compulsion" is presented later in this chapter, under the heading, "Dynamic Abstractions."

service of reaching the original goal. For example, if the wish "to be a lawyer like father" is incorporated, it becomes the motive for developing interest and skill in reading, and reading becomes a valued and interesting activity. On the other hand, if father appears disinterested in reading (or, in the extreme, downright antagonistic), a boy may have to block his own interest in order "to be a man like father." (These factors are also related to the sense of identity, and will be discussed in Chapter IX).

When one falls short of one's ego ideal, the subjective feeling of *shame* results which creates a sense of failure and evokes anxiety.[9] The attempt to avoid these painful feelings impels the individual to strive harder to achieve the sought-after goal—i.e., to measure up to the ego ideal—and is a powerful motivating force for learning and acculturation.

The superego, then, is the internal standard with which one's needs and impulses must be reconciled, and is a reflection of the external patterns of acceptable social behavior learned during childhood. The effectiveness of the superego is the measure of the presence or absence of "the policeman at the elbow." This particular psychological policeman is susceptible to all the forms of bribery, coercion, stupidity, and blindness to which its real-life counterpart falls prey. These problems will be discussed in more detail.

DYNAMIC ABSTRACTIONS

The most recent abstractions to be evolved in psychiatry are the *dynamic*. Although psychological homeostatic concepts are generally viewed as the brainchild of Freud, Jeremy Bentham, a legal philosopher who wrote fifty years earlier than Freud, clearly delineated this

[9] The importance of the ego ideal would appear to be greater in those cultures where freely accessible aggression is an advantage. For example, the Sioux Indians, during their pre-Columbian period, were a nomadic, hunting culture. In their child-rearing techniques, they fully utilized the ego ideal of the powerful, aggressive male, and the boy or man who did not come up to this ideal was shamed. This facilitated a successful adaptation to the physical demands of this culture. As Erikson has stated, "Sioux child-training forms a firm basis for this system of centrifugality by establishing a lasting center of trust, namely the nursing mother, and then by handling the matter of teething, of infantile rage, and of muscular aggression in such a way that the greatest possible degree of ferocity is provoked, channelized socially, and finally released against prey and enemy." Erikson would relate this reaction of shame to the period of life when the child is first striving to some external demand, as during the period of toilet training (25).

concept. "Nature has placed mankind under the governance of two sovereign masters, *pain* and *pleasure*. It is for them alone to point out what we ought to do, as well as determine what we shall do. On the one hand the standard of right and wrong, on the other the chain of cause and effects, are fastened to their throne. They govern us in all we do, in all we say, in all we think: every effort we can make to throw off our subjection, will serve but to demonstrate and confirm it. In words a man may pretend to abjure their empire; but in reality he will remain subject to it all the while" (9). He then goes on to define what he calls the "principle of utility"(10).

Quite early in Freud's writing he described human behavior as motivated by the search for pleasure and the avoidance of pain. This concept is clearer in the original German, where they are called *Lust* (pleasure) and *Unlust* ("unpleasure"). This indicates more precisely that pain and pleasure lie along a continuum and do not in fact reflect opposite feeling states.[10] The essence of Freud's pain-pleasure principle lies in the idea that the organism always strives for the state of optimum tensionlessness. It is always shifting the balance of inner and outer stimulus in order to achieve as comfortable a state as possible. This is similar to what Walter Cannon, quite a few years later, designated the "homeostatic principle."

It is immediately apparent that an organism which strives merely for pleasure will not survive long. Aesop's "Grasshopper and Ant" fable illustrates this fact and underscores the pressure of reality. Man, or any other organism, oriented just to pleasure, cannot survive the rigors of psychological Winter. This new adaptive principle is perceived by children quite early in life. Freud called it the *reality principle*.[11] Adaptation to the multitude of pressures from the outside environment heavily molds and influences the nature of each individual's personality. *It is in response to these specific and individually experienced reality pressures that character delineation occurs.*

Another aspect of the principle of homeostasis is the concept of

---

[10] When Freud set forth this hypothesis, he thought that he was following up an idea stimulated by the German physiologist, Fechner. However, many years earlier Freud had translated some of the works of John Stuart Mill, who wrote about the philosophy of Jeremy Bentham, and utilized many of Bentham's concepts in his own philosophy. It was probably from this source that these concepts found their way into Freud's thinking (105).

[11] Bentham and Mill described the same concept as "the principle of utility."

fight-flight—a means for reaching environmental homeostasis. When an organism is threatened by either external danger or internal anxiety, it may respond by either fighting to destroy the threat, or fleeing to get away from the source of danger. When external (or internal) danger threatens, there is always physiological mobilization to meet the danger, responsive to the fight-flight alternatives. This involves increased heart and respiration rates, increased blood circulation to the voluntary muscles (the ones with which you fight or run), a tendency to perspire ("to break out in a cold sweat"), a tendency to lose control of the sphincters (no need to quote the vernacular here), dilation of the pupils ("wide-eyed with fear"), and contraction of the skin muscles ("hair stood on end" and one has "gooseflesh"). All of these responses are caused by the massive release of epinephrine (adrenaline), and produce fight-flight readiness. Concomitant with these changes, there is a tendency to impulsive muscular reaction and obscuring of rational judgment by the pressures for motor expression.

Many readers will recognize this state as an example of the physical condition of the person who makes a "mistake" and kills in "self-defense" out of fear of an imagined or misapprehended threat. The law quite correctly removes this kind of mistake from full culpability. A person reacting with violence against such a "threat" is doing the only thing he can do biologically when in such "danger." Some jurisdictions attempt to settle this problem with the "reasonable man" formula, while others, with more regard for psychological facts, view this question in the light of the particular defendant's state of mind (the "objective" versus the "subjective" test).

Quite clearly, not all men "mistake" a pipe for a revolver and kill out of mistaken self-defense motives. In fact, few of us would be likely to have a weapon on hand to use for such self-defense. Such a mistake is often related to faulty ego functioning and should properly raise the same psychological factors we encounter with questions regarding criminal responsibility. Such a degree of misperception and inappropriate action often approaches a state of emotional disability which may properly be called "mental illness" (i.e., "insanity"). It is a "fight-flight reaction" as the law correctly recognizes, but since it is initiated by a faulty ego, it is psychodynamically and logically close to the legal question of criminal responsibility.

The next dynamic concept we shall describe is that of the "determined" nature of all behavior—one of the basic assumptions of psychoanalytic psychology. By this we mean that every act is carried out for a specific reason or reasons, and that while we often cannot discern immediately what the reasons are, they may be found through adequate psychological investigation. This does not mean that any specific action is the result of a single motive. The concept that multiple factors motivate any single action is called the principle of *overdetermination* (4). There is also an algebraic summation of motives, some of which are positive and some negative in terms of their effect on the end action. In any given situation, a person arrives at the decision to act after weighing (not necessarily consciously) the various competing, reinforcing, or neutral values which are to be found in the reservoir of his experience.[12] We shall see as we develop our theoretical construct that the interaction of the individual's own pleasure-seeking wishes, of reality, and of his past experiences in similar situations will determine what he does in any given circumstance.

This leads us to the next concept—that of the *repetition-compulsion*. In simple language, this means that the methods used successfully to solve problems in the past will be remembered and repeated in future problem-solving. In much the same way as Pavlov conditioned his dogs (82), the human ego is conditioned by prior successes. These patterns (techniques) are taken into and become a part of the personality. They are used automatically and repetitiously to meet all new situations which the ego perceives as similar to the earlier conditioning experiences. One of the characteristics of such repetitious behavior is that much of the nature of the original situation is "forgotten"—buried in the unconscious where it is not available to ready recall. The obvious import of this fact is that the repetitious solution may be manifestly inappropriate to new circumstances. Quite often, when the reasons for a person's behavior are questioned and he is pressed to explain it, the forthcoming answer is "just because." No amount of questioning will bring further elucidation, the reason is lost. It has always seemed to me that Lorenz's description of the water shrews' learning of their trails beautifully exemplifies this process (68). Their near incapacity to change their

---

12 Alexander has aptly described these varying determinants as "vectors" (3).

behavior, even in the face of grave danger, reflects a repetition-compulsion and seems a prototype of neurosis.

Repetitious patterns of behavior are not unknown to the police. In fact, in scientific crime detection centers such as the F.B.I., elaborate catalog systems are maintained of the detailed descriptions of crimes. These are systematically associated with proven participants in past crimes and are used to track down the unknown culprits in new crimes. Experience has shown that, like all technicians, criminals have characteristic approaches which are nearly as reliable as a signature or a photograph for identification purposes. Through the use of these files, many arrests are accomplished.

Just as these "behavioral" files are systematically utilized by the police, so the psychiatrist, through a careful analysis of a patient's repetition-compulsions, is able to anticipate future behavior with reasonable accuracy. These predictions necessarily must deal with the fact that the environment itself is capable of infinite variation and that each variation affects an individual's psyche in a particular way. Therefore, predictions of future behavior must be stated conditionally: "If such and such should happen to the person, he will probably react in a certain way." Presumably, since there are many possible future events, an equally lengthy series of predictions is necessary. While this method of analysis has limitations, it affords one of our best predictive tools at the present time.

DEVELOPMENT OF THE EGO

We have so far commented on some of the aspects of the ego's functioning and suggested some of the forms of malfunction. The classic controversy is whether serious malfunction is the result of heredity or environment. We may say from the outset that, at least, inherited characteristics of the personality afford varying patterns of sensitivity to the environment which affect the direction of the ego's development. We know that various intrauterine conditions may affect the growth and development of the foetus, although in the past, it was felt that this was not true. Folklore is being vindicated currently as more and more evidence accumulates showing that there can be influence on the child *in utero*. There are many biological factors which may impinge on the unborn child, such as toxic substances taken by the mother or maternal infections such as German measles and syphilis (74).

Montagu states: ". . . the expression of genes is both a function of their nature and their nurture. *The organic potentialities do not develop at all in the absence of environmental influences.* This is true of physical potentialities; it is even more true of mental ones. The development of the mental potentialities presents virtually infinite possibilities under the action of varying environments. We can, of course, say that no two persons are ever born with quite the same potentialities, and that at birth those potentialities may be said to exist apart from any significantly influencing environmental factors, and thus recognize that on the one hand there exists a complex of potentialities which may be called the heredity of the individual, and on the other, a complex of environments which must be distinguished from heredity" (78).

At birth, the ego has a varying potential capability for perceiving the nature of the reality around it. Its sole psychological and physiological purpose is to maintain as comfortable and tension-free an existence as possible. "At the beginning of its development, the newborn baby seeks to attain a state of satisfaction merely through insistent wishing (imagining), whereby it simply ignores (represses) the unsatisfying reality, picturing to itself as present, on the contrary, the wished-for but lacking satisfaction; it attempts, therefore, to conceal without effort all its needs by means of positive and negative hallucinations" (32). This first stage of ego development is called the *period of unconditional omnipotence* (34). This state is not, after all, contradicted by prenatal experience. After birth, as Ferenczi says, "From the subjective standpoint of the child, the previously unconditional 'omnipotence' has changed merely insofar that he needs only to seize the wish-aims in a hallucinatory way (to imagine them), and to alter nothing else in the outer world, in order (after satisfying this single condition) really to obtain the wish fulfillment. Since the child certainly has no knowledge of the real concatenation of cause and effect, or the nurse's existence and activity, he must feel himself in a position of magical capacity that can actually realize all his wishes by simply imagining the satisfaction of them" (35). This is called the period of *magical hallucinatory omnipotence*. The child has only to fall into a sleep state and he can seemingly reproduce his previous condition of strength and omnipotence. Adults, when they sleep, maintain the same magical powers through the capacity to manipulate dreams freely. This is one place where great "power" persists throughout life.[13]

With the growth of perception and the development of more complex wishes, reality begins to force a modification of this sense of omnipotence. The sense of helplessness is diminished as the child gains motor capacity and he is better able to view himself as having other magical powers. "The child gradually learns also to stretch out his hand for the object that he wants. From this is developed later a regular gesture-language; by suitable combinations of gestures the child is able to express quite special needs, which then are very often actually satisfied, so that . . . the child can still appear to itself as omnipotent: *Period of omnipotence by the help of magic gestures*" (36).

Later on, with an increased perceptive capacity and an increased ability to understand the world around him, "The child learns, it is true, to be content with having only a part of the world, the ego, at his disposal. The other world, however, often opposes his wishes, but there still remain in this outer world qualities that he has learned to know in himself, i.e., ego qualities. Everything points to the conclusion that the child passes through an *animistic period* in the apprehension of reality, in which every object appears to him to be endowed with life, and in which he seeks to find again in every object his own organs and their activities" (37). This capacity to view the outer world in terms of the self is commonly demonstrated by children and primitive peoples. In fact, all primitive religions seem to originate from this concept of the external world.

As the child learns to talk, he begins to possess yet another way of dealing with the world around him. He "controls" the world by reducing it to a series of comprehensible abstractions or symbols. "Speech symbolism best gets substituted for gesture symbolism: certain series of sounds are brought into close associative connection with definite objects and processes, and indeed gradually identified with these. . . . The mimic expressions that continually accompany thinking (particularly so with children) make this kind of thought-

---

[13] The "proof" for such views comes from clinical observations of children as well as the adult's memory derivatives which occur in the course of psychotherapy. See also Lewin (68).

reading especially easy for adults; and when the child actually formulates his wishes in words, the entourage, ever-ready to help, hastens to fulfill them as soon as possible. The child then thinks himself in possession of magical capacities, is thus in the period of magic thoughts and magic words" (38).

It is only reluctantly that the growing child gives up his feelings of omnipotence in favor of a more realistic acceptance of himself and of external reality. This reluctance is so great that we never fully abandon all of our claims to secret power. The doctrine of free will, for example, makes part of its appeal through these fantasies of omnipotence. Most adults experience some sensation of anxiety at the suggestion that free will does not, in fact, exist. A great deal of human activity is directed toward maintaining the feeling of control over external reality. Man's eternal preoccupation with fairy tales, science fiction, and other stories of fantastic power and capacity is a reflection of his longing for the security he feels he has lost. (We might also recall Lord Coke's comment that ". . . The knowne certainty of the law is the safety of all" [18].) It provides motivation for scientific investigation and much of man's search for truth. While in fact he may never regain his lost sense of omnipotence except in neurotic form, the development of good reality testing can provide external as well as internal security.

The wide variety of possible ways in which the sense of reality may develop can be inferred from the above discussion. The kind of reality, the parental system of permissions and prohibitions, the example of adult figures, all determine the form in which the child's capacity for reality testing will be expressed. This kind of help is so vital to all infants that lawyers, when they are called up to assay whether a child's "best interests" are being furthered (as in an emotional neglect case), must assay the presence of this ingredient.

In this context, the whole area of teaching methodology and public education could be discussed. For our purposes it is enough to note that every child needs to replace magical thinking with reality-testing skill. This is a difficult task, not accomplished without the presence of both limits and freedom. Permissiveness offers freedom to explore, but withholds the support of guidance for testing experience. Rigid methods force guidance, but withhold freedom to explore. Either of these extremes offers a technique much superior to magic. However, a balanced system which offers children the opportunity to experiment with and test the environment, guided with forethought and kept within their best capacity, offers an optimal learning experience. While there may also be defects in the amount of instinctual energy available to the child, and while there may be some defect in the incorporated value system of the superego, it is the reaction to these in the ego which does damage to the health of the individual. To understand the functioning of ego, then, is of the utmost importance in understanding human behavior.

In summary, we see that the activities of the ego lie at the very core of psychological adaptation in the human organism. All psychological difficulties which cripple a person in any sphere have some relationship to a failure of ego functioning. When lawyers seek information about any kind of human behavior, the data should relate to the ego and its operations.

DEVELOPMENT OF THE SUPEREGO

As previously noted, the manner in which the superego, or conscience, develops is of the utmost interest to lawyers and others interested in man's social behavior. Some aspects of psychiatric and psychological knowledge about the superego generally prove startling to the layman. A survey of the important aspects of this subject is in order.

In his early formulations, Freud stated that most of the basic structure of the superego was established during the "oedipal period." At this time (four to six years of age), the growing child first sees himself in social, competitive relationships and must face clearly the needs, wishes, and goals of the people around him. According to Freud, children of this age group are actively engaged in a love competition for the parent of the opposite sex whom they want for their own exclusive purposes. The way in which the parents react to this competition determines the nature of many superego value judgments.[14] Decisions that "I *will* be like Daddy" or "I *won't* be like Daddy," are of major importance in building the superego. While these early superego attitudes are deeply ingrained, they are usually "slowly modified by later influences" (5).

---

[14] For the manner in which the oedipal conflict is resolved, see Chapter VII.

Childhood Superego

The mechanics of childhood superego functioning are important to the understanding of the psychological effects of the judicial process. As noted before, "The sovereign principle which governs the psychic processes is that of obtaining pleasure . . . , the instinctual impulses can no longer seek direct gratification—they are required to respect the demands of reality and, more than that, to conform to ethical and moral laws by which the superego seeks to control the behavior of the ego" (49). Here we have a statement of the manner in which the adult conscience functions. How does the maturing personality achieve this level of efficiency?

As the newborn child grapples with the manifold problems of a "separate existence, . . . he *accidentally*[15] discovers behavior patterns which are useful in gratifying biological needs" (6). A series of experiences accrue in which pleasure and loss of tension are achieved by the application of certain techniques *under certain conditions*. As growth continues, these vague "feeling memories" regarding specific conditions also accumulate. Memories include the information achieved through minute observation of the way in which parents and others solve problems.

We refer to this as the process of *identification*, i.e., someone else's patterns of how to behave properly and successfully are taken into the person, "swallowed," as it were. (Our language makes colloquial use of this idea in the expressions "I can't swallow that," and "he swallowed the idea whole.") These early identifications are indiscriminate and are taken "whole." This leads the immature conscience to incline toward a rigid, nondifferentiating, "black or white," "good or bad" value system. It operates in a rough sort of way to make the child conform to the demands of his surroundings.

These original standards come from *outside* the person. An act which runs counter to these values brings forth punishment and/or deprivation from *without*. Mother and father disapprove, spank, or withdraw love from the child. In the child's state of helplessness, parental love and approval in fact are necessary to biological survival. His ego perceives prohibited activity as threatening survival, and its relationship to punishment and deprivation are remembered.

---

[15] Italics added.

Even after these memories are "forgotten" and have become unconscious, they form a part of the internalized superego.

After this internalization process has taken place, a new kind of conforming is possible, for now the child possesses the capacity for self-observation. When the wish arises to perform an act contrary to the internalized values, the ego perceives this wish as dangerous, just *as though it were responding to the previously external prohibition*, and anxiety is aroused (85). Thus the superego with its automaticity makes it easier for the child to thread his way through the complex, mystifying, external world. It facilitates psychic economy by providing ready-made response-solutions to specific types of situations. These responses have the same advantages and disadvantages as conditioned reflexes. The ability to call up automatically a response which will avoid pain is, in the last analysis, pleasure-directed. To quote Alexander, "To act on the unmodified pleasure-pain principle would eventually cause the organism more pain than pleasure; in fact the organism could not survive. The reality principle means carefully planned and coordinated behavior, which often requires voluntary imposed restrictions and effort, but insures more gratification. It represents the best deal the organism is able to negotiate with reality under given conditions and therefore can be correctly called an improved pleasure principle" (7).

In economic terms, these responses are advantageous because the ego does not have to go through the process of "judgment" each time action is called for (97). This is equivalent to the conservative regulating aspect of the law. By having a body of statutes and common law decisions available, many of the pros and cons of an issue are more or less settled—the outcome can be predicted and re-evaluation of policy is not necessary for each decision. In the law, social energy is conserved; in the mind psychic energy is conserved.

Another advantage, especially important to children, is that values may be incorporated and responses learned at a time when many problems are largely incomprehensible to the child. For example, a child may learn it is "bad" if he steps out into the street. This is not based on the ego perceiving the dangers of vehicular traffic; rather, the parent says it is "bad," and the child will lose parental love if the curbstone is crossed. The usefulness of this kind of learning for children is apparent; it saves their lives.

In the ancient writings of the Egyptians, as quoted by Breasted in

The Dawn of Conscience, the first codes of behavior did not contain such words as *right* and *wrong.* Instead are found the expressions, "He who does that is loved," and "He who does that is hated" (13). These words from the fourth millennium B.C. (16), clearly describe ego perceptions of external pain and pleasure situations. They are not so much ethical terms, as primitive ego terms. An act is good if it results in pleasure (being loved). It is bad if it results in pain and loss of love. Here is an archeological-historical example of the "childish" conscience which antedates by far the appearance of the more abstract concepts of right and wrong in man's social conscience and his language. Apparently, the collective conscience of society, as represented in laws and codes, must go through the same type of internalization as the superego of the individual does. It was a long, slow process before "the emergence of the individual as a moral force, an individual aware of conscience as an ultimate authority at whose mandate he may confront and arraign society" (15). Not until this point did behavior and conscience become a social force (14). Two thousand years elapsed in the historical period of man's existence before this occurred. The appearance of a socially oriented conscience followed a slow and difficult process, and it must be apparent to all observers that the "conscience" of society still leaves much to be desired.

Early in its development the law became much concerned with the state of mind of the criminal (12). Using the concept of *mens rea,* there has been an attempt to establish the nature of the criminal's *guilty* intention. Although it varies from crime to crime, there has been an effort to establish a specifically defined state of mind in relation to specific criminal acts. Psychiatrists also, from the beginning of their study of mental motivations, have been concerned with the nature of guilt. While the early writings of Freud and his associates tended to attribute the sense of guilt to conflicts about sexuality, later work established that it is also (and possibly more frequently) related to feelings about aggression (56, 88). Exactly what is guilt, then, and how does it function to help the individual control his primitive impulses and meet the demands of society to conform?

To recapitulate, in infancy the child learns to sense which aspects of his behavior and impulse life elicit punishment, rejection, or loss of love. He slowly builds up associative memories of rejection or punishment around actions based on certain impulses. In time, merely to think of these impulses, to have the wish, reflexly produces the associated anxiety which we call guilt (31). This feeling of discomfort becomes the secondary motive for blocking and controlling the projected act. By reacting to this *internal* warning stimulus, *external* acts are avoided and the internal anxiety is diminished. Even though anxiety is uncomfortable as is frustration, it is clear that a pleasure gain has been made. To build up such "reflexes," there must be consistent external patterns to which to respond. This consistency helps the child to learn to establish controls over his behavior and is one of the most vital "needs" of all children (92).

If we remember that the infant and the very young child differentiate poorly between thoughts and actions, it is easy to see why the ego regards some thoughts as being quite as dangerous as actions and treats them equally (39). Evidence of the conscious continuation of such "reasoning" can be seen in the religious practices of voodoo, in such superstitions as the "hex" and the "evil eye," and in the obsolete English common law where it was a crime to think of the death of the king. In the magical thinking of the psychotic, such primitive logic continues as an important part of much of his intellectual activity.

Under the ancient *lex talionis,* the punishment prescribed fitted the crime, so that it was "eye for eye, tooth for tooth, hand for hand, foot for foot" (26). This closely reflects infantile conscience expectations, especially those produced by a very restrictive or punitive environment. Now, not only does the mere *wish* for the forbidden stir up anxiety about punishment, but it also creates a need for "appropriate" punishment. If appropriate punishment is not meted out, the ego fears a more drastic punishment such as the total loss of love, best understood intellectually as death. A healthy child can usually tolerate guilt feelings and regard them as sufficient punishment for the forbidden wish.[16] Those persons who develop a strong conscience with excessive guilt reactions have a need to carry the self-imposed psychic punishment to greater lengths. They carry

[16] To illustrate the reluctance adults have for perceiving underlying feelings of hostility in children, we may cite Coke who, when speaking of punishment for homicide (under what was then "Petit Treason") said, "If the child commit Parricide in killing of his father or mother (which the law-makers never imagined any childe would doe) this case is out of this statute, unlesse the child served the father or mother for wages, or meat, drink or apparell. . . ." In other words not until children were of working age was it felt they could harbor parricidal impulses (19).

out defensive maneuvers to escape guilt and the sense of inner discomfort which necessitate *actual* punishment for alien thoughts, even though nothing was done to deserve punishment, so far as the outside world is concerned.

It is important to understand this process if we are to understand the self-punishing behavior which many persons exhibit. There are those individuals who are always courting some form of disaster, and whose life plan seems to have been conceived to cause difficulty. There are those who select mates who will be "the cross they bear" for the rest of their lives, and from whom they submissively accept mistreatment. To disrupt these patterns may be very difficult.

Another familiar form of self-punishment is found in the syndrome which insurance companies have labeled "accident-proneness." Without psychiatric assistance, insurance companies long ago discovered that there are individuals with a tendency to become involved in automobile accidents. Recent studies indicate that these individuals strive to balance out the demands of their conscience for punishment because of forbidden impulses (23, 24, 67, 75).

There is another group of individuals who use psychosomatic illnesses to punish themselves. They block their conscience-forbidden impulses through the mechanism of guilt, and then punish themselves through some form of physical disability. For example, patients with peptic ulcer long for the pleasures of being cared for as infants or children. They deny these impulses as inappropriate to their age and drive themselves to impossible levels of performance. Their stomach lining (one of the places where effective "babying" makes its impact with the sensation of being well-fed, i.e., loved) becomes the focus for psychophysiologic malfunction and ulcer is the result (108).

Another example of such psychophysiologic conflict occurs in some cases of high blood pressure (hypertension). Persons unable to deal freely with anger because of their fear of losing acceptance from people around them hold it in, are constantly keyed up to fight or flight, and as a result blood pressure rises and stays elevated. They are more or less constantly "hot under the collar," and it takes elevated blood pressure to maintain this state. These mechanisms are familiar to all physicians who must deal with these psychosomatic, or psychophysiologic disorders in their daily practices (109).

Of special interest to lawyers and society alike, are the many criminals who keep repeating crimes in which there is high probability of being apprehended and punished. Some prison psychiatrists have stated that they can predict which men when released from prison are most likely to commit another crime in order to assure their return to prison. This foolhardiness is understandable when we view it as the unconscious irrational demand of a conscience seeking to restore balance in pain-pleasure tensions by expiating guilt through punishment (42, 55, 89). Society, reacting to its vengeance (retributive) impulses, willingly plays "the sucker" and fulfills the neurotic needs of these overconscientious criminals.[17] Roche states that to resolve this social dilemma we must "change the criminal into a neurotic and treat the neurosis" (90).[18] In other words, antisocial behavior which is the camouflaged manifestation of guilty demands for punishment must be changed back to its original form. Only then can the individual learn a more appropriate way to relieve such tension.

It has long been assumed that this is an impossible task. However, since 1950, in the California Medical Facility, a treatment-oriented institution for criminals, this problem has been approached therapeutically with very favorable results. After parole from the Facility, treatment continues in a special outpatient clinic. One interesting sidelight which appears in the preliminary reports is that "Several men have actually asked to be returned to the facility for further treatment because they felt an increase in their anxieties and were fearful of committing another crime" (95). In such men, the *action* solution for the buried punishment need is replaced by feelings of anxiety and the cycle of punishment-provoking behavior has been broken.

From the preceding discussions and illustrations, we can see that the childhood superego performs a useful function during the years when the reality-testing function of the ego is not yet sufficiently developed to cope with the subtleties of life. However, it can also result in severe crippling if it becomes too punitive and persists into adulthood. It may produce such disequilibrium that it prevents effective maturation and limits the ego's subsequent opportunities to learn by pragmatic reality-based experience.

---

[17] Another determinant, not detailed here, is the wish to be taken care of, and a prison does this.

[18] See also, Ferenczi (44).

Mature Superego

From the preceding discussion and illustrations, it can be seen that, while the sense of guilt tends to keep an individual within the bounds demanded by society, it can also cause a secondary disequilibrium with serious social results. Inappropriate guilt reactions are related primarily to childhood conscience functioning carried into adult life. There is a difference, obviously, between this kind of conscience and that of a mature adult.

So far, we have described the normal functioning as well as some of the more severe aberrations of the childish conscience. Infants and children, with their inadequate grasp of the subtleties in the external world, need to have clear-cut and sharply defined "rules" to help them delineate and cope with problems and relationships. They grow accustomed to, and indeed would be quite lost, without these oversimplified rules for reaction.

Many adults continue to function by using the black and white standards of infancy. This is difficult and frequently impossible to do and so may become a source of problems. Conceivably, such a sharply drawn set of rules would work well in a culture or society which was stable and predictable. However, with the world changing as rapidly as it does today, a conscience predicated on such rigidity is likely to lead to difficulties in adjustment. What adults need today is the ability to examine issues in regard to present implications and future possibilities, and then be able to make decisions accordingly. This is related to the ego's function of reality-testing.

An adult who has developed a healthy ego is able to perceive, examine, analyze, and judge the external world critically, and is not obligated to fall back on rigid, reflex patterns of behavior. Without undue anxiety, he can examine new situations and determine in what way they may best be dealt with. In short, he has a conscience which permits the ego adequate latitude for pragmatic, reality-based judgment and action (98). Children function mainly according to short-sighted, short-term, pleasure goals. The mature adult is able to see his behavior in the context of his society, and plan for long-term, as well as short-term, advantages. The automatic, uncritical judgment of the child's superego must be taken over by reality-testing functions of the ego. It then becomes possible to see oneself against the background of the whole social fabric, and to look forward and backward in order to decide how to behave. Obviously, each action cannot be separately weighed, and more or less automatic responses to situations will be evolved. However, contrary to the situation with the infantile superego, these automatic patterns are susceptible to specific examination when necessary, and can be brought into harmony with the current reality. If, for one reason or another, current methods for problem-solving do not work, the whole technique may be critically re-examined. In the child, conscience tends to shroud all value judgments with fear and awe and makes reappraisal of them difficult or impossible. Those judgments are sacrosanct and are regarded as beyond the realm of modification by any properly "moral" person. Studies on the psychological nature of religious attitudes show that much of the reluctance to examine these questions relates to the fear of challenging the parental value system as it is reflected in the superego. What the parent believes to be right has all of the force of the "word of God." Indeed, to a child, parents *are* gods.[19]

How does superego functioning relate to legal administration? One striking similarity which the law has to the childhood superego is the way in which the law strives for an absolute standard which it may invoke systematically and regularly, and thus regulate and control society. While this is a sound judicial ideal, it tends to become exaggerated because so many of the law's administrators share the universal childhood longings for sureness and security. We must remember that all children make an anxious search for some well-defined status which will assure security and safety. This search is never entirely given up, and adults, too, always hope to achieve stability and regularity in their environment so as to permit predictability of their relationships to it. Unfortunately, this cannot be. The passage of time brings irrevocable change. A healthy and mature mind must be oriented to meet this change, and so must a healthy legal system. Law which is dedicated to changelessness becomes sterile and ineffectual. Chief Justice Marshall said, "It is . . . a healthy practice . . . for a court to re-examine its own doctrines. . . . Responsible government should entail the undoings of wrong. . . . Respect for any tribunal is increased if it stands ready . . . not only

[19] For a general discussion see Report No. 48 of the Group for the Advancement of Psychiatry (58).

to correct the errors of others but also to confess its own. [This] . . . blunt, open and direct course is truer to democratic conditions than disguised changes, and marked but unacknowledged deviations from all precedents concealed by technical rationalizing." Marshall believed that "judges should, when justice so requires, engage in candidly creating precedents" (21). This is a great judicial ideal, though we are very familiar with the stubborn resistance to change couched in the theory of *stare decisis*.[20] Many judicial opinions reflect the wish to change coupled with the feeling that, because the law is what it is, no change should be effected. Edmond Cahn, commenting on the opinions of Justice Frankfurter, said, "As the intellectuals of Alexandria once looked to Athens and Jerusalem, so Justice Frankfurter has searched the thoughts of Holmes and Brandeis. On occasion he writes as though he possessed no personal commission of office and could merely wield the continued authority of theirs; with the passing of the years, he has found it less and less satisfying to ask: how would Holmes (or Brandeis) have coped with this or that issue, which never arose in his lifetime?" (17).

There is another aspect of superego functioning which has important implications for law. A child is *willing* to conform to the rules of society as they are reflected in the rules of his own family only if he senses a spirit of justice therein (8, 40). If he feels he is going to be dealt with inconsistently and unfairly he will be inclined to resolve problems more in accordance with his own wishes and impulses. In other words, there is a strong desire and a great need to know that he and his problems are understood, and that insofar as possible they will be dealt with fairly, equitably, and in a more or less gratifying manner. This attitude carries over into his relationship to society and his feelings about law. The will to get along with society and conform to law stems mainly from an expectation of being treated fairly as an individual. A person on trial for a crime is permitted to defend himself, to bring character witnesses, or to make what explanations he can if he admits to committing the crime. In this highly individualized process, even though the accused has breached the standards of society, he can feel that he is being considered as an individual. Not only can this have a positive effect on his ego, but more important, its deterrent effect on

---

[20] This was especially true in Great Britain until recently (99).

society is increased by enhancing the superego identification with the law. Some loss of respect for law occurs when the jury feels that the law does not deal fairly or understandingly with the accused and his problems (84). This feeling may be supplemented by an unconscious identification with the accused, and he may be acquitted even though he is felt to be guilty (the process of nullification). It would be interesting to study and evaluate why juries acquit some individuals even when there is obvious guilt.[21] The process of allying positively with law is probably more closely related to the feeling that law is "wise," "fair," and "just" than it is to a fear of punishment.

Superego functioning has another implication for law in relation to the kind of sentences imposed. It is true that the infantile superego begins its development on the basis of "an eye for an eye" expectations, and more ethical considerations are not involved. While the death penalty might seem appropriate to this infantile, nonethical layer of superego, it presents problems for the conscience which is even one degree more advanced. Every parent knows that while a child can be taught not to hit by hitting him back, he cannot, by this method, be made to think that hitting is morally wrong. Most members of our society believe that physical aggression leading to death not only is to be feared but is also a deeply immoral action. Therefore, when the law uses death as a means of enforcement it tends to create a divided superego image: on the one hand, to kill is evil and immoral; on the other, to kill in the name of legal punishment is all right (106). Conceivably, it is possible to maintain such a rationalization, but the average person's ego tends to handle physical aggression in childish (*not* infantile) terms. It deals with impulses to kill by totally barring them from consciousness. Therefore, to kill in the name of morality and law is a distressing problem for the ego. It has been observed in states where certain crimes are capital offenses that the accused is often found guilty of a lesser crime in order to avoid capital punishment. This would tend to substantiate the above premises. It would seem that public respect for law and correction would be improved if it

---

[21] Indeed, the recently published study by Kalven and Zeisel seems to establish this fact. The critical consideration, according to the investigators, is whether or not the jury can sympathize with the defendant (66).

were more psychologically consistent in its attitudes toward physical violence.

Although these few considerations do not exhaust the practical aspects of superego functioning, they give some indication of its importance for effective laws and effective legal administration. It is important in relation to the individual criminal and his subsequent behavior to assay the manner in which his conscience functions so that punishment may have a positive learning impact. Some of the proponents for change in our "treatment techniques" utilize this concept fully. Robert Waelder outlines a method whereby these factors are fully and individually studied before the sentencing occurs (101). He suggests that evaluations be made with regard to the individual's potential relationship to society, as well as his treatability. The disposition of each individual should then be related to (1) the degree to which the offender is dangerous to society, (2) the degree to which he is deterrable, and (3) the degree to which he is treatable. Depending on the evaluation of these three factors, questions of probation, custody, and treatment can be decided. This is an area of legal administration which deserves much greater attention by courts, legislatures, and the public if we are to approach the goals of deterrence and rehabilitation with psychological realism.

The primitive and punitive aspects of conscience should be noted again before leaving the subject of superego functioning. As indicated above, the childhood conscience has an absolute expectation of retributive punishment whenever the rules are broken. Unfortunately, civilization has not yet advanced to the state where this retributive impulse and expectation are absent. As Zilboorg and others have pointed out, much of the determination of guilt and punishment of criminals is motivated by unconscious, retributive impulses (41, 111). We see this most clearly in those crimes which are regarded as "heinous." The state of mind of the criminal makes little difference when savage and mutilating acts have been committed, and juries under those circumstances rarely pay much attention to the notion of *mens rea*. In 1883, Sir James Stephen (96) stated that crimes of this sort "emphatically justify and gratify the public desire for vengeance upon such offenders." At the time of the Renaissance, vengeance was expressed in the form of mutilation and, at times, the public itself was permitted to inflict the torture (110).

Today, having reached a "more advanced" level of civilization, we no longer permit the public at large to apply the punishment (even though, on rare occasions, in some parts of the country such primitive acts do take place). The law has assumed the function of applying the punishment, and there is a slowly increasing objection to using violent means to act out retributive impulses.[22] For some time to come, we may expect that an unconscious residue from infantile conscience will continue to influence legal decisions. Although we must accept this as an unavoidable part of our primitive heritage, only as we minimize its effects will law work toward achieving a safe and sane society (43). This goal can be sought through various procedural changes in the trial which will minimize the effects of unconscious attitudes by forcing them into cognition.

CONCEPTS OF AWARENESS: THE THEORY OF THE UNCONSCIOUS

One of the most controversial of Freud's contributions to mental science at the time he made it was the concept of the unconscious. It would not be accurate to say that Freud was the first to describe the unconscious, but it was Freud's clinical investigations which first gave us scientific evidence of its existence. Many philosophers had postulated the existence of an unconscious mental life. Bentham, in some of his writings, mentions obliquely the possibility of various levels of mental activity. Sir William Hamilton outlined three levels of consciousness which were very close to those postulated by Freud (60). We know that Freud did translate some of the essays of John Stuart Mill, who wrote a two-volume dissertation on the philosophy of Hamilton (76). Whatever the historical antecedents

[22] For example, see *Douglas v. U.S.* (239 F.2d 52). (Defendant took appeal to ask for reversal and a directed verdict of not guilty by reason of insanity, on the basis of the "ignored" expert testimony in the case.) The Court of Appeals reversed and remanded the case to the trial court because ". . . after according due deference to the verdicts of the juries and to the denials by the trial court of new trials, we are constrained to conclude that it would be inconsistent with applicable legal standards to hold on the records as presently constituted that punishment for criminal conduct, rather than treatment for a mental disease, was the remedy." In this case the main thrust of the prosecutor's argument to the jury was that the defendant was obviously lying and malingering, and what he needed was punishment. The jury apparently acted on this suggestion coupled with ungrounded fear that the man would be released into the community to continue his felonious behavior.

to Freud's concept of the unconscious, there is little controversy over the fact that he was the first to provide substantial evidence of its existence. We recall that Anton Mesmer, working with hypnosis, evolved the concept of "animal magnetism." This was a metaphysical concept, an attempt to explain unconscious phenomena which he observed and, in fact, could manipulate. However, the skepticism of the French Academy of Science was sufficient to sidetrack any further investigations of this phenomenon for many years (113). We have noted that Pierre Janet used the word unconscious, but disavowed its similarity of meaning when Freud wanted to acknowledge Janet as the discoverer of the unconscious (114). Bernheim and Liebeault also delved into some of the manifestations of the hypnotic state, but did not arrive at any systematic description of the unconscious (115).

When Freud began to study the neuroses, he was soon able to demonstrate that his patients were capable of remembering many "forgotten" incidents from their early life. A crisis in his career occurred when he discovered that these "remembered" events were not necessarily true. This upset his whole theoretical structure, and for a time so deeply disturbed him that he was on the verge of giving up his research into the field of mental behavior. However, he continued his investigations and was able to reformulate his concepts, incorporating his new findings. Slowly, he formulated the process whereby people "forget," and he described what this forgetting meant in the mental economy.

Freud found that when things were forgotten, it was generally due to the fact that the forgotten event was associated with some painful emotional experience. To illustrate, a child might attack an envied baby brother and provoke painful parental disapproval. He would then find it necessary to block off and "forget" the desire to harm the baby. In subsequent behavior, such *unconscious* hostility toward the sibling may be manifested in various ways. For example, the older child might be assigned the task of taking care of the younger, and might "accidentally" allow him to fall from a swing. He would maintain that it was not his fault; it was an accident. This would not be a lie, but would reflect the effect of an unconscious desire motivating motor behavior which resulted in an "accident." The "cause" for the accident would have been long "forgotten."

One of the convincing demonstrations Freud offers in relation to everyday evidence of unconscious activity is found in the first part of his lectures on *A General Introduction to Psychoanalysis*. In the second lecture, "The Psychology of Errors," he very neatly goes through his proof for the existence of the unconscious as it is manifested through what are known as "slips," or *parapraxes*.[23] This dissertation proceeds so logically and smoothly that, as Freud himself warns, if you follow him through and accept each step of the argument, you are driven to accept the theory of the unconscious (52).

Dreams also contribute to our knowledge about the functioning of the mind and testify to the presence of the unconscious. Freud felt that his principal scientific contribution was his book, *The Interpretation of Dreams* (50), which gives a detailed description of the manner in which dreams may be analyzed and understood. First published in 1900, it was to have significant impact on American psychiatry. It was the first psychoanalytic book published in America.[24]

According to psychoanalytic theory, the function of the dream is to protect sleep. At night, people attempt to withdraw from the world of reality in order to be restored and revitalized, and they must get away from the day's unsolved problems and irritations if this is to be accomplished. Dreams demonstrate clearly the manner in which the ego deals with the internal forces of instinctual demands (id) as well as the impact of conscience limitations (superego). These techniques for adaptation relate to the individual's past history as well as to current struggles. We shall discuss the psychoanalytic interpretation of dreams later in this chapter, and at that point, demonstrate the manner in which the unconscious is specifically revealed through them.

Levels of consciousness have been variously described during the

[23] An example: Several years ago during Queen Elizabeth's state visit to the United States, many people were gathered in a side hall at a large and congested social function. According to protocol the truly festive portion of the evening had to await the Queen's departure. The guests were becoming politely restive when a functionary came into the hall and proclaimed in a loud voice, "Ladies and Gentlemen, I *regret* to announce that the Queen has not yet departed." The reactions of the group were not reported, but behind the inevitable suppressed smiles and laughter, there must have been full recognition of how the poor fellow got himself into such an embarrassing spot. This was a slip of the tongue.

[24] A. A. Brill translated and published the first American edition in 1913.

development of psychoanalytic theory, but this discussion will be limited to current theories. First of all, psychic awareness exists on three different levels: *conscious* (Cs), *unconscious* (Ucs), and *preconscious* (Pcs). The particular level of consciousness has no relationship to the dynamic importance or to the strength or weakness of a given impulse or idea. Rather, it relates to the degree of accessibility to volitional attention. When a person can turn his attention to an idea, thought, or impulse, their content is *conscious*. Conscious elements are available for rational manipulation by the ego. The *unconscious*, on the other hand, is totally inaccessible to rational deliberation, and the nature of its content must be drawn by inferences from data which indicate the presence of unconscious ideas and attitudes. While the effects of conscious rational experience can impinge upon the unconscious, this is a roundabout process at best. Likewise, the effect of unconscious attitudes comes into conscious thoughts and acts, but their origins are lost.

The term *Preconscious* applies to the reservoir of memories and impulses which are not immediately available to recall but which can be recovered by associative maneuvers, concentration, and as the result of stimuli in both waking and dream states. Much of the resynthesis of past and present experience appears to take place at the preconscious level. Now let us examine the dynamics of these levels of awareness.

Characteristics of the Unconscious

Certain conditions exist in the unconscious which appear strange to conscious rationality. First, the unconscious energies, attitudes, and impulses are directed solely by the pleasure principle. They have only one goal—to achieve pleasure and to relieve tension. The second condition is the maintenance of the fantasy of omnipotence. All of childhood's magical ability to manipulate and alter the reality world is preserved here. This is clearly revealed in dreams where the dreamer is able to accomplish the most unlikely things, and any aspect of life can be altered to suit his whims.

In the unconscious, opposites are always potentially alike. Black and white may be equated and may be used interchangeably to symbolize the same state. This tendency, by the way, may be seen in children who, as they begin to master language, very often use one word to denote two opposite conditions. This characteristic also may be found in primitive languages, where a single sound or word is used to denote opposite conditions and distinctions are made by use of supplementary gestures.

Another reality reference which is juggled freely in the unconscious is time. Details may be moved forward through time; past may be present or future, and future may be past. The infant, child, and adolescent live side by side in the adult unconscious. In short, the unconscious is timeless. The psychic utility of this fact will be demonstrated in the descripton of dynamic effects which take place in dreams.

Unconscious content is expressed through the use of dramatization and symbolization. For example, the dream may appear as a theatrical production in which symbols are utilized (or, as Shakespeare wrote, a play within a play). Such qualities are seen also in the surrealistic and dreamlike paintings of Salvador Dali, the drawings of William Blake, and the work of Hieronymus Bosch. In such dreams and paintings, despite the fact that the manifest symbols and actions *seem* to have no meaning, the dreamer or observer is convinced that they do have meaning. The process of free association used by patients in psychotherapy usually reveals what these meanings are.

Not only are the conditions of unconscious mental functioning different from those of reality-centered consciousness, but the unconscious follows different laws of logic. One characteristic of unconscious logic is called *secondary elaboration*. By this we mean that a thing or symbol, or a feeling which starts off as a simple one, may be extended, complicated, and elaborated to include a multitude of concepts. Part of this may be in the service of expressing a complex of associated incidents and can be recognized in those dreams where some readily apparent stimulus from the day is extended into a very elaborate concept in that night's dream.

Other characteristics of the unconscious are those of *condensation* and *displacement*. By condensation is meant the fact that one symbol may represent a multitude of concepts, feelings, or events. The art critic Bernard Berenson has said, "Thinking is never more than trying to inscribe within a circle the polygon that comes nearest to coinciding with it" (11). It is the ingenuity of the unconscious mental process to be able to use polygons directly, thus expressing in a single figure what would take pages of logical exposition. For example, an apple in a dream might represent some forbidden sexual fantasy, a reference to the Biblical Garden of Eden, a recollection of an enjoyable dessert, the job of spraying the apple orchard which must be accomplished the next day, and an effort to win teacher's approval. All of these meanings may be condensed in the single symbol, "apple."

Displacement, on the other hand, occurs when an idea or a feeling is shifted from the object of its origin to another less obvious one. To continue from the previous illustration, all of these meanings might be shifted to the symbol of an orange. Displacement serves the purpose of disguise.

All of the topographic areas of the psyche are represented in the unconscious. There are unconscious id impulses, unconscious ego defenses, and unconscious superego value judgments. Unconsciousness is not the characteristic of any one of the topographic compartments of the psyche. Rather, it is all mental activity below the level of conscious awareness.

Consciousness deals with the world of reality. It must abide by all of the rules of reality, and any attitude or technique which does not conform with the ego's knowledge of reality will create anxiety. Consciousness is characterized by logic, appropriate sense of time, and adherence to the reality principle. The manipulation of consciousness itself is an ego function. The ego is aware of emotions and value judgments, and through such perceptions admits id and superego forces to consciousness within the framework of reality principle limitations.

Factors Which Determine the Level of Consciousness in Experience

The level of psychological maturation sets limits on the degree of consciousness possible. A new-born infant functions almost totally on an instinctual basis. He is incapable of sorting out sensory stimuli into well-defined perceptions and cannot even clearly distinguish his own body from the rest of the environment. There is little of the conscious rationalizing process as we have described it, and yet the infantile mental state can hardly be called "unconscious." As soon as rudimentary conceptualization of reality becomes possible through the maturing of the nervous system, such distinctions can be drawn. With maturation of the ego, there comes into existence the capacity to erect barriers with which to screen those impulses from consciousness which are inconsistent and produce conflicts with reality. With growing experience, a child perceives that certain impulses, acted upon, bring anxiety or pain. He learns to *repress* these impulses—to drive them below the level of conscious awareness.

We will not discuss the process of repression here except to say that the psyche has the capacity to drive painful thoughts and feelings into unconsciousness where they are incapable of producing conscious pain or anxiety. Some of the reasons for repression were discussed in relation to conscience functioning, so we shall not repeat them here. This need to deal with some perceptions by repression is related to the child's inadequacy and incapability in relation to reality manipulation. As growth and maturation occur and social independence develops, many previously impossible situations come within reach of possible ego control and mastery. Effective child rearing includes opportunities to stir up from the unconscious some of the previously repressed experiences. If this does not occur (and there is a tendency for it not to occur), repression continues and matters remain in the unconscious which, in adults, should come under conscious control. Biological and psychological maturation exerts a healthy pressure on unconscious forces, tending to press them toward consciousness. Unfortunately, it sometimes happens that the defenses which maintain segments of experience unconscious may be reinforced and perpetuated in such a way as to block such movement outward. While it is not necessary or particularly desirable for all of one's past experience to be recallable, major distortions of the past should be accessible to re-evaluation when they create trouble. Generally, we have no reason to review our whole past consciously in the light of present experience. But, when it is necessary, the ego should be capable of doing so without too great anxiety. If some neurotic need maintains the repressions intact and strong, then many past experiences *must* remain permanently below the surface in the unconscious, no matter what the adaptive advantages for altering behavior patterns.[25]

[25] Freud, in his book *The Ego and the Id,* describes the dynamics of consciousness clearly. Earlier, in *Beyond the Pleasure Principle* (53), he explained some of the reasons for the need to block off and obliterate from awareness some of the incoming stimuli. In his concept of the *Reizschutz* he visualized a sort of protective screen of "denial" in which the organism has the capacity to block off and screen out some of the multitudinous stimuli which are impinging upon it. This is necessary to avoid

The concept of the unconscious is basic to an understanding of psychic functioning. No theory which omits it can account for the observable activities of the psyche. Although workers in the various behavioral sciences use different names for the unconscious, there is virtual unanimity about its existence. With all this acceptance, it is curious how difficult it is to believe. Almost anyone can be convinced that *other* people behave for reasons they don't know about, but it is quite a different thing to believe it about oneself.

Perhaps a few remarks should be made about the relationship of consciousness and unconsciousness in the normal person. This issue arises quite frequently in various legal contexts. For example, during the trial procedure, questions are often raised relative to whether a witness is lying.[26] By definition, lying relates to a *conscious* distortion of the fact. Almost everyone distorts the facts, sometimes grossly, without any intent to lie. Some distortion is due to unconscious pressure to alter facts in order to balance out psychological needs. For example, a person whose reaction to some threat was cowardly may be unable to tolerate the fact of cowardice and so may present his story in a very much altered form. Since this alteration is unconscious, the person will argue strongly and believe his highly inaccurate story. This is not a lie, but rather is the result of unconscious defense maneuvers to obscure the unpalatable facts. There are other kinds of situations which cause distortion and difficulty for the law. For example, it has been found that many of the child "victims" of sexual seduction either have not experienced the seduction at all, or if they did, have precipitated the seduction through their own behavior (81). They do not lie; these children do not *know* what happened, although they are "sure" that they do. Here again we see imperative unconscious needs which must be kept unconscious due to superego prohibitions, but are manifest on the level of behavior, nevertheless. In situations like this, the law very often requires corroboration by someone other than the complaining witness. Such a decision is psychologically wise.

When psychiatrists are asked to testify, the question of conscious-

---

overstimulation and is conservative in its nature. He speculated that sometimes, when *internal* stimuli are too disturbing, the individual may "project" such stimuli outward so that they must re-enter through the screening device (54). While this is purely speculative, it possibly explains one of the methods whereby the ego protects itself from too much anxiety-producing stimulation.

[26] See *U.S. v. Douglas* (239 F.2d 52).

ness is an important one. To a psychiatrist, whether or not a motive
or impulse is conscious is extremely important in understanding the
person's behavior. If, during questioning or in reports, they are not
permitted to draw clear distinctions between conscious and unconscious, they may be forced to give misleading impressions. This is
intolerable to a physician of integrity, and many such men will refuse to testify rather than be compromised in this manner.[27] While
part of this hesitation, in my opinion, is due to a misapprehension of
the role of expert witness, it nonetheless results in keeping many
competent experts from the courtroom, where they are badly
needed.

As understanding of psychic functioning becomes more generally
understood, it should lessen the possibility of trial lawyers appealing
to the ignorance of juries by confusing those questions which relate
to level of consciousness. Along with this change, psychiatrists with
the greatest skill and training hopefully will become increasingly
willing to work with the courts.

DREAMS: THE FINGERPRINT OF THE PERSONALITY

Dreams have always fascinated man. From the earliest days of
recorded history, there have been efforts to interpret dreams and
to discover their meanings. Even the most sophisticated cannot rid
themselves of a sneaking belief in them. Aristotle regarded dreams as
following the laws of the human spirit with something akin to the
divine. He stated that "dreams are defined as the mental activity
of the sleeper in so far as he is asleep" (56). An almost universal
phenomenon is the "dream book." Such a book attempts to apply
an interpretation to each dream symbol, and while these interpreta-
tions persist to the present day, they bear little relationship to the
scientific technique of dream interpretation.

Let us make a few general comments on the psychoanalytic theory
of dreams. Analysts feel that all people dream nightly, even though
most people have at least some nights when they believe they have
not dreamed.[28] There are many popular theories about the causes of
dreaming, many of which attribute this activity to some direct,

[27] For various psychiatric opinions on this point, see Guttmacher (59), Weihofen
(107), Waelder (102), Szasz (97), Zilboorg (113).
[28] This proposition has now been well documented by the work of Dement (20).

physiological stimulus, such as eating mince pie before retiring. While it is true that the day's activity does provide the immediate stimulus, it is not such a direct and uncomplicated one. (We call the day's stimulus *day residue*. The analyst may usually discern it in the dream with little difficulty.) Ordinarily, a person has no motivation to recall dreams, and unless they are heavily charged with some emotional quality, active memory of the dream rarely survives the period of immediate awakening. The recollection of not dreaming is usually indicative of a highly successful dream, i.e., one which has dealt with the left-over stimuli of the day so thoroughly that there is no breakthrough of emotion into consciousness. Thus, the feeling of not dreaming is a sign of efficient dreaming.

We may ask what evidence there is for this thesis. It comes from several sources: (1) Electroencephalographic studies of brain activity during sleep are similar to those which occur during known dreaming; (2) Patients in analysis, who claim they rarely dream, begin to report dreams. These appear to have no direct relationship to any suggestion that one *should* dream in order to be analyzed; (3) Various studies on the relationship of dreaming to hypnosis, drugs, and normal sleep (20, 45, 46, 47, 71, 72). To the psychoanalyst, the most convincing evidence is his day-to-day clinical experience, which clearly indicates that awareness of dreams is related more to factors influencing memory than to the question of their occurrence.

Freud called the dream the "royal road to the unconscious." This view is shared by all analysts today and it is through dreams that a person's peculiar mental functioning may be most clearly revealed. Analysts use dreams as a cross-sectional diagram of what is going on in the id, ego, and superego at both conscious and unconscious levels.

Many will raise the question of whether or not there is a standard meaning for a given dream symbol. While there is some degree of similarity in dream symbols, this does not make it possible to translate them as simple equivalents. Carl Jung, in his studies of the unconscious, has explored the nature of symbol formation and its relationship to the cultural past of the human race (65). There seems to be no doubt that there is some thread of continuity in symbol formation, but that thread has not yet been adequately described for practical use. Clinical experience clearly demonstrates that we are not entitled to utilize dream symbols in the manner in which "dream books" do. To quote Ferenczi, "The derisive remark was once made against psychoanalysis that, according to this doctrine, the unconscious sees a penis in every convex object and a vagina or anus in every concave one." This overstatement of the case pays heed to the fact that the important communications of a dream are found in the action, the circumstances, and the style rather than in the content alone.

Recalling the characteristics of the unconscious (omnipotence, timelessness, pleasure principle), it follows that each bit of action in the dream reveals these principles as they express an adaptive aim. Freud stated, "When the work of interpretation has been completed, we perceive that a dream is the fulfillment of a wish" (50).

Remembering these conditions and the special logic of the unconscious, let us examine a dream and analyze it so that we may gain some understanding of this very important analytic tool. While this is not an exhaustive exploration, it touches the important points.

Before relating this dream, the patient casually mentioned that something "unusual" had happened and told the following story: She had returned alone to her place of business the night before because her husband was busy. As she passed a dark corner, a young Negro man stepped out "without a stitch of clothing on." He made no move toward her, and her only conscious reaction to this event was that she "was afraid that the poor soul might catch pneumonia." During and just after the event, she had the feeling that she "was in a dream. In fact, this morning I feel unsure about what was the dream and what was real." After relating the above, this dream was told to the analyst:

I was in my office. I was sitting talking to someone. I looked up and then the man was standing there fully clothed. I tried desperately to see if it was the same man. I couldn't be sure because of the darkness of the room. Then I started getting Christmas cards signed, "Percy." Then letters. They kept getting more and more personal. I was worried about it. In one card he had written the note, "Disregard the previous card. This one is more for youth." I don't know how the dream ended up. The last part is fuzzy in my mind, but it was violent. Somehow Percy grabbed hold of me. There were policemen around and he used me as a hostage. Finally a policeman got around at an angle and shot him and killed him. I saw him lying on the floor, dead and bleeding. Someone said, "You shot someone else, too." It was my husband. He was lying there unconscious, but I could see he had only a superficial shoulder wound. I knew he wasn't dead.

In this dream, we shall first consider the *manifest content* (51). This is what the dream communicates without any interpretive efforts: It is clear that the patient is being subjected to more and more pressure which seems to involve sex (The man is "fully clothed"—a clue to concern over *being* clothed. "This one is for youth . . . kept getting more and more personal." These last two elements suggest sexuality in a more roundabout way). Also, the manifest content of the dream involves violence and death, two subjects rarely discussed by this patient prior to this point in treatment. The policeman brings in the idea of law, order, rules (and in a dream, often relates to the superego). We can also see some of the ways this woman protects herself from forbidden impulses. For example, the "getting too personal" is the act of someone other than the dreamer, and the violence and killing are also carried out by others. Since *all* of a dream's content refers to the dreamer, we see here a method for shifting the blame to others.[29] More extensive speculations could be made from the manifest content, but they would only be utilized by the analyst as working hypotheses, awaiting corroboration through more specific associations.

To get at the meanings behind manifest content, the analyst has the patient free-associate. Each element of the dream is associated to, without any effort to rationalize a meaning. It is what the dream piece "reminds you of" (50). From these associations, the deeper, unconscious, *latent content* of the dream is obtained (51). This patient gave the following associations:

The first item she reacted to was the "Christmas card." This led to associations about a Christmas tree, which was described as being "tall, straight, graceful, and beautiful." Next was the man's name—"Percy." The only Percy known to the patient was a very elderly colored man, who was said to be "very peaceful and harmless." Further, she considered "Percy" a very effeminate name. The other element extensively associated to was that of the husband's presence

---

[29] Ego defenses will be specifically explored in Chapter Four. This particular defense is called *projection*.

in the dream. She stated that if her husband had been willing to go with her instead of working on the night of the encounter, she would not have met with the situation and the whole thing would have been avoided.

We now have some raw data from which this dream can be interpreted. Before we do this let us first note the kinds of facts about the dreamer which are characteristically revealed in dreams.[30]

1. The dream may or may not reveal aspects of a person's conscious attitudes. Often the dreamer cannot even suggest a reason for the dream, or any part of it.

2. The dream reveals many of the unconscious attitudes of the dreamer from the id, ego, and superego. These have a relationship to the circumstances of the present, the childhood past and, if the dream occurs during psychotherapy, of attitudes toward the treatment and the therapist (50, 51, 93).

3. The specific nature of the patient's ego defenses is illustrated. These may be taken as evidence of the person's specific repetition-compulsion. Using this fact, the analyst may know in some detail the exact nature of the patient's neurotic problem, what defensive maneuvers must be removed by interpretation, how the patient will relate to the doctor in the therapy,[31] as well as the approximate course which therapy will take.

4. All elements of the dream, since they are representative of the dreamer's psychic functioning, relate specifically to him on some level of consciousness, and in the topographical areas of id, ego, or superego.

With these facts in mind, let us now at least partially analyze the dream. One of the most striking aspects of this dream is the great difference between the patient's conscious attitude toward the *precipitating event* (there can be little doubt what triggered this dream) and the manifest emotional content of the dream. In the former, all was sympathy and solicitude for the "poor soul" who accosted her, and in the latter the scene is bloody and body-strewn. During the "event" the patient was almost unaware of the nudity

---

[30] It is not always wise or possible at the time of a dream to analyze *all* of its meanings since there are other considerations to be dealt with during a therapeutic session besides the dream. Therefore, the time needed to exhaust all of the dream potential is not always invested and some meanings will not be discovered until later as the treatment proceeds.

[31] See Chapter I on the "transference reaction."

except as it related to "the cold," while in the dream there are many thinly veiled allusions to sex. From these inferences, the *interpretation* was made to the patient that "you must have been very frightened by this encounter and seemed angry about its having happened. Did you think this man had an erection?" (The cue for this interpretation came from the Christmas tree associations). To this she laughingly responded that she recalled now that she had looked at his pelvis, but there was too much shadow to make anything out. (The emotional response of laughter usually indicates a release of tension, and is a good clue that the interpretation is correct.) We can say then that she perceived in this event a danger of sexual attack, but her conscience forbade acknowledging the sexual aspects (which, though only inferred here, were amply illustrated in previous treatment data). The id reaction to this threat was to wish to attack and/or emasculate her fantasied sexual assailant (in the dream this was expressed by the man's death, and his effeminate name of Percy). This primitive desire was also prohibited by superego, so it was defensively modified by projection to the policeman who does the killing, thus keeping all impulses and attitudes in balance.

The element of the husband being shot in the dream is easily seen as her anger at him because he had not accompanied her and protected her against this incident. The "wounded husband" also reflected and was partially determined by the transference feelings toward the therapist, since he had "helped" her to become sensitive and thus vulnerable to such events, and this provoked some anger toward him.

This dream bears out what was already very clear about this patient—in the face of any serious anxiety-producing situation, she resorts to the defenses of denial (not being consciously aware of the threat she perceived to be present) and projection in order not to feel overt anxiety which can lead to a problem-solving response. These adaptive maneuvers represent a part of this patient's repetition compulsion. The problems they encompass are those to be analyzed during the therapy. Continuing interpretive efforts were made to bring insight into these mechanisms, and to obviate their necessity. This occurred slowly and progressively during the course of the therapy.

As noted above, all of the meanings of this dream are not exhausted by this analysis. However, this fragmentary description demonstrates the manner in which dreams are utilized in analytically oriented psychotherapy, and why they are regarded as being so important and useful as revelations of the unconscious and its functioning (94).

SUMMARY

The concepts described and elucidated in this chapter represent some of the important underpinnings of all contemporary psychodynamic theory. They represent the relatively recent flashes of scientific genius which have resynthesized age-old observations on the workings of man's mind, and which have produced a new method for studying and treating normal and abnormal mental functioning. The idea of a dynamic, influential unconscious, the concept of specific personality patterns of psychological defenses which are predictable and genetically understandable, and the theories on the development and function of conscience are but a few of the crucial theoretical conceptions. They provide a unified theoretical approach to the whole man and his internal and external environment. It has been stated emphatically that while much of this theory remains to be "validated" and tied to more fundamental observations of neurophysiology, it does provide the conceptualizing tools to pose the questions for future research and to collect and collate the data of today's explorations. As is true in all scientific research, we must consider these ideas as "voidable" by tomorrow's study.

PROBLEMS

Example

The State Bar Committee for Revision of the Criminal Code is exploring the law of homicide and particularly the whole question of criminal intent. One of the older members of the Committee turns to you (a younger and more recent law graduate) and says, "Is there any information we could get from psychiatry which might help us in these deliberations?" Having been exposed to some of these materials in law school, you volunteer to explore the matter and perhaps bring an expert consultant to the Committee for consultation. Describe how you would proceed with your work on this matter.

First of all, from past experience with nonlawyer experts, it is clear that one must have clearly formulated questions to put to them. Also, one must be prepared to explain to the expert all important aspects of the legal questions and legal process in comprehensible terms. For this reason, the first task is to develop such a set of questions so that their legal relevance may be explained to the expert.

Since the Revision Committee is dealing specifically with the law of homicide, that subject may be used as a prototype exploration for all of the questions about "criminal intent" or *mens rea*. Presumably, the policy questions developed in this context might have general applicability. They may then center around these issues:

(a) How does one psychogically assay levels of awareness, choice-making, and action control in criminal behavior (that which is couched in such legal expressions as "malice aforethought," "premeditation," "deliberation," "willful," "irresistible impulse," etc.)?

(b) How difficult of proof are these different mental states? How reliable is the evidence of expert psychiatrists on these subjects? How can it best be handled by counsel in a trial? Are there any better or worse procedures for presenting and "proving" such evidence?

(c) How do these different mental states portend future risk to society so far as repetition of similar (different?) criminal behavior?

(d) What are the treatment implications of these different conditions? Can a person who makes a "mistake" and kills someone who he thinks is attacking him be "cured" of such a proclivity? If so, how long will it take? What kind of treatment will he need and how should it be given? If he cannot be cured, what are the chances of the mistake being repeated?

(e) If effective psychological treatment is not available, what alternative courses are there? What kind of controls (incapacitation) need be imposed to secure society if risk continues? What are the effects in future of different kinds and durations of incapacitation on such a person?

(f) How would the psychiatric expert best go about effectively presenting his material to the Revision Committee? Will they be able to understand him? How may this communication process be made most effective?

These questions provide the shape for a series of discussions with expert or experts from the psychological sciences, and such persons can now be approached.

As the conferences with the expert proceed, the data he provides in response to the above questions may be developed into a written memo. It would be organized to meet the anticipated challenges and questions from the Committee so as to elicit and elaborate their fears, doubts, concerns and ignorance. When the expert is testifying, he should be told to bear in mind that the Committee hearing is in one sense similar to testifying before a jury. *He* will bear the burden of making his data comprehensible and communicative.

The Committee could be told that their comprehension (or lack of it) reflects the problems in utilizing such scientific data. If they find the expert's information useful, it may be assumed that the jury would do likewise.

In using the scientific data in this way, the important principle is to organize it so that it first deals with questions at the level of the Committee's relative ignorance. It should then carry them systematically forward through theory, evidence and data in support of the theory, and then to the conclusions drawn from it relating to the explicit legal and legislative questions. In other words, the Committee has to be educated to understand this alien material and be led through its logical implications from beginning to end.

From prior knowledge, one would expect that the information which the expert would apply to the legislators' questions would include: theory and data on levels of consciousness; development and functioning of conscience; the manner in which learning is accomplished; questions of treatability (the latter subject will be dealt with in a later chapter). Also, consideration should be given to the psychology of the *role* of expert witness, so that this expert's effectiveness before the Committee is maximized.

If all of these matters are dealt with effectively, the Committee should be able to incorporate the latest *useful* knowledge about human behavior into the statutory language and develop trial procedures which will facilitate the use of all available and relevant knowledge for consideration of the issue of *mens rea*.

1. In a recent television movie production, *Twelve Angry Men*, which is a sensitive depiction of a jury's deliberations in a murder case, one of the jurors (Lee J. Cobb) is shown exercising his fullest influence to convict the young defendant of first-degree murder. With great emotional fervor, he presses his argument, stressing, among other things, the fact

that the accused had been heard threatening to kill his father. During the course of the jury's discussions, the audience gradually learns that this man has a son who apparently rebelled against his father's somewhat heavy-handed domination. At one of the crises in the deliberations, this man angrily raised the murder weapon and "threatened" to kill the soft-spoken juryman (Henry Fonda) who challenged his interpretation of the evidence. At this point, he and several of his fellow jurors gained some of the insight which ultimately resulted in acquittal.

(a) What does this episode show us of the nature of the id?

(b) Of the ego?

(c) Of the superego?

(d) Relate this jury episode to the man's relationship to his own son in meaningful psychological terms.

2. How do you relate the legal concept of deterrence to the functioning of the ego? The superego?

3. What do you consider to be the psychodynamic factors involved in the current problem of "school desegregation"?[32] What do these factors suggest to you in regard to administrative and judicial policies?

4. What is your understanding of the scientific competency of the psychiatrist when the question of "responsibility" is raised in a criminal trial?

(a) How does this competency apply under the rule of McNaughten?

(b) The rule of Durham?

5. It has been correctly pointed out by some commentators on Durham that under this rule a psychiatrist could honestly testify that in his opinion there was no responsibility in the vast majority of criminal episodes. What are the problems raised by this point, if indeed it is true? How might these problems be met practically? Does this pose social advantages or disadvantages?

6. What are the differences in the manifest and the latent dream content and what are their significance.

7. Susan, a strictly reared, single woman of 28, met a young man while drinking in a bar one evening with a group of friends. After several

32 For an extensive description and analysis of these factors see Group for the Advancement of Psychiatry, Report Number 37: "Psychiatric Aspects of School Desegregation" (57).

hours of pleasant social conversation, the young man offered to drive Susan home. They decided to go for a short ride before going home. After stopping the car in a secluded spot, the young man proceeded to have sexual intercourse with her. She offered no resistance, and in fact reported that her memory was a "complete blank" from the time he started the act until "some time later" when she recalls finding him seated beside her with his head in her arms. She was certain they had had inter-course, and she felt very frightened and panic-stricken when she realized what had happened. When Susan saw her psychiatrist two days after the event, she was still in a very anxious and overwrought condition.

(a) How do you explain this episode from the standpoint of the functioning of the id? The ego? The superego?

(b) Did Susan give her "consent" to this act?

(c) Should this event become involved in litigation, what problems of credibility might be raised? Do you think competency could become an issue?

8. Explain the psychodynamic theory in regard to levels of conscious-ness, relating it to the incident presented in question number 7, above.

9. Following is an excerpt from the case study of a seriously aggres-sive nine-year-old boy, who was being cared for in a special treatment center for "Children Who Hate" (87):

Bill, who ordinarily is quite positive toward me, was quite rebellious when I reminded him that he wasn't supposed to hit golf balls over into the next door neighbor's yard. Instead of replying with his usual "O.K. Yo-Yo," (his and the group's pet name for me) and coming along with the suggestion, he snarled back at me, "yer mammy" and knocked one over the fence de-liberately. When I insisted that this was not acceptable and reminded Bill that I would now have to confiscate the club, he ran away, throwing the club at me. Five minutes later I found Bill trying to break down the office door with a two-by-four because he thought I had put the club in there. I relieved him of the two-by-four and asked him what was bothering him that he should act so "mean" this morning. Bill said that he was going "to take that club to school" or he wasn't going and I said "Now come on, you guys never get to take your golf clubs to school anyway" but he was adamant and refused to go along so the group was taken without him. When I returned, Bill was even more upset and was angrily packing his clothes, saying that he wasn't going to stay at this "goddam dump no more" etc. I said nothing but just stayed with him, finally bringing out that something must be bothering him and that I was sure it wasn't just the golf club— what was it? First, Bill said that nothing was wrong and then angrily threw out, "That goddam Danny, he thinks he can shove everybody around." I replied that I hadn't seen Danny do anything special this morning to Bill or anyone else. Was Bill sure that was it? He didn't answer and I said, "O.K., if you don't want to talk about whatever it is, I guess we'll have to skip it but I think it would be better if you came out in the open. . . ." Finally Bill, in a gust of feeling, said, "I didn't keep none of it and I ain't going to get blamed for it. . . . Last night Mike went over to that old lady that lives next door and gave her some flowers. I was with him and we saw she had a roll of bills this big [rolls up his fist]. Mike said for me to watch out in the yard this morning and he would go over and swipe it and I did but I ain't got any of it and I won't get blamed for what he did. The wallet is hidden in the garage. . . .

(a) How would you describe the state of the superego in this boy? The ego? The id?

(b) Explain the dynamics of psychological guilt which are operative in this case.

(c) What are the "treatment" implications for this kind of behavior?

REFERENCES

1. Alexander, F., *Fundamentals of Psychoanalysis*. New York: Norton, 1948, pp. 86-87.
2. *Ibid.*, p. 82
3. *Ibid.*, pp. 44-45.
4. *Ibid.*, p. 108.
5. *Ibid.*, p. 83.
6. *Ibid.*, p. 95.
7. *Ibid.*, p. 90.
8. Alexander, F. & Staub, H., *The Criminal, the Judge, and the Public*. Glencoe, Ill.: The Free Press, 1956, pp. 3-5.
9. Bentham, J., *The Works of Jeremy Bentham*, Vol. I. Edinburgh: W. Tait, 1843, p. 14.
10. *Ibid.*, pp. 1-4.
11. Berenson, B., *Aesthetics and History*. Garden City, N. Y.: Doubleday, 1954, p. 26.
12. Biggs, J., Jr., *The Guilty Mind: Psychiatry and the Law of Homicide*. New York: Harcourt, Brace, 1955, p. 20.
13. Breasted, J. H., *The Dawn of Conscience*. New York: C. Scribner's Sons, 1947, p. 39.
14. *Ibid.*, p. 213.
15. *Ibid.*, p. 177.
16. *Ibid.*, p. 34.
17. Cahn, E., Judging a Judge. (Book Review on *Of Law and Men*. Felix Frankfurter Papers, Ed. P. Elman). *New York Times Book Review Section*, May 27, 1956, p. 18.
18. Coke, E., *The First Part of the Institutes of the Lawes of England or a Commentary on Littleton*. London: M.F.I.H., 1639, p. 395.
19. Coke, E., *The Third Part of the Institutes*. London: M. Flesher, 1648, p. 20.

20. Dement, W., The Effect of Dream Deprivation. *Science*, 131:1705-1707, 1960.
21. Douglas, W. O., Law and Psychiatry. Graduation Address at W. A. White Institute of Psychiatry, Psychoanalysis, and Psychology, Jan. 28, 1956, p. 2.
22. Drever, J., *A Dictionary of Psychology*. Harmondsworth: Penguin Books, 1952, p. 201.
23. Dunbar, F., Medical Aspects of Accidents and Mistakes in the Industrial Army and the Armed Forces. *War Medicine*, 4:161-175, 1943.
24. Dunbar, F., Susceptibility to Accidents. *Medical Clinics of North America*, 28:653-662, 1944.
25. Erikson, E., *Childhood and Society*. New York: Norton, 1950, p. 140.
26. *Exodus*, 21:24.
27. Fenichel, O., *The Psychoanalytic Theory of Neurosis*. New York: Norton, 1945, p. 57.
28. *Ibid.*, p. 55.
29. *Ibid.*, p. 18.
30. *Ibid.*, p. 106.
31. *Ibid.*, p. 105.
32. Ferenczi, S., Stages in the Development of the Sense of Reality. In: *Sex in Psychoanalysis*. New York: Basic Books, 1950, p. 213.
33. *Ibid.*, p. 227.
34. *Ibid.*, p. 219.
35. *Ibid.*, p. 222.
36. *Ibid.*, p. 225.
37. *Ibid.*, p. 227.
38. *Ibid.*, p. 229-230.
39. *Ibid.*, p. 231.
40. Ferenczi, S., A Lecture for Judges and Barristers. In: *Further Contributions to the Theory and Technique of Psychoanalysis*. New York: Basic Books, 1952, p. 432.
41. *Ibid.*, p. 431.
42. Ferenczi, S., Psychoanalysis and Criminology. In: *Further Contributions to the Theory and Technique of Psychoanalysis*. New York: Basic Books, 1952, p. 435.
43. *Ibid.*, p. 434.
44. *Ibid.*, p. 436.
45. Fisher, C., Dreams and Perception: The Role of Preconscious and Primary Modes of Perception on Dream Formation. *J. Amer. Psychoanal. Assn.*, 2:389-445, 1954.
46. Fisher, C., Dreams, Images, and Perceptions. *J. Amer. Psychoanal. Assn.*, 4:5-47, 1956.
47. French, T. M., *The Integration of Behavior: Vol. I, Basic Postulates*. Chicago: University of Chicago Press, 1952, pp. i-xi, 1-272.
48. Freud, A., The Ego and the Mechanisms of Defense (1936). *The Writings of Anna Freud*, 2. New York: International Universities Press, 1967.
49. *Ibid.*, p. 7.
50. Freud, S., The Interpretation of Dreams (1900). *Standard Edition*, 4, 5. London: Hogarth Press, 1953.

51. Freud, S., On Dreams (1901). *Standard Edition*, 5:629-683. London: Hogarth Press, 1953.
52. Freud, S., A General Introduction to Psychoanalysis (1916-1917). *Standard Edition*, 15 & 16. London: Hogarth Press, 1963.
53. Freud, S., Beyond the Pleasure Principle (1920). *Standard Edition*, 18:7-64. London: Hogarth Press, 1955.
54. Freud, S., The Ego and the Id (1923). *Standard Edition*, 19:12-66. London: Hogarth Press, 1961.
55. Freud S., Dostoevsky and Parricide (1928). *Standard Edition*, 21:175-198. London: Hogarth Press, 1961.
56. Freud, S., Civilization and Its Discontents (1930). *Standard Edition*, 21:57-146. London: Hogarth Press, 1961.
57. Group for the Advancement of Psychiatry, Report No. 37: Psychiatric Aspects of School Desegregation. New York: G.A.P., 1957.
58. Group for the Advancement of Psychiatry, Report No. 48: Psychiatry and Religion. New York: G.A.P., 1960.
59. Guttmacher, M., The Psychiatrist as an Expert Witness. *Univ. Chicago Law Rev.*, 22:325-330, 1955.
60. Hamilton, W., *The Metaphysics of Sir William Hamilton*, Ed. F. Bowen. Cambridge: Sever & Francis, 1862, pp. 235-253.
61. Hartmann, H., *Ego Psychology and the Problem of Adaptation*. New York: International Universities Press, 1958.
62. Hartmann, H., Comments on the Psychoanalytic Theory of Ego. In: *Essays on Ego Psychology*. New York: International Universities Press, 1964, pp. 113-141.
63. Hartmann, H., Kris, E. & Loewenstein, R., Comments on Formation of Psychic Structure. *The Psychoanalytic Study of the Child*, 2:11-38. New York: International Universities Press, 1946.
64. *Ibid.*, p. 14.
65. Jung, C., *Archetypes and the Collective Unconscious* (1935). London: Routledge & Kegan Paul, 1959.
66. Kalven, H. & Zeisel, H., *The American Jury*. Boston: Little, Brown & Co., 1966, Chapt. 15.
67. LeShan, L., Dynamics in Accident-Prone Behavior. *Psychiatry*, 15:73-80, 1952.
68. Lewin, B. D., *The Psychoanalysis of Elation*. New York: Norton, 1950.
69. Lorenz, K. Z., *King Solomon's Ring*. London: Methuen, 1952, pp. 107-111.
70. Lorenz. K. Z., The Past Twelve Years in the Comparative Study of Behavior. In: *Instinctive Behavior*, Ed. C. H. Schiller. New York: International Universities Press, 1957, pp. 288-310.
71. Luborsky, L. & Shevrin, H., Dreams and Day-Residues: A Study of the Poetzl Observation. *Bull. Menninger Clin.*, 20:135-148, 1956.
72. Malamud, W. & Lindner, F. E., Dreams and Their Relationship to Recent Impressions. *Arch. Neurol. Psychiat.*, 25:1081-1099, 1931.
73. Margolin, S. G., The Behavior of the Stomach During Psychoanalysis. *Psychoanal. Quart.*, 20:349-373, 1951.
74. Medawar, P. B., *The Uniqueness of the Individual*. London: Methuen, 1957, pp. 175-184.

75. Menninger, K. A., Purposive Accidents as an Expression of Self-Destructive Tendencies. *Internat. J. Psychoanal.*, 17:6-16, 1936.
76. Mill, J. S., *An Examination of Sir William Hamilton's Philosophy*, 2 Vols. Boston: W. V. Spencer, 1865.
77. Miller, J. G., Psychoanalysis and Systems Theory. In: *Science and Psychoanalysis*. New York: Grune & Stratton, 1958.
78. Montagu, A., *The Direction of Human Development*. New York: Harper Bros., 1955, pp. 83-84.
79. Munn, N. L., *The Evolution and Growth of Human Behavior*. London: G. G. Harrop, 1965, pp. 193-195.
80. Munroe, R. L., *Schools of Psychoanalytic Thought*. New York: Dryden Press, 1955, pp. 337-343.
81. Overholser, W., *The Psychiatrist and the Law*. New York: Harcourt, Brace, 1953, pp. 51-55.
82. Pavlov, I. P., *Experimental Psychology and Other Essays*. New York: Philosophical Library, 1957, pp. 245-270.
83. Penfield, W., The Interpretive Cortex. *Science*, 129:1724-1725, 1959.
84. Pound, R., The Causes of Popular Dissatisfaction with the Administration of Justice. *Baylor Law Rev.*, 8:11-12, 1956.
85. Rangell, L., On the Psychoanalytic Theory of Anxiety. *J. Amer. Psychoanal. Assn.*, 3:403, 1955.
86. Redl, F. & Wineman, D., *Children Who Hate*. Glencoe, Ill.: The Free Press, 1951.
87. *Ibid.*, pp. 107-108.
88. Reich, W., *Character Analysis*. New York: Orgone Press, 1933.
89. Reik, T., *Myth and Guilt: The Crime and Punishment of Mankind*. New York: G. Braziller, 1957, p. 28.
90. Roche, P. Q., Criminality and Mental Illness—Two Faces of the Same Coin. *Univ. Chicago Law Rev.*, 22:324, 1955.
91. Saul, L. J., *The Bases of Human Behavior*. Philadelphia: J. B. Lippincott, 1951, pp. 32-38.
92. *Ibid.*, pp. 110-112.
93. Sharpe, E., *Dream Analysis*. London: Hogarth Press, 1951, Chapt. I.
94. *Ibid.*, Chapt. II.
95. Showstack, N., Preliminary Report of the Psychiatric Treatment of Prisoners at the California Medical Facility. *Amer. J. Psychiat.*, 112:824, 1956.
96. Stephen, J. F., *History of the Criminal Law of England*, Vol. II. London: Macmillan, 1883, p. 83.
97. Szasz, T. S., Some Observations of the Relationship between Psychiatry and the Law. *Arch. Neurol. Psychiat.*, 75:309-311, 1956.
98. *Ibid.*, pp. 310-311.
99. *Times,* Lords Relax Judicial Precedent Rule. *The Times.* London, July 27, 1966, p. 10.
100. Voltaire, *Candide*. London: Penguin Books, 1947, p. 20.
101. Waelder, R., Psychiatry and the Problem of Criminal Responsibility. *Univ. Pa. Law Rev.*, 101:390.
102. *Ibid.*, p. 380.
103. Walter, G., *The Living Brain*. New York: Norton, 1953, p. 247.
104. *Ibid.*, p. 16.

105. Watson, A. S., Freud the Translator; Some Contacts with Philosophy. *Internat. J. Psychoanal.*, 39:326-327, 1958.
106. Weihofen, H., *The Urge to Punish*. New York: Farrar, Straus & Cudahy, 1956, p. 168.
107. *Ibid.*, pp. 38-44.
108. Weiss, E. & English, O. S., *Psychosomatic Medicine*. Philadelphia: W. B. Saunders, 1949, pp. 445-446.
109. *Ibid.*, p. 316.
110. Wolfgang, M. E., Political Crimes and Punishments in Renaissance Florence. *J. Crim. Law, Criminol. & Police Sci.*, 44:5, 1954.
111. Zilboorg, G., *The Psychology of the Criminal Act*. New York: Harcourt, Brace, 1954.
112. *Ibid.*, pp. 109-136.
113. Zilboorg, G. & Henry, G. W., *A History of Medical Psychology*. New York: Norton, 1941, pp. 342-350.
114. *Ibid.*, pp. 376-377.
115. *Ibid.*, pp. 367-369.

IV

The Ego and Its Defenses

In Chapter III, we described the means by which the ego accomplishes the task of adaptation to internal and external reality. In the words of Hartmann, Kris, and Loewenstein: "Functions of the ego center around the relation to reality. In this sense, we speak of the ego as of a specific organ of adjustment. It controls the apparatus of motility and perception; it tests the properties of the present situation at hand, i.e., of 'present reality,' and anticipates properties of the future situations. The ego mediates between these properties and requirements, and the demands of the other psychic organizations" (23).

We have stated that in this adaptive capacity, *the ego*, out of deference to the biological and psychological need for comfort, *resorts to defense maneuvers to achieve or re-establish that comfort, under difficult conditions.* The ego must achieve some degree of instinctual drive gratification within the limitations of "reality," protecting itself at the same time from the massive pressures of instinctual drives. While the ego juggles the forces of instinctual drives, reality, and superego judgments, it must protect itself from all three as well.[1] Any one of these may threaten to overwhelm the ego under certain conditions, and the ego must anticipate and deflect such developments. For example, in a situation which would

[1] As these concepts are discussed, there is often the implication of teleology: "The ego guards against . . . ," etc. The ego in fact reacts to situations adaptively and thus has an *etiological* relationship to them. Because we are describing this adaptive process in terms of abstractions which have no base in anatomy and only a remote connection to physiology, it is exceedingly difficult to avoid this useful manner of expression. However, let me emphasize that we are dealing with etiological, not teleological relationships.

arouse such a powerful impulse to kill that the person might "lose his mind," the ego can prevent the whole thing by screening *all* aggressive feelings from conscious awareness. The ego must limit and control instinctual drive gratifications in relation to external considerations. An individual with a healthy functioning ego recognizes full well that sexual impulses, for example, may be acted upon only under certain circumstances of time, place, person, situation, etc. Also, instinctual impulses must be handled in ways which fit in with superego dictates. For example, if conscience disapproves severely of particular sexual or aggressive impulses, then the ego must block them from awareness to avoid the shame and guilt which would be caused by "knowing" of their presence.

In carrying out its defensive functions, the ego must see to it that excessive anxiety states are avoided. All of the conflict situations above create anxiety,[2] and have the effect of potentiating defensive activity by the ego. In addition to the primary conflict, prior experience may cause the ego to regard the anxiety as a potent source of danger. The sequence of events is as follows: Whenever any threat occurs which may create anxiety, some defensive maneuver is invoked to disguise the source of risk. While this provides a modicum of comfort, it does not totally eliminate the anxiety which continues in a nonspecific form. Since it is not related to a recognizable source, it is called "free-floating anxiety." This form of anxiety is frightening and painful, and therefore the ego must seek to neutralize and bind it through a defensive maneuver (such as attaching it to some object which can be manipulated and "controlled." This would produce the symptom of *phobia*.) This kind of ego activity is very important to psychic adaptation.

From reading the above, as well as other psychiatric and psychoanalytic materials, one may get the impression that anxiety is "bad" and should be abolished at all costs. This is very far from true, since anxiety is essential for mobilizing the physiological and psychological mechanisms for dealing with stress situations. Anxiety mobilizes adaptive behavior and acts as a warning to the psyche that it is in some kind of real or potential danger. The healthy ego treats anxiety as a signal to prepare itself for action, does so, and in the process masters the anxiety by eliminating its cause. A sense of well-

[2] This concept was first elaborated by Freud in his important book, *Inhibitions, Symptoms and Anxiety* (22).

being arises through the ego's perception that the threat has been realistically handled, and this implies strength and competence. However, if the ego has failed to learn how to deal with stress, the very perception of anxiety may be the signal for a massive panic or flight reaction, and the ego is disrupted by such anxiety. This, while it conforms to the biological pattern of flight from excessive danger, very often it causes a person to take defensive action which is, in fact, counter to biological and psychological security.

We have discussed the fact before that the ego must maintain balance between the demands of the biological, instinctual organism, and the dictates of external reality in the form of natural forces and the customs and laws of the society. Frequently, psychic dilemmas occur. The ego must then resort to some maneuver which will "eliminate" the dilemma and the frustration in order to permit a continuation of effective psychic activity. Under "excessive stress" (and this is a quality which varies in relation to each individual) the ego may have to resort to extreme defensive maneuvers which grossly compromise the perception of reality.[3] A common example is the pain and difficulty in facing the death of a loved person. Often the bereaved person denies the fact that the loved one has died. He may go about in a detached and withdrawn state, acting as if the disaster had not, in fact, happened. Of course, this is a temporary maneuver with most people, and sooner or later they turn back to everyday reality and recognize and accept the death. With some individuals the loss is totally denied, or else they may remain withdrawn and in a depressed state. This illustrates the close proximity between the normal and the pathological use of defense mechanisms, which is an important factor always to keep in mind.[4] Decisions of what to do with those who have committed antisocial acts,

[3] It has been established experimentally that under the stress of being deprived of all or most normal sensory stimulation (as carried out under the conditions of "brain-washing") most persons, in time, respond by hallucinating (25). This very strongly suggests that a person *needs* sensory stimulation and that if he does not get it through the usual routes, he creates it by hallucinating. This is related to the clinical phenomenon observed in the psychoses, where the social disabilities of the patient are reconstituted by delusional and hallucinatory means. A *hallucination* is "a false sensory perception in the absence of an actual external stimulus" (2). A *delusion* is "a false belief out of keeping with the individual's knowledge and cultural group" (3). For example, Daniel M'Naghten shot and killed the secretary to the English Prime Minister because he had been directed to do so by God (6).

[4] Camus, in *The Plague*, brilliantly details the various ways in which grief, disappointment, and deprivation may be managed psychically (5).

and whose behavior necessitates some form of treatment, must be made in terms of the degree and the manner in which such persons utilize these mechanisms. Rational dealing with these problems is made difficult by the fact that those who make the decisions, without realizing it, sense that some of their own inner impulses are identical with those which the criminal has translated into action. Out of fear that these forbidden inner drives may cause prohibited action, the need arises to suppress its mirrored counterpart and the criminal "must" be punished. Such unconscious and irrational (although "normal") reactions slow progress toward more humane and effective treatment of the antisocial or deviant behavior in society, be it criminal, delinquent, or psychotic.

Each individual tends to "specialize" in the defenses which he uses.[5] Each person during his life, under the impact of his own environment which teaches him acceptable and unacceptable methods of dealing with his own impulses and the realities around him, learns to utilize one particular set of defenses more than another. These defenses tend to exist in combinations. We shall see as we discuss them that some are extensions and continuations of others. What are the characteristics of these defenses? *The principal characteristic which all defenses have in common is that they are unconscious.* They function without the individual being aware that he is utilizing them. This is obviously related to the main function of the defense which is to hide forbidden impulses or motivations from a person's conscious awareness and thus avoid anxiety. The fox who "knows" that the grapes are sweet and delectable cannot walk away from them with comfort merely by saying that they are sour. He must convince himself that they are sour. When this is done, frustration is "avoided." The maneuver would have no psychic usefulness if he knew that it was only a dodge, and it is characteristic of all defenses that they attain approximately the same level of unconsciousness. The very essence of almost all psychological treatment rests in disentangling these defense maneuvers and bringing what was unconscious into consciousness (29).

Now, let us turn to specific mechanisms of defense. We shall list and describe eleven of these defenses. Although various authors subdivide and describe them in different ways—some group several

[5] See Chapter III for a discussion of the repetition compulsion.

under a single descriptive name, while others subdivide them in much greater detail—the dynamic relationships of these mechanisms are well understood and well accepted by most psychiatrists. We should note that scientific awareness and understanding of these defenses has been gradual in its growth. Early in the history of psychoanalysis, the defenses were not separately defined but were categorized together as *repression*. With increasing knowledge of ego dynamics, subdivisions have been split off and defined. We shall attempt to deal with them here so as to shed light on the way in which they crop up in relation to the problems of law and legal administration.

SUBLIMATION

Of all the ego defenses, this is the most ubiquitous and the most "normal." Every individual, in the course of psychosexual maturation, accomplishes a large amount of sublimation, since those living in a society must limit and redirect their emotional impulses to a considerable degree.[6] We may define sublimation as that psychological maneuver in which an instinctual drive impulse or an emotion is unconsciously redirected from its original to a more socially acceptable goal. It is a rechanneling and, for this reason, a relatively efficient psychic defense. Although the ego must expend energy to create and to master a new channel for outlet, once this is achieved, the energy thrust of the emotion may proceed largely unrestricted. Let us illustrate this with several clinical examples.

A young man, reared in a family which met any suggestion of aggression with stern repudiation, grew up to redirect and camouflage all forms of aggression. He could not consciously see himself as an aggressive person. As an adult, he got a job as an engineering sales consultant for a manufacturer of heavy earth-moving equipment. These giant machines were unconsciously perceived as powerful extensions of himself, whereby he could express some of his pent-up aggressive feelings. Individuals working on this job had been deliberately selected because they were large and powerful men. The job seemed to be ideal, and he was eagerly looking forward to it. In clinical interviews, he revealed the degree to which he was

6 In a recent paper, Sherfey has demonstrated anew how true is this psychological and sociological maxim (32).

going to use this job as a sublimated outlet for his aggression. He had changed both the aim (expression of aggressive feelings) and the object of the aggression (originally the frustrating persons in his family), and thus achieved sublimation.

Research activities which permit an indulgence of some "forbidden" curiosity are another example of sublimation. Seeking answers in one area of intellectual interest may be a sublimation of the desire to find answers to sexual questions. Such a sublimation is extremely useful to society. The desire to be looked at and to be admired by others, which must be curtailed once childhood is past, may be sublimated in the performing arts where there is a premium on skillful acting or exhibiting of oneself.[7]

Sublimation is often a crucial factor in the choice of career, and law is no exception. The pent-up wish to prove oneself to be right and to know answers, once directed toward parents where it could not be expressed freely, may be sublimated in the practice of law. In this profession, there is a high premium on the ability to argue one's position clearly and aggressively. Thus, verbal aggression may be redirected in terms of its object, and may be a useful motivating factor in the practice of law (37). However, if this sublimatory activity is not successful, the practitioner may suffer inhibition under just those circumstances where aggressive argumentation is called for. He may have the wish to argue aggressively and effectively and, indeed, he may have the skill, but this can be blocked by superego (conscience) prohibition.

"Sublimation, i.e., the displacement of the instinctual aim in conformity with higher social values, presupposes the acceptance or at least the knowledge of such values, that is to say, presupposes the existence of the superego"[8] (20). The ego unceasingly seeks out the external limitations which may cause anxiety or pain when broached. Once these limits are incorporated into the superego, no external watchman is needed to enforce the judgment—the defensive sublimation will redirect impulses toward acceptable outlets.

[7] Indeed, good teachers have a similar capacity.
[8] Displacement is itself a psychological defense, in which energy, initially aimed in one direction, is shifted and redirected toward another. The distinction between displacement and sublimation rests in the fact that displacement does not necessarily involve attaching the instinctual aim to social acceptability. Displacements may, in fact, be absolutely counter to social acceptability. This defense will be described more fully below.

Repression

The second defense we shall discuss, *repression,* is fundamental to all the ego's defense activity. We may define it as "an unconsciously purposeful forgetting of internal urgings or external events which, if conscious, would be painful" (7). In other words, the painful event or affect is first repressed before subsequent defensive activity takes place. In terms of psychic efficiency, this kind of defense is relatively "expensive." We might compare it to the control of a steam by damming it up. We know that merely building a dam across a stream bed is only a temporary technique of blocking the flow downstream. As the water rises behind the dam, it very quickly reaches the spill-over point. If the decision to control the flow further is made, then it becomes necessary to build the dam higher. We also know that with the increase of height, the base must be thickened to hold the increased pressure—the higher the dam, the wider must be its foundation. Also, it may become necessary to change the shape, and instead of a straight line across the stream, the strength is increased by arching the dam backward into the pressure of the water. Repression works similarly.

The original idea or feeling which is repressed touches associatively upon many other ideas and feelings. This necessitates repression of the associated links if the original stimulus is to be blocked from awareness. For example, if an individual experiences a frightening episode with a dog as a child, the fact that dogs are dangerous may be blocked from his awareness. However, since dogs are pets and cats are pets, it may become necessary to similarly repress thoughts about cats. Cats catch rats and this necessitates rats being covered by repression. So the repression must continue until, finally, it may envelop a very large segment of a person's experiences through such tangential associations as these. It is like dropping a pebble into a quiet pond. At first there is a little wave just at the point of impact. Gradually the wave spreads outward until it is lapping on all the banks of the pond. Repression does the same thing, and when the anxiety-provoking capacity of the originally repressed feeling is insufficient, the area of the spreading, secondary repression becomes very extensive and obstructs effective life patterns.

We should also note that, contrary to some of the early thinking about "progressive education" and child-rearing, repression is a necessary psychic defense in early childhood, at the time when the emotions to be handled are intense and frightening. A great deal of what we call "infantile amnesia" relates to the necessity for repressing powerful competitive feelings which exist within the family. With this repression, many of the early associative memories of childhood are also swept out of awareness and "forgotten." This statement reflects one of the basic assumptions of psychoanalytic theory that, in the face of threat and attack, the normal reaction is either to counterattack and fight back, or to run away. Due to the child's weakness and vulnerability, the attack impulse is repressed because of its obvious danger, and the flight technique is carried out through the repression. Thus, in our culture, society "trains out" the child's retaliative impulses very early, and they are controlled by repression. It is clear, however, that such "forgotten" desires are not really lost. They return to consciousness and action when circumstances seem to "warrant."

The latter circumstances are closely related to public reaction toward some types of criminal cases, when there is a great outburst of both public and judicial anger aimed at the criminal. The return of repressed impulses is often the motivating force behind "retributive justice."[9] How, we might ask, do repressed impulses relate to the desire to punish others? The answer to this lies in the fact that repressed emotions and ideas, in order to remain behind the curtain of repression, must not be openly dealt with by the conscious ego. Thus, when a crime which involves primitive emotions and impulses has been committed, it is as if one were looking at oneself in a mirror, and the criminal act is perceived as a reflection of one's own repressed impulse life. The screen of unawareness has been pierced and the spectre of one's own forbidden impulses is clearly seen. For this reason, "crimes of passion" are less likely to be viewed with rational understanding by the public at large and, all too often, lawyers and judges react likewise.

It is in just those cases where criminal acts most clearly demonstrate severe ego dysfunction that we may anticipate the most retributive and punitive attitude on the part of both the public and

[9] The assassination of President Kennedy in America and the recent killing of the three policemen in England called forth this response (34).

the legal profession. Sex crimes, murders, and activities involving "animal passions," draw forth remarks heavily fraught with emotion from the judge on the bench and from the press. There is a great hue and cry for the police to "do something" about this kind of person. It may well be true that this type of individual desperately needs society's attention, but intelligent and appropriate treatment planning necessitates understanding the psychological motivations for the crime. To achieve such understanding, the observer must be able to abide his own repressed identifications with the criminal, or he will "need" to react defensively and retributively against him.

When we consider the defense of repression and attempt to evaluate its usefulness and appropriateness, we must acknowledge the fact that in each individual's childhood repression seems to be necessary for the socializing process. However, as the individual begins to reach maturity, it is also necessary that he reduce his use of this defense to a minimum. With the ego's maturation and its increasing ability to reality-test, it should be possible to accept and recognize the reality of inner impulses, as well as the reality of the external world and its pressures for conforming. On the basis of these two considerations, one can arrive at conscious control and modification of behavior. When this is accomplished, a person is able to utilize his psychic energy maximally and to minimize the amount needed to maintain the patchwork of his psychic defenses. Instead of expending energies to increase the height and thickness of the dam structure, conduits can be installed to run the dammed-up and blocked emotion off into generators and irrigation ditches, or down a reconstructed and rechanneled stream bed. This results in psychic economy. Repression, of course, remains available to deal with extremities of acute stress and shock. However, as the ego recovers, it should be able to remove the repression, accept the shocking facts, and return to a more reality-based set of operational procedures.

PROJECTION

Projection is the mechanism whereby painful or objectionable feelings or ideas are perceived as originating from persons or things in the environment and thus may be seen as not belonging to the self. It is an archaic kind of defense both in terms of personal as well as social development. Children (and many adults) tend to view the "good" things of life as relating to themselves, while the "bad" or evil stem from external sources (8). We commonly see examples of this defense mechanism in primitive societies, and it is the basis for the most primitive form of religion, animism (35). In this form of religion, personal attributes are "projected" onto inanimate objects of the natural world as well as onto natural forces, and their behavior is explained according to these anthropocentric concepts. Very young children freely demonstrate projection. It is not uncommon for two- or three-year-olds, when that which they are just on the verge of learning is disapproved, to turn to father and say, "You're bad, Daddy."

This type of defense is potentially dangerous since it so markedly disturbs the perception of reality. "Psychoanalysis assumes the early process of differentiation between inside and outside to be the origin of the mechanisms of projection and introjection, which remain some of our deepest and most dangerous defense mechanisms. . . . In projection we experience an inner harm as an outer one; we endow significant people with the evil which is actually in us" (15). Freud postulated an interesting theory to explain the psychological economy of projection. He stated that the ego is much more capable of screening and controlling stimuli from outside the body than it is of dealing with internal stimulation. Therefore, in order to make use of this defensive screen, (which he called the *Reizschutz*) projection is effected (22). As the ego becomes more capable of perceiving and understanding the nature of the internal stimulation of the body, is better able to master these and relate them to external reality, projective defenses become less necessary. To whatever degree projection is utilized, distortion of external reality will occur. This defense may produce severe problems for an individual, even though it alleviates immediate anxiety.

We may think of myriad examples to illustrate projection. They range from the idea expressed in the popular song, "Put the Blame on Mame, Boys," to the bizarre auditory hallucinations of the schizophrenic. Also, the visual hallucinations of delirium tremens and acute alcoholism, the pink elephants and purple mice running up the walls, are all examples of projection. The paranoid is often victimized by the mechanism of projection. His self-perception gives him the feeling that he is "homosexual," but this thought is so dis-rupting that he must get rid of it and have somebody else "assert" the idea. His delusions of persecution exemplify the mechanism of projection. For example, the defendant in *Fisher v. United States* (328 U.S. 463, 1946) showed evidence of paranoid delusions in his attitude toward the librarian whom he killed. Senile persons often believe that they have been mistreated by relatives and therefore feel that they should leave their property to a nurse or housekeeper who has "really loved" them. Occasionally, a business partner will begin to feel that he is being cheated in a mysterious way by his associates and will reason that he should therefore leave the partner-ship. (The latter case stems from his own repressed and projected desires to take advantage of partners, while the former may repre-sent the testator's desire to get rid of the sense of helplessness by blaming others for it, i.e., "they mistreat me" instead of "I am weak, helpless, and feel mistreated.") We have discussed previously the psychological mechanisms in retribution. It should be clear that projection is also involved in that instance.

While the bizarre, hallucinatory activity of the overt psychotic is easy to recognize as projection, some of the more subtle types which commonly occur are not so easy to perceive. This is due to the fact that projection tends to utilize some small element of reality and invest it with considerable projected emotion. In these instances, we find individuals over-reacting to an incident which the observer feels is relatively unimportant. The intensity of emotional response is usually due to the projected affect. The ubiquity of this defense in social and personal relationships makes its understanding most important. While it is not unusual for normal people to utilize projection occasionally, it does impair reality-testing. It should not exist to any great extent in healthy people. Its frequent use is one of the criteria which establish the psychiatrist's diagnosis of psychosis. Only to demonstrate projection does not prove psychosis, but it does prove a relative inability to test reality.

DENIAL

Denial is the "mechanism of defense whereby obvious reality factors are treated by the individual as if they did not exist. For one reason or another, the patient finds certain of these factors painful or unpleasant, and he literally denies that they are present. This mechanism, similar to projection, while quite common, is representative of a psychotic state if it is used excessively in adults" (9).

Illustrations of this defense abound in the behavior of emotionally disturbed individuals. For example: a young man was very fearful of driving an automobile. Instead of responding to this fear by either not driving or by perfecting his driving skill, he plunged "fearlessly" into the task and drove extremely aggressively. In fact, he soon became known as a "wildman" at the wheel of his car. In this instance, the emotion of fear was denied and he behaved with great bravado. However, there were disguised outcroppings of his fear in the form of disabling gastrointestinal symptoms, which not only ultimately took him away from the wheel of his car but nearly brought about surgical intervention. An astute and perceptive physician became skeptical and sent his patient to a psychiatrist. Bringing his fear to the surface where he could deal with it more appropriately promptly relieved his symptoms, and he went back to learning to drive—this time with his fear on the surface. Many kinds of "daredevil" activities have this sort of motivation. A false sense of power is achieved, but it fails to be reassuring.

Denial is also occasionally seen in social and political events. For example, the famous and ill-fated belief of Chamberlain before World War II, when he thought that he had concluded a peace treaty with Germany at Munich, would appear to be a good example of denial. We should not be too prone to criticize Mr. Chamberlain, however, since a large part of the Western world was more than willing to share his denial with him.

Occasionally denial is seen in social reactions to those who go about directing dire threats toward their neighbors or family. Very often such individuals have given all-too-clear warning of their murderous intentions long before they burst the bounds of self-control. The Unruh case which occurred in Camden, New Jersey, several years ago is a good example of this.[10] Retrospectively, it was clear that he had warned several of his victims repeatedly, but due to the frightening aspects of his threats, these individuals "denied" what they saw and felt and took no remedial action until it was too late. Daniel M'Naghten also tried to warn people of his homicidal

---

[10] A young man (Unruh) went beserk and killed eleven people before he was captured.

intentions and even sought to solicit the help of the sheriff. Unfortunately, he too was not taken seriously (4).

INTROJECTION

This is "a mechanism by which a person incorporates into himself a certain human characteristic, trait or force. This characteristic, trait or force may be incorporated for the purpose of using it or destroying it. In many ways, introjection is the opposite of projection, and both are very archaic in their origins. Like projection, introjection relates back to the infantile feeling that everything 'good' belongs to the self, and everything 'bad' or painful is in the outer world" (10). The child incorporates the traits and attitudes of the emotionally important people with whom he lives. If he feels warmth, appreciation, safety, or respect for the person, he introjects their attitudes and uses them as his own—they become not only *his*, but also *him*. If, on the other hand, he fears or hates these people, he incorporates the feared traits in order to destroy them. While this permits the child's ego to survive for the time, it may have devastating effects on him as an adult. He will then find himself actively hating and/or fearing a part of his personality and waging a blind battle to eliminate somehow this alienated part of his self. Without some outside help, these struggles are usually self-defeating.

The phenomenon of introjection is very plainly seen in depression. When the death of a loved one occurs, it is as though "a part of me is also dead." The identification and introjection in relation to the dead person are forced closer to consciousness by the death, and the individual feels that death has also struck at his own vitality. His recuperation from such a reaction brings about a slow disengagement from the old introject through the formation of a new one. If the relationship with the deceased was also fraught with anger, hatred, or hostility, strong guilt about the death is also present, as though the angry thoughts or wishes had somehow caused the death. Such guilt makes it more difficult to give up the introjection, and the survivor feels he does not deserve to live. Depression caused by such guilt feelings may create difficulty in "getting over" a death. Under such circumstances, the depression may be very profound and may linger on, even bringing about a psychotic reaction. In a transient and small way, this reaction may be observed in relation to most grief, and many rituals surrounding death have been evolved socially to dissipate it. Lawyers should be on the lookout for inappropriate legal moves in their clients which arise from such guilt reactions.

REACTION FORMATION

A reaction formation is "the setting up of a more-or-less rigid attitude or character trait which will serve as a means of preventing the emergence of a painful or undesirable attitude or trait, usually of the opposite type" (11). The joke about the old maid who looks under her bed because she is "afraid" a man might be hiding there is only funny because of the intuitive recognition that the fear is in fact a wish. Reaction formation is a rather inefficient defense since it directs the unacceptable impulse toward a goal opposite to the original, and can thus produce little pleasure or resolution. It is tantamount to trying to make a river reverse its course and flow upstream. It is important to understand this defense in order to see some of the motivational forces in people's reactions in formulating, and in enforcing the law. This was well illustrated several years ago in the play, *The Detective Story* (26). Here a detective, whose father had been a criminal, devoted himself in a crusaderlike fashion to the job of law enforcement. Under the stress of a situation in which his identification with a criminal came too close to the surface, the underlying motivation for his enforcement zeal became clear. To defend himself against his own antisocial impulses (and his identification with his father), he had become the opposite of antisocial—a zealous law enforcement officer.

Many homosexuals comment that one of their most frightening problems is the likelihood that they will try to seduce a plainclothesman from the vice squad. With angry bitterness they point out that these individuals are themselves "queers" who are afraid of their impulses and so go around "catching" other homosexuals by entrapment (31). The homosexual's perception is very often correct inasmuch as he does feel seductiveness and empathy emanating from such a detective. The detective, on the other hand, uses his unconscious feelings and wishes to lead him to the homosexual and to invite him to make a pass. Using this unconscious lead, the enforce-

ment officer invites the homosexual to expose himself and then
arrests him.

Almost all laws involving "morality"—in sex, alcohol, language—are
influenced by the reaction formations of the individuals involved.[11]
The woman who crusades against having panties displayed in store
windows, the antivivisectionist, the prohibitionist—most of these
types are struggling to reverse and eliminate their own strong inclinations. It is easy to take a relaxed and worldly view of such demonstrations since they seem to reflect but a small minority.[12] However, the more subtle reaction formations which strongly influence
legal and legislative decisions regarding issues involving sexuality,
are of the very same nature. It is only through understanding these
psychological forces that it will be possible for us to take a more
rational approach to such legal problems.

UNDOING

"Undoing is a mechanism in which the individual does one thing
for the purpose of 'undoing' or neutralizing something which in his
imagination or in reality was done before, and which he feels was
objectionable. It is a sort of expiation mechanism" (12). This mechanism of defense has been utilized and formalized in religious activities, in child-rearing practices, and in some legal punishments. The
concept of doing penance is predicated on the assumption that the
individual will thus "make up for" his sins. Just as the religious
institution of penance is dependent on the existence of a dogma
which establishes the fact that penance expiates sin, so the mechanism of undoing rests on the superego attitude that this form of
expiation wipes the slate clean. Individuals who use this defense
do so because they learned in childhood that punishments were always exacted in relation to forbidden activities and were necessary
to get back in the family's good graces. It is closely akin to the
guilt/punishment expectations of the childhood superego.[13]

The mechanism of undoing is occasionally revealed when well-
publicized crimes bring forth a spate of false "confessions." Exami-

[11] A good illustration is the crusade for a law to prohibit obscenity in the mails
by Anthony Comstock in 1873 (28).

[12] Sometimes, however, these small groups succeed in making an enormous impact
on the legislative process (27).

[13] See Chapter III.

nation of these individuals would probably show that they are
suffering from guilt due to some "crime" which they imagine they
have committed (33). When they read of the unsolved crime, their
unconscious defense of undoing takes over, and they attempt to get
themselves punished to remove their guilt. They will confess even
at the risk of capital punishment. The need for punishment is so
great that possible death does not deflect the defensive maneuver.
It is quite probable, however, that since they, at least unconsciously,
realize that they are not guilty of the crime, they do not quite
believe that they will be punished for it. The inconvenience and
difficulty to which they subject themselves by being interrogated
in relation to the crime accomplishes enough self-punishment to
produce considerable homeostatic effect.

The question of differentiating *undoing* from *reaction formation*
rests largely in a temporal quality. Reaction formations are usually
constant attitudes erected against a constantly present attitude in
the unconscious. *Undoing* generally relates to a specific thought or
event, and does not continue in time.

REGRESSION

The defense of regression is characterized by the temporary or
permanent abandonment of a more mature adaptive measure for an
earlier one which was appropriate and effective at a previous stage
of psychological development (13). Since this exacts a heavy toll on
the ego's efficient operation in the present, there must be important
gains or it would not be used. When a person functions at a lower
level of development than his chronological age, it is a serious detriment to successful living. However, this is a defense used even by
normal individuals, and it is one which everyone uses at least once
a day when they go to sleep. This should amply illustrate the fact
that regression is not entirely pathological. In fact, after an individual has lived and worked during a day, struggling with the
problems and tensions of his life, it is biologically essential that he
withdraw himself from his contacts with the environment and rest
and restore his physiological balance. This may be partially accomplished by "recreation" and play (including sexual "foreplay"), and
sleep completes the job. During sleep there is marked psychological

regression. Dreams illustrate this with their almost inevitable expression of some childhood phase of the person's life.

Many examples of regression are familiar to those working with criminal law. For example, there are the old men who indulge in exhibitionistic or other sexual activities with children. They appear to derive more sexual satisfaction from relationships with children than with their own peers. This, no doubt, is a function of their growing inability to adjust to the exigencies of life, a progressive loss of the relationships with their life-long acquaintances and family, and an increasing anxiety about their frustrations and difficulties due to progressive physical debility. Thus they retreat to childish techniques for sensual gratification. This being the motivation, there is no virtue whatsoever in punishing them for their activities. While it is important to keep them from sexual contact with children, there is no possible advantage in punishing them.

Regression cannot be checked by punishment, and its course may be reversed only by removing the stresses which impinge upon the ego and force it to regress. We may say that all neurotic behavior, psychosis, and a great deal of criminal activity is regressive in its nature inasmuch as it is a withdrawal from mature solutions and a retreat to the level where reality considerations are overlooked and pleasure-gratification is immediate.

RATIONALIZATION

"Rationalization is a mechanism of defense in which the ego substitutes an acceptable reason for an unacceptable one in order to explain a given action or attitude. This is carried on primarily to delude the superego into accepting something which might otherwise result in guilt" (14).

This is one of the most common defenses and is employed by everybody. It is a homeostatic maneuver to bring motivations into harmony which are felt to be at odds with the values of the superego. For example, a lawyer may hold certain ideals of objectivity in making decisions. At the same time, he may have particularly strong religious beliefs. Approached by a client of similar religion who wishes to obtain a divorce, he may raise many objections quite unconscious of the fact that they stem from his religious attitudes. Since he cannot advance these reasons and still maintain his appropriate professional role, he will not voice them, even to himself. He may resolve this inner conflict by seeking out some "reason" in the theory of the law to justify not working on the case. While this "reason" may be logical, it is not the real one. This switch is called a rationalization.

Another common event which occurs to both doctors and lawyers arises when a case is not progressing in a way that is professionally and personally satisfying. There is a powerful urge to relieve boredom or frustration by "unloading" the case to another. Very often this kind of case finds its way to the office of a newer and younger member of the professional community under the guise of some rationalization. It would not be easy to get the referring person to acknowledge this. Most people get quite angry when they are told they are rationalizing, and they refuse to believe it. However, the anger itself is symptomatic of the irrational situation and exposes the rationalization. Rationalizations are seldom dealt with consciously (36).

Homosexuals who are referred to psychiatrists for treatment in lieu of imprisonment occasionally exhibit rationalization. They may become more comfortable as homosexuals just because they are in treatment. Their rationalization is that since they are "doing something about it" they are fulfilling their social obligation and therefore may continue with prior behavior. Also, the fact that "homosexual activity is motivated by emotional forces over which they have no control," supports their behavior. While this is entirely true in fact, it sets up a perfect rationalization opportunity which must be removed therapeutically. We should emphasize the fact that rationalization *is* unconscious and not a deliberate effort to malinger or distort.

Another area in which rationalizations probably occur frequently is in judges' opinions. In many cases, it is likely that, by the end of trial argument, the judge has already arrived at a decision. He must then discover legal reasons for having arrived at his decision, and these may take the form of rationalizations. The opinion must rest on established law, and therefore he may not report all of the mental process through which he went to arrive at his decision. This does not mean that the decision is necessarily wrong, but it does mean that the reasons given for the decision may not be the true ones, or at least all of the true ones (19, 38).

DISPLACEMENT

"Displacement is a mechanism of defense by which an affect which was originally attached to one object is displaced to another" (16). This defense is certainly very familiar to most of us, and we all occasionally "take out our spleen on somebody else." For example, one may become very angry with one's employer and be unable to vent this anger. This anger must be obliterated from awareness, but this does not eliminate it. That evening, one's innocent spouse may catch the full blast which was suppressed earlier.

Another example of displacement is seen in some individuals' deep love for pets. This is lucidly portrayed by Dorothy Canfield Fisher in her novel, *The Deepening Stream* (17). In this story a lonesome young girl showers her love on her pet dog with all of the avidity of a lover. Later on, when she is able to move away from her psychological isolation, she directs her affection toward her husband and family, and the intensity of her feeling for pets is greatly reduced.

Many criminals, when they repetitively attack society, are practicing a symbolic displacement from some hated or frustrating parent. After reading the autobiography of the notorious safecracker, Willie Sutton, one could readily say that his fascination for safes and his compulsion to crack them was related to the intense sense of frustration which he felt at his mother's failure to love and support him adequately during his childhood (30).

The foregoing examples illustrate the basic function of all ego defenses—to alleviate anxiety and establish psychological homeostasis. It should be equally clear that the defenses may, and very often do, overshoot the mark and bring about a new imbalance. They thus fail in their purpose and thereby create distortion in some area of the personality. Psychiatrists state flatly that all psychological activity is directed toward ultimate alleviation of tension. This is hard to credit when we observe the vast spectrum of self-punishing and self-destructive behavior common to our world: suicides, accidents, many kinds of illness, and criminal activity which is certain to result in apprehension and drastic punishment. How can we say that these actions are aimed at relief of tension?

The tension here is internal, but none the less commanding for that. The superego's impact and overriding power on the total personality cannot be overestimated. Individuals who commit what their childish conscience views as severe sin or crime need, insist upon, and receive drastic and severe punishment. Sometimes the ego is strong enough to camouflage this "death wish" and, instead of being overtly suicidal, the action is disguised as physical illness or social activity which only indirectly result in punishment. Whether to call this masochism or not depends entirely on how we define masochism. Can it be said that these individuals enjoy their self-punishment? If they do not, according to the classical definition of masochism, this would not qualify.

Psychosis is an extreme defensive operation. Classically, psychosis is viewed as a deterioration or a lack of psychic activity, but this theory fails to account for all the facts. It can be demonstrated that psychosis itself is a defense against anxiety. If the individual fails in his reality adaptation, he may drive his defensive operations to such extremes that they are psychotic by definition.

There is a point of controversy here. Are psychoses different in quantity or quality from neuroses?[14] The difficulty in answering rests on the many ways of viewing psychic behavior. Psychoses, neuroses and, for that matter, normal behavior have the same purpose and abide by the same laws. In this sense, psychoses represent the extreme end of a continuum and are different quantitatively. They are different in quality from neuroses and normal behavior in their exaggerated disregard for reality factors, and so may be considered different in quality. We have drawn a line and said: On this side is normality with all its eccentricities, and on the other are neurosis and psychosis with their own inexorable logic.

It may be that a physiological component to psychosis will be discovered. It is already suspected, and there are hints that it exists (24). If so, the question will be settled in favor of quality. If, however, such a physiological factor is discovered not as a specific agent, but rather as occurring in various degrees in everyone, we will be back where we started—viewing psychoses as extreme forms of normal psychophysiological adaptive maneuvers. To illustrate this in an oversimplified way—an individual who feels so very insecure

14 For example, see the controversy in *Overholser v. Leach* (257 F.2d 667 [1958]).

and inferior that he lives with constant, racking anxiety, may seek refuge in daydreams of glory. These fantasies eventually take over his thought life until he has "delusions of grandeur." He may communicate with higher powers via hallucinations, and thus compensate for a sense of weakness and inferiority. These defensive operations, rather than creating security in a real sense, increase his insecurity and necessitate further withdrawal from reality. There is an inevitable, progressive eradication of the reality sense when psychotic defenses are utilized. Thus the psychotic adapts to a world of his own creation where magical rules facilitate meeting the pressures upon him, and he is "removed" from the source of his frustration and failure in the world of reality.

Psychosomatic illnesses may have the same function as psychoses. When the psychogenic origins of certain physical ailments were first recognized, therapists aggressively set about the task of interpreting them to patients. Frighteningly often, when patients were thus "convinced" that they were not sick, they developed overt psychoses. If they could not be physically ill, they had to be psychotic. This relationship has become well known, and it is clearly recognized that it is dangerous to remove the psychological crutch of the physical ailment until such time as the patient's ego is strong enough to deal with reality problems efficiently. If the patient cannot attain such ego strength, the physical disease is usually preferable to the drastic defense of psychosis, and the wise doctor will leave the patient alone (1).

The functioning of the ego and its defense mechanisms is at the heart of present-day psychiatric theory. All psychotherapy utilizes this knowledge as its cornerstone. Real cure of any psychological illness always necessitates a detailed treatment of the defenses, bringing them to the patient's understanding and awareness so that reality-based techniques for adaptation may be instituted. One of the criteria of maturity is the degree to which ego defenses are needed. The greater the maturity, the less these defenses will be used. Even the most mature person, however, cannot function without the occasional use of defenses. The issue is rather the degree of rigidity and compulsion with which they are used. Maturity results in greater flexibility and makes the defenses accessible to alteration when they lead to inefficiency.

PROBLEMS

Example

A person walks into your office and tells you that he is under indictment on a criminal charge for which he is to appear before a judge whom he was instrumental in having appointed to the bench. He says that his present lawyer seems to feel that it does not matter if the judge sits, but he, the cilent, feels that it would be impossible to have a fair trial before him. The client wants you to make the necessary arrangements to take over the case and do something about the judge. You instruct the client that he will first have to discharge the other lawyer from the case before you can help him. He does so, and you then contact former counsel (who seems pleased to get rid of what he called an "unpleasant client") and obtain his papers on the case.

The situation is as follows: (1) the judge assigned to sit on the case did in fact get his appointment to the bench through the political influence and help of the defendant. (2) Former counsel had made an attempt (clearly half-hearted) to have the judge disqualify himself. (3) The judge had refused, asserting vigorously that he did not see any reason why he could not sit because, after all, he was an honest man and could be perfectly objective about the issues of this case. (4) During hearings on preliminary motions, the judge assiduously avoided so much as a glance at the defendant, even though in the past they had been close friends, frequent partying buddies, and collaborators in many political matters.[15]

With these facts in hand, how might you conceptualize a psychological defense structure in the judge regarding his relationship to the defendant? How would you proceed to handle this case? What kind of information would you want to carry out your plan?

In thinking and feeling oneself into the circumstances of the judge (empathizing), one's first reaction probably would be that one would not like to be in the judge's shoes. One would not want to have to try a friend on a criminal charge. Indeed, the judge has a ready way out, and he may disqualify himself. This would not be an uncommon course to take, and the fact that he does not, immediately raises the psychological question of why not. These two elements then become data for further exploration of the situation.

The next point one would consider is, does the judge even "know" that

---

[15] These facts are close to those of a reported case, *Green v. Murphy*, 259 F.2d 591, 1957 (18).

he is in a tight squeeze? If he does, it might mean one thing, while if he does not, it would mean another. Do we have any data pro or con regarding this question? When the judge gave his answer that he intended to hear the case because "he was an honest man and could be perfectly objective about the issues of the case," he was doing what Shakespeare designated "protest[ing] too much." This assertive and no doubt emotionally stated answer (one would want to find out exactly how he had inflected and "emoted" his answer), is a giveaway for his underlying sense of uneasiness about the case (i.e., a reaction formation). One could readily imagine the judge torn between his sense of gratitude for past help and his sense of professional duty. Whichever way he goes creates strong personal conflict. (The law wisely acknowledges this when it not only permits but encourages one to withdraw in the face of a "conflict of interests.") In order to understand his dilemma, he must be able to think, "I owe something to this man and I want to repay him—a fact that would cause me to behave inappropriately if I were to follow it." To do this, he must be willing to acknowledge "improper" impulses. This taxes a childish conscience, which works its control by *denial* of forbidden impulses. The missing impulse is then substituted by its opposite—"I am *completely* honest and could even sit on the case of my friend."

In order to maintain the latter attitude intact, it must be overasserted by the judge. Instead of making balanced and neutral rulings, he might so zealously avoid the interests of the friend-defendant that they are in fact prejudiced in reverse. This would be the position that counsel should argue, and this should be the reason for the judge to withdraw (or be withdrawn?).

When attempting to remedy the situation, obviously the best solution would be to get the judge to withdraw voluntarily. Since this has already been attempted unsuccessfully, it means that the judge is not readily able to see his part in this situation. Psychologically, he must be helped to become aware of his desire to help his friend. Perhaps the judge of the supervising court of appeals could informally help him to see his dilemma. "George, I sure sympathize with you on this one! You kind of hate to drop out of the case, but I'm sure everyone would expect you not to want to sit on the trial of your old friend. I'd drop out." The goal here is to legitimize the presence of the desire to help a friend, regardless of professional obligation. This opens up the dilemma and permits reason to re-enter the picture.

In the event that this does not work, there would be a need to carry the issue forward in a formal legal procedure (leaving to one side for the moment the procedural question of whether this should or should not be a post-trial remedy). Inevitably, at about this point, counsel would surely seek some expert psychiatric assistance (even if he could think through the situation as laid out heretofore). He would wish to have these dynamics substantiated with precise statements about the data, its reliability, and the theory upon which it is built. While most people without psychological sophistication can *sense* the nature of the judge's dilemma, it must be made explicit if it is to be used as a legal argument subject to cross-examination.

The data set forth above and the analysis drawn from it (by the sophisticated counsel) could be supplemented by further observational data about the past relationship between the defendant and the judge. From these, the expert would be able to fill out in more detail the basis for the judge's behavior (i.e., the evidence of repeated patterns of similar concern in other issues of the same psychological nature). These observations would all be drawn from what was *publicly* visible about him and what could be supplied by the defendant from his own personal experience with the judge. Out of this data, a persuasive argument could be built which would bring verbal explicitness to what nearly all who observed this situation would feel.

The question of whether this should be a pre-trial or a post-trial remedy is a problem for broader policy consideration. In the case cited[16] the appellate court (and I personally believe, correctly) did not consider the merits of argument about the judge's prejudice. They settled it as a purely procedural question, stating that it was a post-trial remedy. This foreclosed the possibility of myriad pre-trial appeals to bar a judge from hearing a case. Most judges in such a circumstance are all-too-eager to withdraw and do, since refusal would merely open the gates for dilatory tactics. It is interesting to note, in conclusion, that once the judge in the cited case obtained "permission" to hear the case, he withdrew. This serves as final proof of his problem. He had several options to withdraw voluntarily.

1. Read the dream and its associations on pages 98-99.

   (a) What defense mechanisms are illustrated in the patient's handling of this dream?
   (b) What do they tell you of the patient's personality structure?
   (c) How do these defenses serve the function of homeostasis?
   (d) In a hypothetical prosecution for rape, in which this patient was the prosecutrix, would her personality structure raise any problems of credibility?

16 See this chapter, footnote 15.

2. An adult male patient receiving psychotherapy brings up the following early memory:

I am hanging on the railing of a stairway which leads down into the basement of the house, and I am chinning myself. Up above, on the porch, is another boy watching me, and egging me on. I think that I regarded him as being sort of a sissy or something.

(a) Recalling that we may use these early memories in the same way in which we utilize dreams, what mechanisms of defense are illustrated in the memory?

(b) What are the id (instinctual) elements revealed here?

(c) How do you think this man consciously views himself? Unconsciously?

(d) How do you think this man's personality influences his day by day living effectiveness? What kinds of problems might he have? In what kinds of legal problems could you visualize his involvement?

3. (From *Gregoire v. State*, 128 A.2d 243, 244)

David testified at the trial of the case on May 3, 1956, in which he was the prosecuting witness in the first case tried, that he was fourteen years of age and in the ninth grade at school. He identified the appellant in court and stated that a week before Christmas, 1955, he was walking on 65th Avenue about 1:30 p.m., and saw the appellant turn his automobile around and come up 65th Avenue. He stopped and asked David whether he knew the location of a certain street. He then asked him whether he would ride there with him and show him where it was. As David had nothing to do, he got in the car with the appellant. Appellant turned on Central Avenue and went the wrong way. He told appellant that he was going the wrong way but appellant turned to go to Addison Road, then to Ritchie Road, and onto Walker Mill Road. As appellant went down the road he told David he had had a fight with his girl and she was supposed to do something to him. Appellant then drove into a side road in a wooded area just a little way off Walker Mill Road and "unzippered" David's pants and committed an act of oral perversion. He was too scared to run away. The appellant did not abuse him or hurt him in any way. He made no objection to anything that appellant did, although he knew it was wrong. He said he was afraid of the appellant because he did not know what he was going to do. He was just "scared stiff." Appellant did not tell David his name, and the next time David saw him was in the police station. After the act was committed, both David and the appellant "had to go to the bathroom." Both got out of the car, but David said he was too scared to run. Appellant took him back to Central Avenue and let him out of the car. David then walked behind the car and got the license number, 1955 Maryland registration JF-4242, and remembered that it was a blue and white two-door Mercury. He then went home, called the police station and, with the registration number, asked about the owner of the car. He said he was still too scared to tell his mother, so he went to the movies. After he got home he told his mother about it and she called the police. He and his father went to the police station that night, and he identified the appellant there. When asked whether he could have gotten away at the time, he answered that he "might have been able to."

    (a) Can you build a psychological theory accounting for all of the "facts" stated in the opinion? Outline this theory.

    (b) Do you think the complainant a party to complicity in this act?

REFERENCES

1. Alexander, F. & Szasz, T., The Psychosomatic Approach in Medicine. In: *Dynamic Psychiatry*. Chicago: University of Chicago Press, 1952, pp. 369-400.
2. American Psychiatric Association, Committee on Public Information, *A Psychiatric Glossary*. Washington, D. C.: American Psychiatric Association, 1957, p. 20.
3. Ibid., p. 11.
4. Bousfield, R. M., *Report of the Trial of Daniel M'Naghten*. London: Henry Renshaw, 1843, pp. 64-65.
5. Camus, A., *The Plague*. New York: Alfred A. Knopf, 1948.
6. Diamond, B., Isaac Ray and the Trial of Daniel M'Naghten. *Amer. J. Psychiat.*, 112:651-656, 1956.
7. English, O. S. & Finch, S. M., *Introduction to Psychiatry*. New York: W. W. Norton & Co., 1954, pp. 56-66.
8. Ibid., pp. 57-58.
9. Ibid., pp. 58-59.
10. Ibid., p. 60.
11. Ibid., p. 61.
12. Ibid., p. 62.
13. Ibid., p. 64.
14. Ibid., p. 66.
15. Erikson, E. H., *Childhood and Society*. New York: W. W. Norton & Co., 1950, p. 221.
16. Ibid., p. 67.
17. Fisher, D. C., *The Deepening Stream*. New York: Grosset & Dunlap, 1934.
18. Forer, L., Psychiatric Evidence in the Recusation of Judges. *Harvard Law Rev.*, 73:1325-1331, 1960.
19. Frank, J., *Law and the Modern Mind*. New York: Tudor Publishing Co., 1936, pp. 152-153.

20. Freud, A., The Ego and the Mechanisms of Defense (1936). *The Writings of Anna Freud*, 2. New York: International Universities Press, 1967, p. 56.
21. Freud, S., Beyond the Pleasure Principle (1920). *Standard Edition*, 18:7-64. London: Hogarth Press, 1955.
22. Freud, S., Inhibitions, Symptoms and Anxiety (1926). *Standard Edition*, 20:87-172. London: Hogarth Press, 1948.
23. Hartmann, H., Kris, E. & Loewenstein, R. M., Comments on the Formation of Psychic Structure. In: *The Psychoanalytic Study of the Child*, 2:15. New York: International Universities Press, 1946.
24. Heath, R. G., Martens, S. et al., Effects on Behavior in Humans with the Administration of Taraxein. *Amer. J. Psychiat.*, 114:14-24, 1957.
25. Heron, W., The Pathology of Boredom. *Sci. Amer.*, 196:56, 1957.
26. Kingsley, S., *The Detective Story*. New York: Random House, 1949.
27. Marmor, J., Bernard, V. & Ottenberg, P., Psychodynamics of Group Opposition to Health Programs. *Amer. J. Psychiat.*, 30:330-345, 1960.
28. Paul, J. C. N. & Schwartz, M. L., Obscenity in the Mails: A Comment on Some Problems of Federal Censorship. *Univ. Pa. Law Rev.*, 106:217, 1957.
29. Reich, W., *Character Analysis*. New York: Orgone Institute Press, 1949, pp. 64-66.
30. Reynolds, Q., *Smooth and Deadly*. New York: Popular Library, 1953.
31. Secretary of State for Home Department (Committee on Homosexual Offenses and Prostitution), Report of the Committee on Homosexual Offenses and Prostitution. London: Her Majesty's Stationery Office, Sept. 1957, pp. 43-48.
32. Sherfey, M. J., The Evolution and Nature of Female Sexuality in Relation to Psychoanalytic Theory. *J. Amer. Psychoanal. Assn.*, 14:28-128, 1966.
33. *Time,* Case of the Spattered Ceiling. *Time,* Nov. 15, 1956, pp. 21-22.
34. *The Times,* Resist Stampede for Hanging. London: *The Times,* Aug. 16, 1966, p. 8.
35. Tylor, E. R., Animism. In: *Primitive Heritage*. New York: Random House, 1953, pp. 46-52.
36. Vail, A. A., Annulment in Church and State. *DePaul Law Rev.*, 5:377-385, 1956.
37. Watson, A. S., Reflections on the Teaching of Criminal Law. *Univ. Detroit Law Rev.*, 37:701-717, 1960.
38. Yankwich, L. R., The Art of Being a Judge. *Univ. Pa. Law Rev.*, 105:377-385, 1957.

V

The Psychological Growth and Development of the Personality

In order to understand the psychoanalytic theory of personality, one must understand the concept of *genetic process* or psychosexual development of the individual. Organized on biological principles, it assumes that individuals in growing from infancy to adulthood pass regularly through several specific stages of development. Each stage patterns neurological and psychological organization which, though it may later be further elaborated, remains fundamentally the same throughout life. While there have been changes in specific conceptualization of this developmental theory, all present-day analytic theory makes use of some form of the genetic process concept (40).

Since most early psychoanalytic investigation dealt with problems of the instincts, early theory tended to focus on the organizing principles involving libido. Also, since the data was derived largely from adult patients, early theories were based on memories of childhood elicited from adult patients. All workers found that their patients' associative material was filled with such memories and their reactions to them. In 1905, Freud published *Three Contributions to the Theory of Sexuality* (23), in which he developed his theory about the way libido is modified and developed as children grow up. For the next decade or so, Freud, Abraham, Ferenczi, Rank, and others built up a more complete picture of the instinctual

139

modification which comes with maturation. As the years passed, it became more and more apparent to investigators that what was being described included not only developing instincts but also the impact of a specific culture. With an increased understanding of ego functioning and of social forces which impinge upon it, theories of genetic development began to reflect this increased knowledge of the interplay between individual psyche and cultural environment. As psychoanalytic theory began to influence the work of anthropologists and sociologists, the interchange of ideas increased, and today the concept of genetic process is viewed by most behavioral scientists as a biological, cultural, and psychological interaction (11).

As these concepts gained currency, the need to make direct observations on children became apparent. In recent years, "psychoanalysts have begun to study infants *as infant*, with the paraphernalia of scientific method. . . . The research of René Spitz is illustrative of the new, direct approach to study of the infant, and Anna Freud, Fried, Ribble, Katherine Wolf (as Spitz's collaborator and in her own right), Escalona, Isaacs, Mittlemann, and others have also carried out noteworthy psychoanalytically oriented studies of infant behavior" (41). These investigators have substantiated and clarified the theory of genetic process in their work with children. As such work continues, we may expect modifications and additions to genetic theory which, though largely the result of reconstruction, has gained much substantiation by direct observation.

In outlining psychosexual development, we shall not strictly follow Freudian formulation because it tends to omit details of social impact on psychological maturation. The work of Erik Erikson is perhaps the best formulation of the psychosociological interrelationship and includes the basic Freudian insights (16, 21). His concepts provide us with a unified theory encompassing both biological facts and basic cultural factors and are illuminated by the latest knowledge and understanding of the functioning of the personality. This theoretical construct is largely devoid of cultural coloring and comes from an investigator with long experience in dealing with children directly, both as a teacher and a psychoanalyst.

Development is divided into periods of time, and these periods are named according to the principal psychophysiological focus of the period. Before embarking on detailed description, let us summarize and identify these developmental phases.

The earliest stage is called the *period of orality*. Freud and Abraham divide this stage into two substages which are called the "oral-sucking" and the "oral-biting" phases. Erikson calls the whole "oral sensory." In this phase of development, instinctual primacy centers on the oral cavity and the skin surfaces. It is a period of mainly passive receptivity for food, comfort, and all forms of external stimulation. The next stage is the period of body mastery, called the *anal period*. Freud and Abraham divide this into the "anal-retentive" and the "anal-eliminative" phases, while Erikson calls the entire phase the "anal-urethral-muscular" stage. Freud's designation reveals a cultural emphasis on bowel training, while Erikson sees it in broader terms as the period of life when the infant learns to control his whole body.

In the next phase of development the child becomes more socially involved with his parents and has a growing awareness of their sexuality. Freud calls this the *phallic* or *oedipal* period, while Erikson calls it the "locomotor-genital stage." During this phase the principal emphasis centers on the increased ability to use the body in the service of achieving social goals.

For the subsequent stages of development, we shall use the nomenclature of Freud and the earlier analysts while employing some of the descriptive dynamics of Erikson. The latter designates subsequent development as pregenital and genital, while, according to classical description, the next phase is designated as the *latency period*. This name comes from the idea, no longer credited, that the child, from the sixth year to pubescence, is without sexual expression, or is "latent." During the latency period, the child's principal interests are in assimilating the cultural tools of his environment. Latency is followed by *puberty* and *adolescence,* during which sexual maturation occurs and final social orientation is achieved. We shall also outline the periods of *adulthood* and *maturity*. These latter two stages involve, essentially, the evolution of mature social, vocational, and philosophic relationships to society. We shall describe the principal emotional problems which must be resolved in each of these stages and focus especially on how they relate to social controls.

The Period of Orality

Physical and Psychological Status at Birth

The newborn infant arrives in the world after nine months of warm, dark, effortless existence in which feeding is automatic and it is not even necessary to breathe. There is ample evidence to support the idea that the unborn fetus is sensitive to its environment and reacts to it (39). Various investigators have demonstrated that it is capable of learning a typical Pavlovian conditioned reflex.[1] This forces us to assume that it is not unaware of the pleasurable, comfort-giving surroundings in which its prenatal existence is lived out. Birth catapults the infant out of its comfortable state and delivers it, after hours of massive stimulation, into a world in which it must actively breathe, eat, and sort out, and categorize the mass of noisy, bright, harsh stimuli beating in upon it. Birth can easily be understood as the first "psychic trauma" in life. This impression led one early psychoanalyst, Otto Rank, to formulate his entire theory of psychological functioning around this event. He believed that the character of this experience was prototypical and shaped all later methods for dealing with anxiety (43). While all analysts recognize the importance of this event, it is not generally regarded as the central psychological experience.

That this first stage of life should be called the period of orality will not seem strange to anyone who has lived with an infant. The care of a newborn child, with the exception of keeping it clean, centers around its mouth. For the first several months of its life, the baby's main demand on its environment is in its expectation of food and other types of pleasure, such as rocking and cuddling. To eat and to sleep comfortably seems to encompass its total needs.

The child in its new environment, still neurologically immature and lacking the capacity to perform any goal-directed activity, functions extensively on a reflex basis. Several of the most significant of these reflexes center around the mouth and face and have obvious survival importance. For example, when an object of any sort is

[1] For example, when the abdomen of a pregnant woman is stimulated by a sharp jab, the fetus reacts with motion (primary reflex). Then the jab is coupled with a buzzer sound simultaneously applied to the abdominal wall. In time, the jab may be discontinued, and the buzzer alone will produce the fetal activity. This is a *conditioned reflex*.

placed in the mouth, the newborn infant will begin to suck reflexively.[2] Also, if the side of the infant's face is touched, it will automatically move toward the side touched. We can readily see that these two reflexes, in combination, facilitate the child's moving toward and sucking of the breast. The need for this kind of reflex is obvious in the absence of a capacity to think and an inability to learn such a complicated procedure soon enough to survive.

A significant factor at each stage of development is the manner in which the individual achieves pleasure. The infant gives every evidence that sucking is an intensely pleasant activity. In fact, an infant who nurses to satiation, toward the end of its nursing, will make the movements which we associate with adult sexual orgasm.[3] After satisfying hunger and sucking needs (for the child needs to suck beyond nutritive requirements), its next reaction is to fall into a deep sleep. By the third month, a happy and contented infant goes through this cycle without a hitch and shows his pleasurable reaction in various ways.[4]

At this early stage of life, all manner of strange new stimuli impinge upon the child's perceptive apparatus. It is clear that it enjoys being warmly held with close and firm support. Also, it shows pleasure at the pleasant sounds made by loving and admiring elders and, on the opposite side, loud noises or sharp sounds, rough handling, and other unpleasant stimuli produce whatever withdrawal movements the newborn is able to make. Infants who are either ill-treated or totally deprived of pleasurable sensory experiences develop signs of serious physiological impairment. The work of René Spitz (47) and others (12) demonstrate clearly the impact of deprivation of love and maternal care. Spitz observed children reared in a setting barren of maternal closeness, although with adequate physical care. They rapidly developed signs of profound psychological withdrawal and serious physical disability. These infants soon looked like nutritionally starved infants in spite of adequate food intake. Beyond any doubt, they would have died had they not been restored to loving maternal care. In short, all of the stimulation and attention which

[2] A *reflex* is a pattern of organized neuromuscular events which occur automatically when the appropriate stimulus is applied. Once the stimulation has occurred, the individual is not capable of stopping the course of the reflex response.

[3] See the photographs of Balinese children in *Growth and Culture* (37).

[4] For a detailed description of the psychological orientation of the oral period see *The Rights of Infants* by Margaret Ribble (44).

we associate with the process of good "mothering," means to the newborn child not only love, but also physical survival. Love, then, is an essential ingredient of biological survival to the newborn, and we will see that it is also essential to the adequate growth and development of the personality throughout life.

Let us now turn to the psychological status of the newborn and in somewhat more detail describe its concept of the world. We have observed the fact that the newborn child is completely helpless and vulnerable to its surroundings. It would appear that, initially, the healthy and well cared-for infant is unaware of this fact. He perceives the universe according to the manner in which he is handled (22). If he is promptly gratified, he concludes that he has the power to manipulate and control his surroundings by gesture and sound according to his needs. Also, we believe that the newborn who is well cared for, very likely cannot distinguish between himself and his mother (29). He visualizes his mother as an extension of himself, responsive to his own whims, and this does not tend to facilitate distinguishing between the two.[5] When, however, the mother does not immediately answer the infant's demands for attention, a sense of impending danger and vulnerability are soon forced upon the infant, and a growing awareness of the existence of "me" and "her" follows. When hunger pangs go unaltered, the primitive ego is compelled to regard these instinctual needs as dangerous forces which threaten great discomfort and potential injury.

In terms of his emotional relationship to others, it is also clear that an infant is totally self-interested and self-centered. He not only has no knowledge of others' needs and problems, but his whole orientation is to self alone. We say that his libido is *narcissistically* directed.[6] This narcissistic orientation is entirely appropriate from

[5] Evidence for this conclusion comes from the material brought forth by schizophrenics, which shows clearly that they are not able to distinguish between themselves and others in the outside world. Also, we can see that this is not an illogical conclusion for an infant who has just ended the truly symbiotic intrauterine relationship. Under these conditions, where in fact no physiological distinction of importance exists between the mother and the foetus, it is easy to see how the organism's primitive perceptual capacity makes it unable to delineate and distinguish between "self" and "nonself."

[6] This is an example of Freud's use of mythology to illustrate common human motivations. We recall that the youth, Narcissus, child of the gods, came to difficulty only after he discovered his own beauty, and admired himself to the exclusion of all other activities. It was at this point that the gods turned the handsome youth into a flower.

a biological point of view. The newborn needs all his energies for survival, and such self-interest and self-directed love continue for several years. They are modified only according to the exigencies of the external environment based on the biological requirements of adaptation.

We have discussed the concept of "body image." It can be seen from the remarks above that at this early stage of life the infant's ego capacity to differentiate is so poor that it is impossible to delineate self from mother. Therefore, the body image at this time incorporates the mother as she is perceived by the child, as though her body and that of the child were contiguous.

As growth and maturation occur, the ego's perceptive capacity improves. The impressions of persons in the environment are taken in much the same indiscriminate fashion in which feeding occurs, and we speak of these early perceptive experiences as being "incorporated." In other words, they are taken in by way of the senses and become part of experiential memory. Just as the infant is unable to decide rationally what kind of food he may usefully digest, so he is unable to distinguish between various types of experience and stimulation. The newborn has indiscriminate "taste," and takes in all experiences with very little judgment about their relative value. To differentiate and "digest" stimuli selectively is an ego skill associated with a later stage of development.

From this description of the newborn's perception of his surroundings, it follows that many of his assumptions about the nature of life are affected by the way in which he is handled in these initial months. For example, if he is cared for according to a rigorous schedule, he can only feel that life is a touch-and-go situation, continually threatened by some mysterious order which bears no semblance to his own internal rhythms. He will associate gratification with some anxiety and uneasiness. Erikson, in describing child development, sets up contrasting pairs of ego qualities, characteristic and specific for each stage of life. They are "criteria by which the individual demonstrates that his ego, at a given stage, is strong enough to integrate the timetable of the organism with the structure of social institutions" (17). The first ego qualities developed during the oral period are *trust* versus *basic mistrust*. "The first demonstration of social trust in a baby is the ease of his feeding, the depth of his sleep, the relaxation of his bowels. The experience of a mutual regulation of his increasingly receptive capacities with the maternal techniques of provision gradually helps him to balance the discomfort caused by the immaturity of homeostasis with which he was born. In his gradually increasing waking hours, he finds that more and more adventures of the senses arouse a feeling of familiarity, of having coincided with the feeling of inner goodness. Forms of comfort, and people associated with them become as familiar as the gnawing discomfort of the bowels. The infant's first social achievement, then, is his willingness to let the mother out of sight without undue anxiety or rage, because she has become an inner certainty as well as an outer predictability. Such consistency, continuity, and sameness of experience, provide a rudimentary sense of ego identity which depends, I think, on the recognition that there is an inner population of remembered and anticipated sensations and images which are firmly correlated with the outer population of familiar and predictable things and people. Smiling crowns this development" (18).

Toward the end of the period of orality, the teeth begin to develop, and there is a strong physiological need to bite. Biting helps to alleviate the sensation of gnawing discomfort which erupting teeth produce in the infant's sensitive gums. Infants, at this stage, obviously enjoy biting on whatever objects are at hand, including the breast or the bottle nipple. If the child is being nursed, pain will cause the mother to react strongly, and she will probably decide to discontinue breast feeding at this time. From this, the child deduces that its biting impulse is a dangerous one and "out of this . . . comes that primary sense of badness, that original sense of evil or malevolence which signifies the potential loss of all that is good, because we could not help destroying it inside [the mouth], thus driving it away outside . . . this experience of an urge turning upon the self has much to do with the masochistic tendency of finding cruel and cold comfort in hurting oneself whenever an object has eluded one's grasp" (19). By the end of the oral period, the infant experiences feelings of *ambivalence*.[7] While the mother is loved and desired, she may withdraw her love (her breast or her care) precipitating anger and rage, which in turn increase the desire to bite and at the same time increase the need to block and turn the im-

[7] For a discussion of ambivalence, see Chapter VI.

pulse inward. If, in the course of facing these frustrations, the parents provide an inadequate quantity and quality of "sensitive care of the baby's individual needs and a firm sense of personal trustworthiness within the trusted framework of their culture's life style" then the child cannot achieve the closeness and trust which will provide it with "a sense of identity which will later combine a sense of being 'all right,' of being oneself and of being what other people trust one will become" (20). In this earliest period of life, the stage is set for nurturing in the child the desire to belong to a group and behave the way the group wishes. If, instead of this sense of trust, the child develops its opposite, basic distrust, then there is little likelihood that it will grow up appropriately. Child development may be likened to the erection of a pyramid. If the basic foundations are not laid down, then the structure above will also be lacking. Weight above must be supported from below. Whenever subsequent "superstructural" attitudes are missing, it is possible, though usually difficult, to go back and fill in the missing foundations. The earlier these formations occur in the developmental timetable, the more difficult it is to fill them in later on.

A child who is happily and trustfully reared will gain the impression of great power and omnipotence, due simply to the fact that his need signals have always been answered. This attitude, while appropriate in the very young infant, must slowly be modified and brought into relationship with external reality through growth. The effective parent inevitably and slowly introduces frustrations into the child's life so that he not only learns to deal with frustration and anger, but also learns to perceive environmental limitations as well as his own capacities accurately and effectively (30). Growth must include increasing ego ability to control and modulate the impulse of anger and rage.

The Impact of Cultural Patterns

The basic psychophysiological needs may be dealt with variously in different cultures. The manner in which they are satisfied greatly affects subsequent personality development. Let us describe three varieties of orality from three very different cultural settings. On the island of Bali, renowned as a tropical paradise of peace and beauty where the natives are happy, optimistic, and comfortable, the period of oral gratification is extended far beyond that of most societies. Children are nursed until they reach the age of three or three and a half, not only by the mother, but also by any other woman who happens to be around when the infant indicates its wish to suckle. In the absence of women, even a man may pick up a child and suckle it. Mead and MacGregor, in their study of Balinese growth and development, give us some fascinating photographs of Balinese children and the manner in which they express their oral pleasures. Since they are nursed sitting upright, astride the mother's hip, they are free to move their arms as they wish. During the suckling process, they strike the postures we associate with oriental dancing, with its elaborate finger and body movements (36). Later on, we shall discuss the characterological effects of oral gratification, but at this point we shall note only that there is an apparent relationship between the happy, optimistic attitude of the Balinese people and the intensive oral gratification which they receive in childhood.

A brief description of a primitive society of people found in New Guinea, the Mondugumors, provides a contrasting example. These people live in an isolated, mountainous region, where bare survival requires constant attack on the environment. Here the feeding process seems to be one of continuous tantalizing in which the infant responds off and on throughout the course of feeding with violent rages stemming from angry frustration (35). These children grow up with the well-conditioned attitude that only frustration can be expected from their environment. Through long experience, beginning in infancy, they learn how to cope with it skillfully.

In our society, sleeping infants tend to be left alone in their beds, and we more or less take it for granted that crying is a "normal" way for an infant to demand its food. Observers of rural India comment that only rarely, if ever, do they hear an infant cry. Since the many collateral members of the family often live in one household, and since someone is always on hand to gratify promptly all the infant's needs, there is never a need to cry to signal uneasiness (42). Mere restlessness is enough to get attention. The Indian people have shown a great capacity for passive endurance of difficulties, and it is likely that this relates, partially at least, to the long period of oral gratification which they enjoy in infancy. As these children grow up, continued easy gratification provides little opportunity for them to become familiar with techniques for handling frustration and the controlled use of aggression. For this reason, it is not surprising that these people also have been capable of violent outbursts of fury, not readily controlled.

From these three illustrations, we can see the wide variation in the way orality is handled in different cultural settings. We may tentatively consider that the way in which biological-instinctual need for feeding and sucking activity is met by the specific culture influences the manner in which personality forms.

In the context of our rapidly changing "American culture" (which is so highly variable as to really not exist as a distinct culture), attitudes toward child care have varied greatly from place to place and from decade to decade. Today's grandparents can recount several changes in the child-rearing style which have occurred within their life span. A recent study by the Children's Bureau reviews changes in child-rearing techniques as reflected in their own publications over the past fifty years. Originally, there was the "strict schedule" which gave way to the concept of "permissiveness and self-demand," and this in turn has changed to recognizing "mother's rights." Such peregrinations of expert opinion convince us that there are many ways to rear a baby, and it is highly unlikely that there is only one "right way" (50, 56). Nevertheless, the specific way a child is reared affects its development and personality (13).

In justice to the experts, let us recognize that while they have shifted emphasis, the facts which are at the center of any theory are demonstrable and remain facts. Further, certain seeming disagreements among experts reflect different audiences with differing sets of assumptions. For example, in talking to women who believe an infant should eat four ounces every four hours, the expert may stress variability of needs and the principle that the child should be kept comfortable and happy. Talking to women who feed a child every time it cries, the same expert may stress the biological fact that it takes time to empty the stomach and that infants cry for other reasons besides hunger (49).

The child-rearing process is a reciprocal relationship of mother, child, and society (10). The child arrives on the scene aware only of and interested in his own instinctual needs. These impinge on the mother and her feelings. The way in which she and the child interact determines the subsequent development of the child's techniques for need gratification. If the mother-child relationship is a mutually pleasant one, things will go well. Evidence now available shows that mothering is not just an instinctual reaction but is also a means by which the mother satisfies some of her own needs (5). Experimental evidence with animals demonstrates that if the mother's own need gratifications are *not* supplied by the offspring, she gives up her mothering activities and abandons the offspring (34). Studies of withdrawn children show the same reciprocal relationship. A mother will withdraw from a child who, for one reason or other, does not respond sufficiently to give her the pleasure she needs, and her withdrawal in turn reinforces his (14). The close interlocking of family psychopathology is now a well documented fact (3, 28, 52). Treatment of withdrawn children is very difficult because, to be successful, both mother and child must be treated simultaneously. An illustration of such a relationship occurred in the treatment of a seven-year-old schizophrenic boy, who was brought into treatment with the "conscientious and earnest interest of his parents." Their cooperation continued only until the child began to come out of his withdrawn state and to express some of the anger and rage for previous deprivations. As soon as he began to react more as a normal child with angry outbursts and temper tantrums, the parents began to express great anxiety. Finally, they withdrew him from treatment and placed him in an institution. Because of geographical problems, it was not possible to treat the mother and avoid this therapeutic failure.

The manner in which the mother touches the child, speaks to it, feeds it, and clothes it, tends to reflect what she has learned from her social surroundings. This may be through direct emulation or, with more "sophisticated" mothers through reading expert sources (48, 55). Society dictates the manner in which children are to be reared. Each society passes on its values through the child-rearing process, and this begins immediately at birth. Today we frequently read allusions to the childbearing practices of primitive man and of various contemporary medical techniques predicated accurately or inaccurately on assumptions about the nature of such primitive childbearing methods. Thus we have "natural childbirth" and "rooming-in" designed to bring the mother close to the child and to overcome the intervention imposed by modern medical techniques.[8] Whatever we think of these specific techniques, and whatever their worth in fostering effective mother-child relationships, it is true that the modern hospital is designed for maximum sterility and mass care. Concern over emotional satisfaction has only recently become a major consideration. To repeat, successful mothering involves mutual satisfactions for both mother and baby. Any procedure, even if invoked in the name of more hygienic and safer childbirth, which places barriers between the mother and her baby may well have negative effects which deserve attention and reconsideration.

In this context, because of its relevance to many problems in the area of adoption and custody, it might be well to say something about the relative status of the natural mother and the foster or adoptive mother. Common law and most statutes tend to emphasize the blood relationship between the natural mother and her child as though this were something so basic and indestructable that very little, if anything, can disrupt it. While this is one of the closest of all human relationships, there are many ways in which it may be disturbed and attenuated.

When a woman has carried a child for nine months and then been delivered of it, she has had the opportunity to invest in the child and its well-being a major part of all the psychic drives which provide her with feminine identity. This bond is so deep and so intimate that it would be no exaggeration to say that the mother needs her child to maintain a sense of wholeness as much as the child needs her to secure its survival. This mutual need creates a tie so firm that it can sustain the fantastic demands that child-rearing places upon it, as it provides a pervasive sense of well-being and gratification. We may readily agree that in the case of a "normal" mother-child relationship the law is quite correct in refusing to disrupt it, except under "extreme" conditions. (We will defer until later the questions of when and how this relationship should be terminated for the well-being of the child.) There are many circum-

[8] "Natural childbirth" is the method where the mother receives little analgesia so that she may participate more fully in the delivery process and handle and care for her baby immediately postpartum, with full consciousness and awareness. "Rooming-in" is the ward management technique where the newborn baby is kept in the same room as the mother most of the day, and the mother assumes very nearly complete care of her infant.

stances, however, which can prevent or destroy this vital relationship, and which necessitate alternatives.[9]

The description above obviously refers to the ideal mother-infant relationship. However, whenever anything tends to deflect the mother's free attention from the comfortable contemplation and consideration of her new role relative to the unborn or newborn, the bond is threatened, at least, by doubt and, at worst, panic and a full turning away from the child. There are also situations which will physically separate mother and child, such as illness or death, the need to work outside the house, or all the psychological and social forces which can result in abandonment. Once these manifest or covert separating forces are initiated, the bonding force of the ongoing relationship is diluted, and the mother's and child's adjustment to each other has to shift to new measures which must be instituted to meet new situations. For example, if the natural mother falls ill, there will be a substitute mother who (it is to be hoped) will provide everything the child needs, including love. Since there is no magic in this mother-child bond, if the substitution is initiated sufficiently early and persists long enough, the infant will look upon the substitute as if she were the natural mother. The same effect will take place in the mother surrogate. If she cares for the baby during its early months of utter helplessness, the same sense of satisfaction and attachment which occurs in the natural mother will develop in the surrogate. In time, the bond may reach the same level of intensity which is to be found in natural mothers.

We can see then that natural mothers have the initial advantage of what we might call a "biological narcissistic investment" which gives them a powerful motive for further and continuing involvement with their children. However, anything which attenuates this relationship and brings substitution of others in the mother role lessens the importance of the natural mother to the child. It also cuts into the mother's "natural" capacity to develop into the person of prime importance for that child. In other words, the "stuff" which creates the ties that carry a child and its mother through all of the vicissitudes of growing up is made up mostly of the ongoing experiences that come to signal for both, predictable and mutual satisfaction.

[9] For an excellent description of the problems and dynamics of adoptive parents, see Kirk (33).

Psychological Resultants of Orality

Let us examine in more detail the two principal phases of the oral period. The oral focus of pleasure predominates from birth until about 14 or 16 months of age. The first phase, called the oral-sucking phase, is characterized by the child's primarily passive, receptive, dependent relationship to its surroundings. The site of the main sensual pleasure is around the lips and mucosal surfaces of the mouth, although the skin surface as a whole also provides pleasure sensations. Pleasure is derived through the release of the unpleasant tension of hunger and also from the sucking which at times has no relationship to nutritional function. We may say categorically that the child in the early months of life has a purely hedonistic orientation, and all of its reactions relate to the presence or absence of pleasure (45). Frustration at this age cause the child to hang on to the pleasure source by the "skin of the teeth." If frustrating removal of breast or nipple is attempted, it will try to hang on in order to continue the pleasure-giving sucking. If such a practice occurs very often, it may result later in an attitude of stubborn tenacity.

The second phase of the oral period is initiated by the eruption of teeth. The first tooth appears at about the sixth or seventh month. While the child experiences considerable oral discomfort for the next nine to twelve months, it appears that much of the restlessness in young children attributed to the eruption of teeth is due to other sources of deprivation. Tooth eruption is uncomfortable, but it is not generally regarded as producing marked disability.

In our culture, when the teeth begin to erupt, there is an alteration in feeding habits. Solid foods are introduced not much later than the fourth or fifth month of life. These new foods ultimately may be pleasure-producing themselves; initially they necessitate new adaptations, and the child does not "just naturally" take to them. Each change in patterns of care or feeding necessitates new adaptation on the part of the child's ego in order to avoid anxiety. As these initially frustrating events occur, the child experiences the reciprocity of his relationship to his parents (55). He perceives that if he can fit himself into the new requirements, he ends by receiving more than when he refuses to accommodate to the new situation (assuming that parental handling is normal and straightforward). If parents are too uneasy (and unfortunately many "sophisticated" modern parents are), they may fear to press the child toward more mature adjustment. A "good parent" does not sanction and encourage the child's remaining at the more immature level of accommodation, so that with each new demand the groundwork for comfortable give-get relationships is laid down (31).

Toward the end of the first year, neuro-muscular maturation is nearly complete and increasingly coordinated patterns of motor activity are possible. The child begins to reach out into the environment and to "devour" his surroundings in his efforts to gain knowledge and meet the challenges around him. He uses oral techniques for these early investigations, exploring and testing new objects by way of the mouth. "He puts everything into his mouth," and it seems as if his mouth serves as eyes, ears, and hands, bringing in all of these forms of sensory data. Of course, by this time, the eyes are well-developed, well-coordinated, and capable of observing and reacting to motion. Sounds also provoke reaction, and there is a beginning capacity to respond to the outside world with smiles, frowns, anger, and even well-differentiated physical withdrawal. By the end of the oral period, most children are able to creep and possibly stand without assistance, although they are still quite limited in their ability to move out actively into the surroundings. For the latter reason, they are still passively dependent on those around them for most of their experience and gratification.

We have stated that all developmental stages leave residual traces in later levels of personality integration. Perhaps it is superfluous to mention that eating and drinking, chewing, smoking, and kissing are obviously pleasure-producing activities centered in the mouth and are derived from the oral period. Sucking also persists and may be gratified in various ways, including sexual, later on in life (1, 2, 25, 26). We call these activities "continuations," and they are historical remnants of the pleasure-producing activities of infancy.

Not all individuals carry these pleasures forward in undisguised fashion. For example, a person who becomes a gourmet carries on and emphasizes a somewhat exaggerated interest in eating pleasures and does it in a way which is socially acceptable. We have already referred to this device as sublimation. Other oral sublimations which are common, and which may have special importance to lawyers, have to do with the function of talking. The person who enjoys oratory is taking pleasure in oral activity. We are familiar with the sharp-tongued individual who is always ready with some witty comment. "Biting sarcasm" is also well known, and represents sublimations of some of the biting impulses of the later stages of orality. Last, an attribute of great importance to all students is that of epistemophilia, which is the pleasure in learning. The healthy newborn alertly and pleasurably "takes in" everything in his surroundings provided he is not frustrated or made anxious about this process. The person who enjoys learning is usually expressing the fact that in his infancy he was pleasantly fed and continues to enjoy absorbing new material (15, 51). It should be emphasized again that, despite the fact that these are primitive and childish impulses, they are not inappropriate. The process of maturing does not eliminate childish instinctual impulses; they are merely redirected by the adaptive functioning of the ego within the limitations of the specific environment.

Not all individuals move away from the oral period comfortably and without conflict. Some persons show great concern over food and have food fads which are obviously strongly invested with feeling. For example, it is not an uncommon analytic finding that individuals who are vegetarians fear their biting impulses. The idea of eating something which was once alive comes too close to unconscious biting fantasies, and these fantasies must be avoided by denying interest in any form of meat, fowl, or fish.

Sometimes conflict over biting impulses takes the form of preoccupation with teeth, either providing or requiring dental attention. Unreasonably intense fear of dental work may stem from the same source. We must remember that our need to achieve an anxiety-free state necessitates the erection of defenses. Thus, if oral frustration in childhood has been pronounced, some form of biting activity or biting inhibition may very likely show up later on.

The most thoroughly incorporated prohibition in our culture is the prohibition against biting and devouring those whom we either love or hate—i.e., cannibalism. The mere suggestion that cannibalistic impulses are deep within us all may elicit strong reactions in some readers. This is not surprising since we all have been subjected to the same acculturation process where the prohibition against cannibalism is very intense. An interesting aspect of this repression may be seen in the case of *Regina v. Dudley and Stephens* (7, 8, 9).

The defendants in this case had committed homicide and canni-

balism in order to survive a shipwreck. Lord Coleridge deals at
length in his opinion with the definition of murder and the circumstances under which a man may kill in order to survive. It is clear
that the court was sympathetic to the "temptations" which caused
the homicide ("We are often compelled to set up standards we cannot reach ourselves, and to lay down rules we could not ourselves
satisfy" [7]). However, defense counsel could not get the court to
consider (at least in the written opinion) the psychological and
biological similarity of homicide in self-defense to homicide for
self-preservation. This was simply brushed aside with the comment
that there was no precedent for doing so. Since there were past dicta
favorable to the defense, it would have been possible for the court
to hold that this was an act of self-preservation and a justification
for homicide.[10] Therefore, it seems likely that emotion was extremely
important in this holding, despite the fact that the court drew a
clear distinction in the circumstances of the victim under the two
situations.[11] The court simply was unwilling to consider that one
might be unable to resist the cannibalistic impulse in order to survive, and thus should not be held guilty. Such a decision would be
just as "reasonable" as the concept that a man under an attack which
threatens his life will try to defend himself and will be homicidally
disposed as he does so.[12]

There is a large amount of psychoanalytic, anthropological and
biological literature on the universality of the atavistic, cannibalistic
impulse and its attendant psychological defenses (32, 53). In our
culture, at least, there is no need for the law to prohibit this act or
to punish it as murder. The occurrence of cannibalism might well be
regarded as a *prima facie* case of either severe mental illness or
extreme biological duress, against which the person was quite powerless to resist. Apparently both the jury and the executive recognized this in the Stephens case. The jury did not wish to find guilt

[10] A recent historical study by Malin (34a) demonstrates clearly that there were
also other irons in the fire. The trial judge, Baron Huddleston, was attempting to
clarify a matter of substantive definition through invoking an ancient procedural
device. This does not appear to account for all of the legal activity, however.

[11] That there are many complicated issues in cases like this, each with its conscious
and unconscious emotional elements, was beautifully demonstrated by Fuller in his
hypothetical case of the speluncean explorers (24).

[12] Bruno Bettelheim has raised some interesting points regarding the question
of why men do not defend themselves from mortal attack or social manipulation (6).
Ardrey has summarized the biological aspects of aggressive impulses and their
ubiquity (4).

and only determined the facts, while the Crown commuted the sentence of Dudley and Stephens from death to six months' imprisonment (9, 38). The decision to imprison the defendants for six months was probably psychologically effective and appropriate. These men no doubt suffered greatly for their breach of so basic a conscience prohibition, and they probably needed some punishment to alleviate their guilt. This is reminiscent of the ritual followed by eskimos when they are forced to eat their aged and infirm to avoid group starvation. After the crisis has passed, they hold a brief purification rite in which they ask the understanding and forgiveness of the victims' spirit (53). While cannibalism is not controlled by law in these tribes, impulses to eat their fellows seem to appear only under the duress of extreme conditions of starvation.

Brief mention should be made of the pathology which may occur when the problems of the oral period are not adequately resolved. We have already referred to the work of Spitz and others, whose studies involve children with very early and very severe oral deprivation. These children, although they had adequate food, were deprived of the maternal warmth, stimulation, and closeness necessary for a sense of security. They failed to develop physically and withdrew into themselves in an effort to accommodate to the emptiness without. This is similar to what we see in the adult schizophrenic who withdraws into his own fantasy world and hallucinates the missing elements. We cannot prove that children are replacing missing ingredients with hallucinations, but their actions are so similar to those of the schizophrenic that this speculation seems justified.

Children who are not totally deprived but whose needs are inconsistently fulfilled also display emotional scars later. The child who has received adequate oral gratification until about the sixth or seventh month of life (the so-called "anaclitic" period), if deprived at that point, will go into a profound depression. This reaction, so well described by Spitz (47), may well form the groundwork for later manifestations of sweeping mood swings between profound depression and euphoria.

Individuals whom we call *schizoid* also have scars stemming from the oral period. Essentially, they lack trust in their surroundings and tend to live anxiously, always doubting that they will receive support from without. Opposite to this kind of person is the one who has been so excessively fed and cared for, and who has so little experience in dealing with frustration, that he feels the world owes him a living. These individuals develop narcissistic personalities and go through life continually surprised that their fellows do not treat them to the same gratifications which they received at the hands of their overindulgent parents.

Yet another class is formed by those who obtain sensual gratification from *perversions*. To the psychoanalyst, a perversion is a continuation of some infantile source of pleasure gratification (46) which would ordinarily be a way-station on the road to adult heterosexual gratification. We have said before that perversions derive from earlier means of sensual gratification which remain *primary* sources of pleasure far beyond their developmental appropriateness. They are regarded as being inversely related to the neuroses. The pervert, instead of experiencing anxiety over some conflict, is able to "act out" his conflict through some symbolic maneuver which relieves tension and facilitates the return to psychic equilibrium. Therefore, perversions represent both symbolic compensatory activities and either retreat from or fixation on some method of infantile gratification. Many of the perversions emanating from the oral period of life have to do with sucking. The same activities, when practiced as way-stations to more mature gratification outlets, are entirely normal. When they become an end unto themselves, they are *by definition* perversions. Individuals, usually homosexually oriented, who achieve their main orgastic pleasures through fellatio or cunnilingus, have not reached adult levels of maturation.[13]

Other common forms of oral perversion are voyeurism and its opposite, exhibitionism. These are also way-stations, stemming partially from the oral period. Since they are very closely related to a later stage of growth, they will be discussed in the context of that period of life.[14]

It is important to note that perversions and other psychic disabilities stemming from the oral period are not mainly due to *gratification* of needs. It is the *failure* to gratify needs that produces difficulty. This fact is obscured by the many instances where gratifi-

[13] For an extremely interesting legal case involving these matters see Goldstein et al. (27).
[14] See Chapter VII.

cations are given as substitutes. For example, an infant who is fed but not handled lovingly will complain. If food is given when the need is for muscular stimulation, warmth, oxygen, or amusement, then the infant may become "fixated" on food. All this means is that food offered the only obtainable pleasure and so is utilized to satisfy other needs. Similarly, as the infant is ready to move around, to bite things, and to handle new objects, he may be restrained from these efforts and food may be given as a pacifier. In these situations, it is not the overgiving which does the damage but the failure to provide for all needs but one.

From the foregoing comments about the very young child, we may see that the law's concern about his environment, as manifested in such matters as adoption, divorce and custody, is very well grounded. Stability and maturity in the infant's environment are absolutely essential for his healthy development, and emotionally disruptive experience during the early months of life can be the harbinger of later antisocial behavior or mental illness.

PROBLEMS

Example

A couple comes to your office and asks you to assist them with an adoption. The wife's sister has located a child who is available for adoption, but they tell you that the court social worker is going to try to keep them from making the adoption. Upon inquiry, you are told the following facts.

This Roman Catholic couple has been unable to have children after seven years of marriage. (There have been exhaustive medical examinations, and they say that they never will be able to conceive a child.) Two years ago, they attempted to adopt a child from a Catholic adoption agency and were told in polite but clear terms that the agency did not consider them to be suitable as adoptive parents. The main reason seemed to be the history of the wife's hospitalization with a "schizophrenic" illness six years ago. (She has had no "recurrence" of that illness nor has she had any psychiatric treatment since her discharge from the hospital.)

The baby is now three weeks old. The couple has had no contact with the parents except through the sister. The sister says that the baby's parents are very eager to have the child adopted by a "good Catholic family," and if they do not find one soon, they will have to place it in an institution, for the mother cannot keep it. (You happen to know, through your work on the Community Services Board, that at the present time there are many "Catholic" babies for adoption but few applicants to adopt them.) You must plan how to help this family with their wish to adopt the baby.

The first thing a lawyer should do in this case, as well as all others, is to ascertain exactly what it is that his client seeks. In this case, he should test how much they really want to adopt the child in order to assure himself that there are no countervening matters which would cause his clients' ultimate dissatisfaction with an adoption. The history of mental illness in the wife, and his knowledge that there is likely to be some sort of interlocked personality difficulty between the wife and the husband, should make him proceed cautiously. He should know that it would be possible for a child's presence in the family to upset a delicate adjustment balance between them. Since he already knows that the court social worker has built her objection around the mental illness question, he should ask his clients to have a psychiatric evaluation so that he might have a clear picture of their psychological condition.

Let us assume, without having precise details of the examination, that counsel decides to take the case and help them proceed with the adoption. There are several things around which he will shape his case (since he will have the initial burden of proving to the court that the adoption petition should be granted). The first issue he must meet is that there is valid consent for the adoption by the natural parents. At that point, he should introduce the parents' wish that their baby be adopted by a Catholic family. While that is not a binding consideration in most jurisdictions (nor should it be), it is a matter to which the court will surely give some weight. He could also point up that if this child does not find an adoptive home, it will probably be reared in an institution, which is a less than satisfactory solution for any child's needs. The timing for the introduction of this data would depend somewhat on the degree of formality of the procedure. Properly, this would be a rebuttal proposition. The judge is likely to be aware of the position his staff worker has taken, and one should erode into that position at every opportunity.

Counsel will also have to demonstrate the virtues of his clients' home as a desirable place to rear the baby. From his psychiatric consultation, he should have a very good picture of the potential difficulties his clients may have as parents. He can begin to deal with this affirmatively in his initial presentation by showing how they intend to minimize the risks of the known difficulty. This will place this couple at some advantage over many parents who must find out by experience, and after the fact, where they have difficulties. This would be an unspecified kind of presentation upon which he could build a specific rebuttal later, after the worker had presented her case. It can, unfortunately, be anticipated that the worker will probably reason that, because the client was diagnosed as schizophrenic, she is *ipso facto* incompetent. This is a specious line of reasoning, which in fact does not deal directly with the *legal* issue. The legal issue is whether or not the petitioner can properly care for the child, not whether there is a history of mental illness. The existence of mental illness may well raise appropriate doubts, but not by the mere assertion of the *label* of illness. The worker should be made to prove that *because* of the illness there is some demonstrable deficiency in child-rearing capacity. This is not often done and is the main defect in most expert testimony. It is because of the need to attack this strategy that counsel must know precisely what his clients' emotional difficulties are or may have been.

After counsel's demonstration of why his clients should be granted the petition to adopt, the court worker would be asked by the judge to present her case. As noted above, this all too often takes the form of merely labeling the patient as having been ill with schizophrenia and therefore unable to care for the child. This may be assaulted vigorously from several quarters. First of all, the label itself can be demonstrated as unreliable. (Indeed, one probably could swiftly prove that the social worker has no business using it as a measure of anything because of her lack of medical competence.) If it is unreliable, how can there be any valid reasoning from it?

The second line of attack is to force the worker to specify where the family will not be able to care adequately for the child. If, indeed, the worker can do this (and it is to be hoped that in time all workers will be able to perform such a function), then the question would be to ascertain how she can *predict* these incapacities. Here again it should be possible for good workers to spell out how they make such predictions. They should always be made to do so. If they can carry this out, then the final element of argument relates to the *validity* of the predictions. Here the worker, if she is honest, must acknowledge that there are many questions about whether or not such predictions are valid. She should concede this point at once if she is competent.

Once this concession has been made, it is time for counsel to confront the judge with the issues he must balance. He should argue that the child needs individual love and attention which are difficult to provide in *any* institutional setting. He should argue that it is crucial that these needs be met as soon as possible because babies can't wait to grow up. Then he should argue, finally, that here are a pair of adults who eagerly *want* to take care of this child, and that the wanting is a crucial part of the motive for bearing the inevitable hardships of child rearing.

When this form of argument is presented, all of the crucial psychological issues of the case will be before the court. Counsel will have done a good job. Even if the issues are successfully met by the opposition staff, he will know that the best possible decision for all of the parties concerned will have been made.

1. (a) What is the principal importance of a "genetic concept" to general psychiatric theory?
   (b) What is the principal distinction between a "genetic psychiatric theory" and "descriptive psychiatry"?
   (c) Relate each of these psychiatric approaches to the question of their usefulness to the law.

2. Alcoholism is a problem of considerable social importance. Psychiatrists quite generally feel that it is a psychological difficulty related to the oral period.

   (a) From your general observations of alcoholism, drunkenness, and the more common "social drinking," spell out this relationship.
   (b) Assuming this thesis to be true, what could you predict might be some of the rehabilitation problems one would face in dealing with alcoholics?
   (c) How does the effectiveness and the lack of effectiveness of Alcoholics Anonymous fit into the above thesis?

3. Most adoption agencies in the past, and some even now, have had the policy of *not* placing their infant charges with the "adopting parents" until the infant had reached at least six months of age.

   (a) What are the psychological implications of this policy to the infant? The adopting parents?

4. Nancy, a 17-year-old unmarried girl from a small town in a remote coal-mining region, upon finding herself three months pregnant, journeyed to the big city home of an older married sister to wait out her pregnancy. Just before her delivery date, she made contact with an obstetrician who arranged to deliver her. When she suggested to him that she wanted to have her baby "put out for adoption," he sent her to a lawyer. The lawyer arranged for the child to be placed in the custody of an acquaintance of the doctor who wanted to adopt the child if it were normal and healthy when born.

After her delivery, Nancy did not see her baby, and on the fifth postpartum day paid her medical bills in full and returned to her own home. She made no further contact with the doctor, and both he and the lawyer lost touch with her since she had apparently given them a false name and address.

When the child was ten months old, Nancy notified the doctor that she wished to have her baby back as she now intended to raise it herself. The doctor referred her to the lawyer who acted on behalf of the baby's now legal custodians.

(a) If you were this lawyer and wished to understand Nancy's attitudes so that you might best represent your clients' interest, how would you conceptualize the psychological issues which resulted in Nancy's "putting the baby out for adoption"? Those which resulted in her wish to keep the baby herself?

(b) How can the court best determine the answers to these questions in order to resolve the legal problems?

5. Occasionally, when parents are accused of being "bad parents" the court is moved to act in its *parens patria* role and remove the children from the home and assume their custody.

(a) What is a "bad" parent?

(b) What are the factors in the parent-child relationship which are *against* the court taking such action?

(c) How "bad" must a parent be to counteract his positive value to the child and psychologically to justify removing the child from his natural parents' custody?

REFERENCES

1. Abraham, K., The First Pre-genital Stage of the Libido (1916). In: *Selected Papers of Karl Abraham*. London: Hogarth Press, 1949.
2. Abraham, K., The Influence of Oral Erotism on Character Formation (1925). In: *Selected Papers of Karl Abraham*. London: Hogarth Press, 1949, pp. 393-406.
3. Ackerman, N. W., *The Psychodynamics of Family Life*. New York: Basic Books, 1958.
4. Ardrey, R., *The African Genesis*. New York: Atheneum Press, 1963.
5. Benedek, T., Parenthood as a Developmental Phase. *J. Amer. Psychoanal. Assn.*, 7:389-417, 1959.
6. Bettelheim, B., The Ignored Lesson of Ann Frank. *Harpers Magazine*, Nov., 1960, pp. 45-50.
7. Boulter, S., *The Times Law Reports: Vol. I*. London: The Times Office, 1885, p. 128.
8. *Ibid.*, pp. 119-124
9. *Ibid.*, p. 33.
10. Bowlby, J., *Maternal Care and Mental Health*. Geneva: World Health Organization, 1951.

11. Bowlby, J., An Ethological Approach to Research in Child Development. *Brit. J. Med. Psychol.*, 30:230-240, 1957.
12. Brody, S., *Patterns of Mothering.* New York: International Universities Press, 1956, pp. 10-14.
13. *Ibid.*
14. Deutsch, H., *The Psychology of Women,* Vol. II. New York: Grune & Stratton, 1945, Chapt. 8.
15. Erikson, E. H., Psychoanalysis and the Future of Education. *Psychoanal. Quart.*, 4:50-68, 1935.
16. Erikson, E. H., *Childhood and Society.* New York: W. W. Norton, 1950.
17. *Ibid.*, p. 218.
18. *Ibid.*, p. 219.
19. *Ibid.*, p. 220
20. *Ibid.*, p. 221.
21. Erikson, E. H., The Problem of Ego Identity. *J. Amer. Psychoanal, Assn.*, 4:56, 1956.
22. Ferenczi, S., Stages in the Development of the Sense of Reality. In: *Sex and Psychoanalysis.* New York: Basic Books, 1950, pp. 213-239.
23. Freud, S., Three Contributions to the Theory of Sexuality (1905). *Standard Edition*, 7:123-245. London: Hogarth Press, 1953.
24. Fuller, L., The Case of the Speluncean Explorers. *Harvard Law Rev.*, 62:616-645, 1949.
25. Glover, E., Notes on Oral Character Formation. In: *On the Early Development of Mind.* New York: International Universities Press, 1956, pp. 25-46.
26. Glover, E., The Significance of the Mouth in Psychoanalysis. In: *On the Early Development of Mind.* New York: International Universities Press, 1956, pp. 1-24.
27. Goldstein, J., Donnelly, J. & Schwartz, R., *Criminal Law.* Glencoe, Ill.: Free Press, 1962, pp. 7-44.
28. Grotjahn, M., *Psychoanalysis and the Family Neurosis.* New York: Norton, 1960.
29. Hartmann, H., Kris, E. & Loewenstein, R., Comments on the Formation of Psychic Structure. *The Psychoanalytic Study of the Child*, 2:20-38. New York: International Universities Press, 1946.
30. *Ibid.*, p. 20.
31. *Ibid.*, pp. 24-26.
32. Heilbrunn, G., The Basic Fear. *J. Amer. Psychoanal. Assn.*, 3:450-457, 1955.
33. Kirk, H. D., *Shared Fate.* Glencoe, Ill.: Free Press, 1963.
34. Liddel, H., *Emotional Hazards in Animals and Man.* Springfield, Ill.: Charles C Thomas, 1956, pp. 36-40.
34a. Malin, M. G., In Warm Blood: Some Historical and Procedural Aspects of *Regina v. Dudley and Stephens. Univ. Chicago Law Rev.*, 34:287-407, 1967.
35. Mead, M., *Male and Female.* New York: William Morrow, 1949, p. 112.
36. Mead, M. & MacGregor, F. C., *Growth and Culture.* New York: G. P. Putnam's Sons, 1951.
37. *Ibid.*, p. 99, plate 3.
38. Michael, J. & Wechsler, H., *The Criminal Law and Its Administration.* Chicago: Foundation Press, 1940, p. 58.

39. Montagu, A., *The Direction of Human Development*. New York: Harper Bros., 1955, pp. 90-94.
40. Munroe, R. L., *Schools of Psychoanalytic Thought*. New York: Dryden Press, 1955, pp. 174-176.
41. *Ibid.*, p. 185.
42. Murphy, L. B., Roots of Tolerance and Tensions in Indian Child Development. In: *The Minds of Men*. New York: Basic Books, 1953, p. 47.
43. Rank, O., *Will Therapy and Truth and Reality*. New York: Alfred A. Knopf, 1947.
44. Ribble, M., *The Rights of Infants*. New York: Columbia University Press, 1943.
45. *Ibid.*, pp. 22-34.
46. Sperling, O. E., Psychodynamics of Group Perversion. *Psychoanal. Quart.*, 25:56-57, 1956.
47. Spitz, R. & Wolf, K., Anaclitic Depression: An Inquiry into the Genesis of Psychiatric Conditions in Early Childhood, II. *The Psychoanalytic Study of the Child*, 2:313-342. New York: International Universities Press, 1946.
48. Spock, B., *Baby and Child Care*. New York: Pocket Books (Cardinal Edition), 1951.
49. Spock, B., Why I'm Re-writing My Baby Book. *Ladies Home Journal*, Sept. 1957, pp. 22, 25, 29.
50. Stendler, C., Sixty Years of Child Training Practices. *J. Pediat.*, 36:122-135, 1950.
51. Thompson, W. & Melzack, R., Early Environment. *Sci. Amer.*, 194:38-42, Jan. 1956.
52. Watson, A. S., The Conjoint Psychotherapy of Marriage Partners. *Amer. J. Orthopsychiat.*, 33:913-914, 1963.
53. Weyer, E. M., *The Eskimos*. New Haven: Yale University Press, 1932.
54. Winnicott, D. W., *Mother and Child*. New York: Basic Books, 1957.
55. *Ibid.*, pp. 51-52.
56. Wolfenstein, M., Trends in Infant Care. *Amer. J. Orthopsychiat.*, 23:120-130, 1953.

VI

The Development of Control:
The Anal Period

When reading a theory of psychological development, it is not difficult for the layman to understand and accept the importance attributed to functions of the mouth. When the second phase of psychosexual development, the anal period, is discussed and the importance of bowel function in psychological development is described, a general withdrawal occurs. If we had blundered into a bathroom in use, such behavior would reflect gentlemanly good manners, but it is carrying genteelism too far to avoid thinking about this fundamental process. It is possible to view bowel function with the same poise with which we consider breathing, and it is necessary to make the attempt if we are to understand human behavior. In the face of considerable resistance, analysts persist in considering bowel function, urination, and toilet training, as well as other forms of training, to be of fundamental importance to the developing personality (1, 16).

The original theory of anal character development tended to emphasize biological facts. Fifty years later, our attitude about these biological facts has been somewhat modified in the light of increased knowledge about cultural influences. Still, bowel training continues to be stressed as a source of potential pleasure and conflict in our culture. One of the earliest and most demanding pressures upon a child is to learn bowel control, and for this reason it is highly invested with psychological significance.

Few categorical demands are made on the infant. Suddenly, with the beginning of toilet training, the child is confronted with the necessity to focus his attention on excretory functions which have always operated automatically and outside of any specific interest. Infants reared in homes where there is much attention given to keeping the child "clean" are strongly influenced in their attitude toward bowel function. Such children find themselves seriously limited in their efforts to discover the nature of excretory functioning because they spend most of their time well diapered and with no opportunity to demonstrate interest in or to explore bodily functioning (29). Those who have observed children in settings where care tends to be restricted more to biological needs than to social standards of "cleanliness," report the universal interest which normal infants have in their excretory functioning. Such children experiment with feces, just as they do with the rest of their body. The same attention which is given to hands and feet may also be directed toward these eliminative operations. It is not infrequent to have an infant indulge early "artistic inclinations," and produce murals using feces for pigment. Small children touch and taste these products and observe their defecatory process with high interest when they may, and it is clear that they feel no repugnance, offense, or reluctance to behave in this way. These are "normal" reactions which, in our culture, are freely expressed only through chance opportunity.[1]

When hygiene and cleanliness are emphasized as a standard of "good" behavior, there are early demands for the infant to learn to be clean. The child must adjust and adapt to this attitude and accept the value judgment that feces are "bad" and bowel activity something which must be closely controlled and properly hidden (17). Instead of following purely physiological need, elimination is "permitted" only at certain times and in certain places. Suddenly, it is pressed into the spotlight, and conforming control is a mark of success or failure in the family-social environment.

The anal period (or what Erikson calls the "anal-urethral muscular stage" [5]) begins when the family "begins it" on the cultural side and when the developing nervous system makes it possible on the biological side. The newborn has all the anatomical parts he will ever have *except* for nerve myelinization. Myelin is the insulat-

---

[1] Perhaps the kind of "bathroom" humor best exemplified by contemporary burlesque, is carried over from frustration of curiosity in this period of childhood development.

ing substance which covers nerve fibers and, without this insulation, nerve impulses short-circuit and voluntary control is impossible. The random movements, unfocused eyes, and reflex behavior of the new-born reflect this constant short-circuiting. Voluntary coordination of muscles is impossible until the myelin sheath of their ennervation is formed. The formation of this sheath begins at once, but is not complete until about the eighteenth month. Up to that time, muscular coordination develops progressively and failures to accomplish motor acts effectively are frequent. By eight months of age, the nerves which enervate the smooth muscles of the anal sphincters have gained enough maturity in some children to permit some degree of voluntary control.

A family obviously may attempt bowel training whenever they feel like it, and there are those who start as early as the baby's second week of life. This urgency to train is clearly a reflection of the mother's needs and bears no relationship to the baby's capability. Any success which may be achieved during the early months of life relates purely to matching the "potty time" to the reflex reactions of the bowel (15). By the age of ten to thirteen months, when voluntary control becomes possible, the reflex is imposed upon by learned, voluntary patterns.[2] Babies who have been trained too early often put up a long and stubborn battle before completely voluntary control is accomplished (36). This is their means of asserting that they, too, have a voice in the matter, and while such resistance may introduce conflict and stress in the family relationships, it is evidence of a desire for autonomy and as such is not unhealthy. It is the beginning of initiative.

From the second to the fourth year, there is a tremendous increase in the capacity for coordinated, voluntary body control and the deployment of normal biological aggression.[3] During this period there appears for the first time a real urge to do as others do, to be like admired people. From the point of view of the biological and psychological facts, it is during this period that excretory control is

[2] The voluntary, or striated muscles, are the large muscles associated with mobility and whose activity is volitional. Smooth or involuntary muscles power the activities of the gastro-intestinal tract, blood vessels, and other visceral organs and are beyond the scope of voluntary control.

[3] Adler and Freud postulated that aggression is a normal biologically based instinct. Contemporary ethological theory is demonstrating the ubiquitousness as well as the adaptive utility of this instinct in ways which have sweeping implications for all psychological theory (22).

most easily and normally acquired. This may be readily seen in un-complicated outdoor societies where children learn how to deal with their excreta by emulation. The young child toddles into the bushes led by an older child and there, unhampered by clothing or plumbing, responds to his physiological signals.

Under the influence of Dr. Spock and others, American mothers (if they are free of conflict in this area themselves) are learning to work with the facts of life instead of bucking the current.[4] In many households, children achieve voluntary control and social conformity seemingly overnight some time between 24 and 36 months with no training efforts whatever. The psychological advantages to the child are great, but there is also considerable saving of effort, time, and temper for the mother.

The important role that toilet training plays in the development of mental illness in highly civilized societies is due to the fact that culture interferes with biology with a ferocity that cannot be overestimated. All the power of disgust, contempt, fury, and iron determination are aimed at the buttocks of the helpless infant. The degree of helplessness, the kinds of gratification available, and the whole pattern of child-parent relationship, determine the nature of the psychological disorder produced. Children who are rigorously toilet-trained tend to develop a sense that somehow the body is beyond control and always will be, and that it will remain a source of shame, disgrace, and pain. The child is alienated from his body and embraces the idea that he has an enemy within. He becomes a house divided. Here is the homely beginning of those philosophies devoted to transcending and controlling the body in the interest of a mystical purity.[5]

By the end of the first year, body muscles are capable of fairly well-coordinated activities and goal-directed behavior. Complicated movements such as rotation of the hands and the finer movements of the fingers do not develop until later (19). The child is able to

[4] In his book, *Baby and Child Care*, Dr. Spock handles this issue with only a gentle indication of the biological facts. He states that he did this in order that the book be accepted in all parts of the country by all kinds of people. In the revised edition, he gives his opinion (as stated here) since he believes general education has progressed sufficiently for it to be understood (37).

[5] The relationship of the need for control to Martin Luther's development of a new theological outlook is examined by Erikson (8). He points out how Luther's early family patterns stewed in the cauldron of adolescence and resulted in the synthesis of a new personal identity and a socioreligious revolution.

crawl toward desired objects and usually can pull himself to a standing position and reach out into his environment. His perceptive capacity has reached a high level of effectiveness and he is extremely sensitive to external stimuli. It is almost frightening to parents when they discover the degree to which these young children can comprehend what is going on in their surroundings. Since he has little need to repress and block out external stimuli for psychological reasons, the infant is well tuned in on activities around him.

At about thirteen months, the child makes sounds which are primitive attempts at word formation. He may begin to respond to words specifically and may call parents "Dada" and "Mama." For those interested in more detailed descriptions of these developmental states, the classical studies of Gesell and his associates outline the maturing psychophysiological, integrative patterns clearly and specifically (18).

Since the process of adaptation at this time of life so largely involves the integration of slowly forming patterns of activity and the new capabilities which increased mobility brings with it, most of the child's psychological energy is focused on matters of muscular control and activity. Our culture further focuses it on the control of the bowel musculature, and this control may come to symbolize all control. In short, bowel function is overdetermined by this cultural pressure. The manner in which this need to control and wish to control develop has much psychological importance for ultimate character development and interpersonal relationships.

Related to the idea of "control" is the idea of "giving" and "taking." These are social attitudes and the context in which they first appear lives on in the unconscious and is the unseen context for future social relations. While they may be modified by progressing development, there are usually important traces in subsequent character structure.

In considering the forces which impinge on a child, we must not overlook the ways in which the child exercises control over the parents by taking advantage of their specific vulnerabilities. The overbossy mother may be neatly paid back by dropping feces in the presence of guests. Or, if this is too dangerous, sleep provides an excellent excuse for "losing control" in order to annoy and maybe even frighten an overdemanding mother. Parents who are terribly concerned can be jockeyed into rewards of candy and toys; they can be compelled to perform rituals, hold hands, stay home for certain portions of the day, and generally dance at the end of a string. And for grabby and frighteningly intrusive mothers, the child can withhold almost indefinitely and then "hurl" feces when mother has given up. Parents are defeated by these maneuvers, but the child wins little of use to him in later life. Unfortunately, these patterns continue even though the circumstances change, and the once triumphant child becomes the self-defeating adult.

The manner and style with which the child is taught control and the quality of "giving and taking" used in his family teach him how to deal with them. Let us illustrate from the history of a patient whose family was so concerned over bowel function that they organized their life around the toilet schedule. In this family, it was felt to be absolutely essential that the child have a bowel movement regularly each day. If no movement was forthcoming, the patient was placed on the potty for a half-hour or so and, if after this length of time he did not perform, he was given an enema. Since this upset the possibility of any kind of regularity, it soon followed that an enema became part of the daily program. This became so much a part of his life that a good deal of psychological energy was expended each day in wondering whether or not there would be a normal bowel movement or in preparing for the daily enema routine. At first, he looked on these enemas as an attack, which indeed they were. His memories were filled with fear and pain and a growing sense of helplessness. In order to maintain psychic equilibrium, he had to dissipate his anxiety. Finally, he achieved a martyred attitude which in itself became a secondary source of psychic pleasure. There was ego gratification in putting up with the painful experience (10, 21). (This ability to obtain pleasure from pain is called *masochism*.[6]) The satisfaction of being a martyr was hardly enough to make up for suffering, and he progressively built up tremendous rage and a burning desire to attack the attacker. As he was only a small child, it was impossible to counterattack parents successfully, and so these feelings had to be either repressed or expressed in an indirect way. The only possibility was through producing anxiety in the parents over the state of his health. During

[6] The word, masochism, is taken from the name of the Austrian writer, Leopold von Sacher-Masoch (1835-1895), whose works are replete with illustrations of persons achieving sexual pleasure through various forms of physical punishment (32).

the course of therapy, it became plain that he had taken great pleasure in frightening his parents with his seemingly faulty physiology. (The ability to obtain pleasure from somebody else's pain or anxiety is called *sadism* [11].[7]) Thus each party to this ongoing battle for control suffered at the hands of the other and gained satisfaction by feeling "good" about the efforts he expended. The parents were long-suffering and conscientious; the boy was patient in his ordeal. There was a fusion of sadism and masochism in each.

Masochism and sadism stem largely from this period of anal-muscular development. The physiological analogue of masochism is the blocking or checking of the pleasure-giving, tension-releasing impulse to defecate under pressure from parental approval. Conversely, inappropriate defecation which can stir anxiety in the parents may gratify the impulse to hurt them and thus becomes sadistic in its implications. When the child is too hard-pressed in learning bowel and bladder control, these impulses may be magnified and exaggerated.

Masochistic and sadistic tendencies represent opposing motivations. If the forces of masochism and sadism are closely balanced, we have a condition called *ambivalence*. This word, which is widely used in psychiatric and psychological literature, is variously defined. Sometimes it is taken to mean the simultaneous existence of oppositely directed psychic forces with no relationship to their quantitative values. In terms of this definition, most persons are ambivalent all of the time. It is much more useful to limit this expression to those situations in which opposite forces are almost evenly balanced, and that is the way this writer will use it. Ambivalence is a terrifying and painful psychological state—a state of total helplessness caused by the inability to act (2). Helplessness is experienced as the ultimate of fear and pain because, in anticipation, every tension is unreleased and every attack is possible. It is a state intolerable to the ego whose every effort is directed to prevent it. If psychic forces do reach equivalence and helplessness does occur, then the individual must take extreme defensive measures to bring helplessness to an end. Children and primitive peoples commonly feel helpless in relation to external reality, and psychotics commonly feel helpless in relation to their psychic reality. Mature adults usually do not feel helpless

[7] This word is derived from the name of the French Marquis de Sade, (1740-1814) whose "sadistic" activities were notorious (33).

except in extreme stress situations and in those circumstances where they are truly ambivalent. The mature adult ego is strong enough to hold mixed and oppositely directed emotions together and act according to reality-tested experience (9). The psychotic, whose reality-testing capacity was seriously damaged in childhood, hallucinates a solution. Primitive man, whose reality sense is intact but who has inadequate cultural knowledge, invokes magic, to resolve his helpless situation. The child, whose ego is too immature to solve the problem, fantasizes a solution which relieves him and restores homeostatic balance.

During the anal period, children must learn to understand and deal with body functions. If cultural pressure is such that a child must hate the people he loves, or hate the self he loves, deep ambivalence with its terrifying helplessness forces the ego to turn away from reality toward magical or psychotic solutions. Every effort should be made to help children achieve reality control without excessive hate or fear. Serious ego damage at this stage of life is not easily reversible by ordinary experience.

We have discussed the psychic efforts made in order to escape the sense of helplessness which ambivalence produces. Another solution to this feeling is to *act out*, that is, to counterattack the society which is viewed as the cause of the helplessness.[8] This may take the form of various kinds of antisocial and criminal behavior. Many criminals openly acknowledge that the "reason" for their crime was to "get even" for real or imagined assaults which they (their ego integrity) suffered in the past (35). Some thieves, after they have completed a robbery, will "give" something in return. Police officers investigating scenes of robberies say that certain thieves always leave behind a fecal calling card. Such a "gift" clearly expresses the thief's mixed defiance and hatred deriving from the anal period. It makes his robbery a "personal" expression.

We have emphasized the concept of ambivalance because it is responsible for much of the anxiety which produces neurotic and acting-out behavior in our society, and which causes children to feel guilt, doubt, fear and rage about the dangers they experience within. When children are reared too strictly and are made to feel

[8] Acting out designates action which expresses a forbidden and unconscious wish, which has been carried over from the "forgotten" past.

that their bodies will get them into trouble, this is incorporated into their self image. The body is experienced as some evil demon whom they must hate and fear, and against whose demands they have no defense (14). This self-hating attitude and attendant unconscious guilt necessitate much self-punishment. The ideal way to get punished is through criminal and antisocial activities which elicit the recriminations and punitive retaliatory impulses of society (3, 30, 31).

Small children, as they learn to control their bodies in reasonably comfortable circumstances, demonstrate guilt directly as they attempt to externalize it through projection (34). For example, a two and a half-year-old boy (just beginning to control his bowel function) had an occasional "accident" when he was deeply engrossed in play. He would get a guilty expression on his face, fleetingly cover his face with his hands, and then turn aggressively to his father and say, "Daddy *bad*." This, in microcosm, is the way individuals and society deal with unconscious attitudes about their own impulses. When we are confronted with forbidden activities in the person of the criminal, we first unconsciously identify with him and then burst out in angry recriminations against him. Such an identification process is a major part of the basis for the retributive impulses of society, and often unconsciously motivates legal decision (38, 39). The little boy's conscience, which was just beginning to form, clearly showed the "childish" and primitive method of control. Social reactions of a retributive nature represent the childish, primitive, and atavistic aspect of society's "conscience." Laws become more understanding and less punitive only when a group feels secure enough to acknowledge its own primitive impulses and does not need to act out rejection through this projective mechanism.

As children achieve greater skill in managing body functions and body musculature, they gain an increased sense of independence and a broader concept of the self. Emotional concerns still focus largely on the self, and narcissism prevails. Because of tremendous inner conflict about themselves and their concern over control of their inevitable aggression, children often lash out in angry and sadistic attacks on parents or parental figures. This is normal for this period of life, and the important thing is that the parents do not punitively counterattack. The child needs help to channel his potentially sadistic impulses. Firm, understanding parental assistance helps to achieve this, but domination through pain and fear increases ambivalence. In maturity, aggressive, angry, sadistic impulses should be accepted with neither inappropriate action nor undue guilt and ambivalence.

In the play, *The Bad Seed*, taken from a book of the same name written by William March, we are presented with the chilling picture of a young girl whose sadistic impulses have gone uncontrolled and untrammeled due to unconscious parental acceptance (23). At the ripe old age of eight, this girl has effected three homicides and "caused" her mother's suicide. Throughout the course of the play, it becomes increasingly clear that the mother was unable to criticize her daughter in clear and nonambivalent terms. Although consciously critical and deeply disturbed by her child's actions, she could not bring herself to express her anger and punish the child. We are led to see the mother's unconscious identification with her own mother, who had committed multiple murders. In the end, when the mother plans to kill the child and herself, her ambivalence still prevents her "desired" action and she kills herself and unconsciously "saves" her child. The playwright, Maxwell Anderson, skillfully utilizing the audience's multiple identifications, turns the play into a blood-chilling, frightening spectacle of unrestricted, murderous impulses. Both the author and the playwright seem to imply that the impulses exist because of some freak of heredity. Perhaps this is because the author and the playwright are unconscious of ambivalence in themselves as well as in the mother they describe. As the play unfolds, it demonstrates clearly what can happen when normal sadistic and aggressive impulses go untrained and unsocialized. It is not a question of bad seed but of the unconscious conflicts in the mothering process. The audience itches to *do* something —revealing their intuitive rejection of the heredity idea—but the mother remains *helpless* to the end.

We have discussed the biological facts of the anal period, the impinging forces of culture by way of toilet as well as other forms of training, and the emotional logic behind the pathology produced by this impingement. More general attitudes and a wide diversity of normal character traits also get their start during this period. According to Erikson:

The anal zone lends itself more than any other to the display of stubborn adherence to contradictory impulses because, for one thing, it is the modal zone for two conflicting modes of approach, which must become alternating, namely *retention* and *elimination*. Furthermore, the sphincters are only part of the muscle system, with its general duality of rigidity and relaxation, of flexion and extension. The development of the muscle system gives the child a much greater power over the environment in the ability to reach out and hold on, to throw and to push away, to appropriate things and to keep them at a distance. This whole stage, then, which the Germans call the stage of stubbornness, becomes a battle for autonomy. For as he gets ready to stand more firmly on his feet, the infant delineates his world as "I" and "You," "Me" and "Mine." Every mother knows how astonishingly pliable a child may be at this age, if and when he has made the decision that he *wants* to do what he is supposed to do. It is hard, however, to find the proper formula for making him want to do just that. Every mother knows how lovingly a child at this stage will snuggle up and how ruthlessly he will suddenly try to push the adult away. At the same time, the child is apt to both hoard things and to discard them, to cling to possessions and to throw them out the window. All of these seemingly contradictory tendencies, then, we include under the formula of the retentive-eliminative moods. As to new social modalities developing at this time, the emphasis is on the simple antithesis of *letting go* and *holding on,* the nature, ratio and sequence of which is of decisive importance both for the development of the individual personality and for that of collective attitudes [6].

The child, as he learns how to manage the excretory products of his body, tends to introject something of the attitudes about those products as part of his own body image. For example, if feces and urine are frowned upon excessively by the environment, then the child looks upon his "productions" as something valueless, dirty, and of repugnance to others. At the same time, if his mastery learning is carried on in a setting of acceptance, so that he may take pride in what he has done (produced), he is able to see himself as a valuable person making valuable contributions. Thus, instead of learning to conform as a self-depreciatory activity, he learns to take pride in contributing. There is an increased sense of security and well-being with increased awareness of his own body and a sense of skill in self-control. Erikson describes the ego qualities which stem from this period as *autonomy* when there is success, and *shame and doubt* when the ego fails at its developmental task.

> [If the child is] . . . denied the gradual and well-guided experience of the autonomy of free choice (or if he has been weakened by an initial loss of trust), he will turn against himself all his urge to discriminate and to manipulate. He will overmanipulate himself; he will develop a precocious conscience. Instead of taking possession of things in order to test them by purposeful repetition, he will become obsessed by his own repetitiveness. By such obsessiveness, of course, he then learns to repossess the environment and to feign power by stubborn and minute control, for he could not find large-scale mutual regulation [7].

In the above quotation the idea of autonomy or free choice appears for the first time as a possibility. When lawyers concern themselves with the problem of responsibility, they regularly utilize the concept of "free will."[9] This is an unfortunate expression to use since it carries theological connotations which are quite opposed to modern psychiatric theory. The view that a man is born with free choices which he may lose only through acts of will belongs to that intellectual era when witches were real and their identity was a fact to be established judicially. It may seem necessary for a legal system to start with the premise that a man is responsible for all his actions unless he is found to be not responsible or "insane." This tends to view the problem of impulse control in black or white terms and does not realistically deal with the wide range in degrees of control which the ego may exhibit. If the ego is not overwhelmed by too stringent or too inconsistent demands during the phase of control development, we may assume that it will achieve a considerable degree of freedom in choice. However, even under optimal circumstances, this freedom is only partial, and some responses will be automatic and outside of conscious control. Indeed, the psychoeconomic necessity of this was discussed earlier.[10] The legal principle of diminished responsibility is therefore well substantiated by psychiatric theory (4, 24).

Even the child who has felt no excessive external pressure to conform and learns to take pride in contributing will still expect his

[9] For a particularly illogical discussion of free will in law, see Nord's paper on "The Mental Element in Crime" (25).
[10] See Chapter III.

contributions to be accepted and valued in certain ways. He will still feel certain aspects of himself to be more important than others. His very freedom from shame and rage may well land him in disagreement with some parts of a society which is so dominated by these emotions. By far the largest part of his behavior will be unconsciously controlled and so be beyond volition. If responsibility should be defined as applying to those acts performed with rational, volitional control, then no one may be responsible for more than a very small percentage of his actions.

Society uses law as a part of its efforts to evolve standards of behavior, deciding what behavior must be limited or proscribed. When we begin to assess methods for bringing deviant members of society into line, we must recognize the means by which intrapsychic controls are evolved. Since antisocial behavior may be activated by a multitude of motives, no system which applies uniform treatment to the offender will work. A chemist may produce a complex compound from many kinds of original substances. To obtain the result he wishes, he must first know the precise structure of the original compound, after which he adds the proper ingredients and produces the correct reaction. Errors in the original analysis or use of an inappropriate reaction will result in failure of the experiment and, occasionally, may even produce a dangerous explosion. So with the treatment of offenders. While treatment must be fair and equitable to be psychologically sound, it must also consider the offender's psychological state if it is to achieve social efficiency. The facts of mental functioning will help us accomplish this goal while rationalizations about "free will" do not.

During the two or three years of the anal-muscular period the reality-testing function of the ego develops considerably. To learn control, it is necessary for a child to evaluate the standards of conformity which are to be met. If a child is permitted freedom to carry out reality testing, he will have gained, by his fourth year, much skill in evaluating both internal and external perceptions. However, the ego, with its relatively short experience, cannot supply adequate judgmental skill, and this must come from without. Standards must still be provided by parents.

Techniques for helping children get the most out of this phase of development are replacing techniques for getting parents through it. The issues raised during this period make more searching demands on parents and require both greater flexibility and greater strength than the oral period. Much of the exploring, testing, and experimental behavior of the child is directed at the parents. Dr. Spock's *Infant and Child Care* has had a remarkable impact on child rearing techniques because of its common sense, sympathetic approach, and the practicality of the suggestions. In relation to the anal period, Spock's clear descriptions of the normal struggles for autonomy, and his excellent advice and suggestions on how to avoid "show-downs with willful children," point the way through one of the principal social dilemmas of this period: the feeling that the child must "learn who is boss" while achieving useful channels for aggression. Although direction must be given, there is no need to drive a child into frightening temper tantrums or cow him for all time. There are less painful ways to learn the realities of social surroundings.

Like the oral stage of development, the anal-muscular period leaves certain character traits which serve socially useful functions and continue into adult habit patterns. Such considerations as saving versus spending, withholding versus giving, cleanliness versus messiness, precision versus sloppiness, all stem from the emotional atmosphere of the training period. Expectations as to whether people will be fair or dishonest, attitudes about power struggles, and accuracy of judgment are heavily influenced. The superego is significantly shaped in several specific ways during this period. For example, sweeping assumptions are made about the basic question of how one may expect to be treated by people. This colors many other specific values which develop later on in life. Important decisions such as whether one will resist passively and defy direction, or take direction while comfortably maintaining personal integrity, are reached during the anal period. The ability to give freely and in a friendly, loving fashion, or the need to hurl what one gives, are also anal character traits.

There are various sublimations which may be utilized to carry over anal activities into future behavior. These have an obvious reality value which adds to their utility as sublimated outlets for the expression of anal activity. All of us have some interest in collecting, or else we may reject collecting altogether. Philanthropy, which is the process of collecting large sums of money and then giving it away, is a socially positive way to express anality. Interest in collecting statistics, bookkeeping, and other activities which place a high premium on the accurate and careful assembly of things are also useful. Painting and sculpture provide an outlet for control skills, and we talk about the "fine control" that an artist or sculptor possesses for his medium. Many of the interests belonging to the period of learning control are dealt with by turning them into their opposites—reaction formation. Adults who feel considerable disgust about bathroom functions are often preoccupied with dirt and the need for cleanliness. Such persons, as well as the prudish, the parsimonious, the pedantic, and the cantankerous are expressing hidden frustration and anger for the demands made upon them during toilet training. When these pressures become excessive, the inner fury which results in the impulse to attack the oppressor may be perceived (through use of projection) as coming from other persons, and will produce feelings of persecution characteristic of *paranoia*.

A frequently seen disease entity which derives from the anal period is *obsessive-compulsive neurosis*, wherein life's problems are dealt with by rigorous and exacting rituals which, if omitted, create massive anxiety. Anal conflicts may also be resolved through sexual perversion, either active or passive, depending on which aspect of anality has been conflicted, thereby arresting maturation. Fear of aggressive impulses, fused with sadistic fantasies, may cause passive submission to the person toward whom the aggression is directed. Such an attitude is a common motive for passive homosexuality. Homosexuals who are so motivated, may indulge in anal intercourse as the passive participants. A parallel may be seen on the monkey island in any zoo. If a young male is caught by the dominant male attempting sexual relations with any of the females, the young male will run away. If he is finally cornered, he turns his buttocks to the older, stronger male and offers himself as a sexual object. In other words, when attack is feared, one defensive maneuver may be to act out the submissive homosexual role, as if to say, "Look, poor little queer me is no threat to your sexual possessions. Here, you may even use me. See how unmasculine and harmless I am to you."

Other forms of sadomasochistic activity include physical brutality, which always has a neurotic flavor. Also, close examination will reveal that many individuals act out masochistic and sadistic fantasies within the context of their sexual life. While these individuals are vaguely aware of the nature of their drives, they are usually completely unaware of their motivation. They cannot alter their behavior without untangling the web of their unconscious conflicts.

The anal period is a fateful one for the formation of basic social attitudes. Ability to conform to the law and adapt to society relates to the character development which evolves from this stage of life. Persons who grow up with unresolved unconscious conflicts about conforming are potentially capable of all kinds of asocial and anti-social activities. Such behavior is not only found in criminals who commit acts of violence, but also in those "white-collar criminals" who commit such crimes as fraud, embezzlement, and tax violations. In addition to individuals who commit overtly antisocial acts, there is also the large number of persons who are eternally engaged in power struggles of one kind or another. This, too, reflects a continuing battle with their surroundings in the effort to gain some position of solidity where they can feel safe and comfortable. Just as during early training, survival was visualized as the struggle to avoid being dominated by others, every social situation is a new test of dominance. This form of self-centered, narcissistic struggle has a multitude of socially devastating effects, and to understand them we must go back to the events of this period.

PROBLEMS

Example

Occasionally counsel comes up against situations in which he cannot understand why the client behaves as he does. The client's stated circumstances and apparent behavior just do not coincide.

For example, a man was charged with the federal felony of filing an incorrect income tax return with intention to defraud the government. When he presented his company's records and accounts to his attorney, it was apparent that there were many gross inaccuracies. When queried about these, he said that his partner took care of the books, and he had been "framed" by him. Although he asserted this vigorously and in red-faced anger, he did none of the things counsel asked him to do in order to prepare a defense or to prove his contention that he had been framed. Repeated efforts by counsel only alienated the client and deepened counsel's perplexity. At this point, instead of unleashing the not unusual lawyer's exhortation that client "had better cooperate or find himself new counsel," he wisely decided to seek psychiatric consultation in order to find out why his client was behaving in this seemingly perverse manner.

Acting upon counsel's written request and a lengthy telephone conversation, the psychiatrist set the purpose of his examination—to find the explanation for the clearly self-defeating behavior of the client.

The client presented himself punctually for his interview and, outwardly, made every effort to cooperate and be helpful. He gave ready and superficial answers to all of the preliminary questions about his business and the nature of his plight. Indeed, he spoke of the former with great pride, notwithstanding his obviously depressed condition (sad expression, slow speech, tired appearance, occasionally yawning). Although he was the principal owner of his company, he dealt only with that part of it involving outside contacts with customers. The administration and record-keeping were delegated entirely to a partner who was a lawyer. When pressed to explain some of the obvious "oversights" in his business awareness, he began to exhibit the same behavior of which his lawyer complained: he became very red in the face, and alleged that he did not know any more about it. (It might be noted here that the client also suffered from severe essential hypertension and had had several episodes of possible mild stroke.) At this point direct exploration of his situation was abandoned and he was asked to tell about his family background. The following sequences are reconstructed from his scrambled and involuntarily evasive answers.

This man, who was 56 at the time of his interview, was the only child of his parents' tumultuous marriage. His father, a hard-working mechanic, was the "strong, silent type." His mother kept house and unendingly nagged her husband about the things he did not give her—to which his response was stolid silence. The client, coming to his teens at the beginning of the depression, remembered his youth as a long series of jobs, often several at the same time. He also helped his father in his work.

The character of this man was greatly influenced by the events surrounding his father's death when the client was seventeen years old. It resulted from a particularly grisly work accident which occurred in his presence. In fact, the father, horribly and fatally injured, died in his son's arms! It became clear shortly thereafter, when the father's estate was being settled, that the mother had stowed away much of the family's scarce money in a bank account in her own name.

Within a few weeks of these upsetting events, the young man "accidentally" encountered his mother leaving a hotel with a man scarcely older than himself. In a moment of blind rage, he lashed out at his mother's consort and broke his jaw. This injury had its not uncommon serious consequence of endangering the latter's life from risk of strangulation. It was to be the very last time the client could ever remember being angry! He never saw his mother again. He turned his attention to the task of self-support, which he did with unusual proficiency, even during the difficult and lean years of the depression.

When this man was in his mid-twenties, he met and courted his wife-to-be. She was described as a gentle and loving woman who "was always on my side." The marriage was "harmonious" and they had three children. Although it was stated initially that there were no marital tensions what-soever, it was clear that the reason for this was his psychological policy of "never fighting with anybody." There was clearly tension in regard to the children. They were greatly indulged by their parents, and there was a long series of difficulties with school, marriages, and their social relationships in general. The father was powerless to "buy" their appro-priate behavior, though he often tried. His wife was reluctant to be firm with them in the face of her husband's inability to deal consistently with their psychological coerciveness. As a result, the children were entirely lacking in discipline and effective, sensible behavior. These problems existed for a very long time and nothing was done to resolve them. To do so would have necessitated acknowledgment of the psychological problems between husband and wife. (After the diagnostic interviews with the consulting psychiatrist, arrangements were made for some therapeutic family discussions. They resulted in some fruitful changes in family arrangements.)

One interesting sidelight, which came up quite accidentally and which revealed much of the way this family managed aggression, was the client's hobby. It involved a relatively dangerous sport, very exciting to participants and spectators, which fostered the sublimated release of great amounts of aggression. At the time he was interviewed, his family was urging him to give up his hobby, because they feared it would upset him further! Needless to say, the consultant urged to the contrary since this man desperately needed some means of expressing aggression.

Many of the client's business associates were friends, relatives, and others whom the patient had decided to "help." (By the time the patient had gotten back to this point, various interpretive comments had enabled him to be more open.) The sequence of such a decision would usually go like this. Someone would approach him and "put the bite on" him. He would size up the situation, reach the opinion that it would be disadvan-tageous to himself to help them, become annoyed (internally and com-pletely beyond his conscious awareness), need to avoid his internal feel-ings by some defensive move, and then "happily" agree to do what they wanted (all of which he "knew" would be contrary to his own interests). This happened to him repeatedly and, of course, it progressively built up his inner frustration and fury. He was incapable of doing anything about it so long as his conscience forbade the expression of anger or resentment.

How is this man to be understood? What do these historical details, as well as his behavior during the interview, tell us about the dynamics of his personality? How does such knowledge help the lawyer and the consultant decide what to do? Last, what might counsel do with the diagnostic information that would increase his usefulness to his client? As we have seen in past chapters, the psychiatrist gains his knowledge about his patients primarily from two sources—the history, and the reactions he sees during the interview, i.e., the transference. Let us examine these data.

In a manner not uncommon to persons with this man's kind of problem, he was not very good at remembering details about his childhood. Try as he would, in the initial interview he could not go beyond the bare details related above. (The reasons for this include a feeling that none of the details are important enough to warrant telling anyone. Also, if he did, they would only create jeopardy for himself. "I am not a nice person, and if I tell you about myself you will be critical of me." These attitudes are all below the level of conscious awareness, and all one can see is the resultant behavior. At this point of the explorations, the man doesn't "know" that he feels this way.) The examiner was forced to infer information about his early childhood. Clearly, by the time this man had reached his teens, he had developed solid work habits and could keep himself hard at his chores. Indeed, he was able to do this by denying that he had any other interests in life at all. (One can readily assume that this is not true of anybody. All have desires to indulge in pleasure-oriented activities.) Life was purely work and duty. To be lovable one had to give of oneself entirely and not be concerned with the getting. To take was bad and selfish (like mother). Similarly, one must hold feelings in because failure to do so could be very dangerous and cause loss of love and acceptance. These conclusions, drawn from his early experience, led to progressive narrowing of activities until they consisted mainly of work. In work there could be free expression of aggressiveness because to work is "good." Thus, a neurotic motivation became a very "useful" force, except that it was coupled with ongoing deprivation and incapacity to express most of the normal spectrum of emotions freely. (This is *not* to say that work is neurotic. Rather, there are motives for working that can be neurotic. This overdetermined condition thus produces satisfaction even as it causes accumulation of displeasure and frustration.)

As this man grew older, he progressively experienced the emotional conflicts which would ultimately face him with a dilemma. His denial would lead him into successive self-defeating courses, and the resultant internal anger and frustration would fill him with a volcanic fury which he could not express. Something would have to give.

In his reaction to the interview (and to the interviewer) we see a reiteration of the same factors. He came to see the consultant at considerable expense in time and money and then did not talk to him! This is not to say that he did not wish to do so; his automated defenses just would not permit him to. As he sat helpless and angry in his speechless impotence, his discomfort and misery mounted. If some interpretive intervention had not taken place, he would ultimately have left without help. His psychological assumptions would not let him run the risk of expressing anger in the situation where he also wanted help (symbolically, acceptance and love.) Only after he had been helped to find that it was safe and indeed possible to express annoyance and anger in modulated form could he discover that he was filled with mixed emotions about many things. In short, he suffered from the condition of ambivalence which had rendered him helpless. This was repeated in the treatment situation exactly as it had arisen in the lawyer's office. The psychiatrist was able to provide some explanations for the man's past behavior in relation to a particular set of events as well as to estimate future reactions. He could explain his behavior with his partners as well as with his family. More important, he was also in a position to make recommendations which might alleviate the man's difficulties.

At this point the lawyer and the psychiatrist should have a conference in order that each might educate the other about the relevant issues in the case. The lawyer can explain to the psychiatrist what it is that he will want to do with the consultative information. For example, did his client have a conscious desire to defraud the government? Did he have a *mens rea* for the defined crime with which he was charged? There is now evidence with which to explain how this man *could* turn over the books to his partner and avoid at all costs anything which would necessitate his "discovering" facts which would stir anger. Now the situation makes sense, and there is a logical explanation for the client's strange behavior. He was acting quite logically, *given the premises from which his internal value judgments originate*. Now counsel has a case which he can argue vigorously on his client's behalf. This is an *example* of the way the consultative data can be used. Clearly, counsel must teach the psychiatrist what *mens rea* is about if he is to apply and present his findings logically and comprehensively. There will, no doubt, be other places in the case where the data will also have relevance.

Another important part of the psychiatrist's recommendation would be to urge the man to get enough psychiatric help to enable him to learn how to avoid this kind of problem in the future. Probably it would be suggested that he have some joint help with his wife since her personality problems dovetail with his. (This was demonstrated in this case during the interview with the wife. It is always true!)[11] If they both learn how their problems interlock and reinforce each other, they will be in a better position to help each other to avoid the psychological pitfalls which have assailed them in the past.

1. In his collaborative autobiography written with Quentin Reynolds, Willie Sutton describes his feelings about bank robbery. He states, "Once, even though I had $30,000 in my pocket, I went by a bank and I just had to meet its challenge. I took that bank, all right, even though I did not need the money. I just felt I had to take that bank. I have often felt that way about banks" (27). Also, "The thought of out-witting a safe or vault was much more exciting to me than the thought of either blasting or burning through it" (28).

Willie describes how he started his career of getting "easy money," by pocketing family food money after stealing some of the groceries. As he describes these early escapades, one is curious about why his parents were not suspicious of his behavior. Another interesting aspect of Willie's criminal behavior is the way in which he carried out all of his crimes in disguise. One gains the impression that he obtained a great deal of satisfaction by fooling people in this particular way.

Throughout the book, it is clearly evident that Willie views himself as a very superior individual, capable of manipulating police, the courts, and people in general. At the same time, Willie was always surprised at the intelligence the police showed in their ability to catch him.

  (a) How would you account for Sutton's behavior, as outlined above, in relation to the developmental events of the anal-urethral-muscular stage?

2. In discussing "the illusion or dogma of legal certainty" Jerome Frank writes, "Notably, there is the insistent effort to achieve predictability by the attempt to mechanize law, to reduce it to formulas in which human beings are treated like identical mathematical entities. . . . The law is dealt with as if it were settled for once and for all; its rules are supposed to operate impartially, inflexibly: justice must be uniform and unswerving. . . . Little allowance can be made for justice in the particular case: thus the law is written and thus it must be applied. Novelty and creativeness must not be permitted" (12).

  (a) Comment on the psychological implications of these remarks.

11 See Chapter X.

3. Describing the system of justice in early English law, with its "hot irons," trial by combat, etc., Hancock writes, "All this brought a sense of peace and security to many minds whatever the actual facts might be. Indeed the very prevalence of so much crime and violence only served to increase the community's need for the comforting illusion that the law was being vigorously enforced" (20).

In a recent newspaper account, following the commutation of a death sentence in a murder case, a prominent lawyer wrote, "I shall not argue whether there should be capital punishment. There are certain antisocial people who are more dangerous than mad dogs, and after that is proved in a court of law, I do not object to their extermination" (26).

(a) What are the psychodynamic factors in both of these situations?
(b) How do such treatment techniques reassure people about crime and criminals?

4. "As we have seen, judges and lawyers are astute enough in their observation of the effect of non-rational factors in the thought-processes of *witnesses*, while as to the effect of these factors on the thought-processes of *judges*, they are singularly blind. Such consciousness as exists of these components of the judicial process is usually vague and only partly articulate; such few references as are made to them are made surreptitiously or by way of gossip. For the most part, awareness of these factors seldom rises above the level of avowed knowledge" (13).

(a) What are the psychodynamic implications of this statement?
(b) Are there any ways in which this problem may be approached practically?
(c) Are there any ways in which judges could be trained to be more effective in handling the interpersonal aspects of their judicial role?

REFERENCES

1. Abraham, K., Contributions to the Theory of the Anal Character. In: *Selected Papers of Karl Abraham.* London: Hogarth Press, 1949, pp. 370-392.
2. Brody, M. W., Clinical Manifestations of Ambivalence. *Psychoanal. Quart.*, 25:509, 1956.
3. Dalman, C. J., Criminal Behavior as a Pathologic Ego Defense. *Arch. Crim. Psychodynam.*, 1:555-563, 1955.
4. Diamond, B., Criminal Responsibility of the Mentally Ill. *Stanford Law Rev.*, 14:59-86, 1961.

188 PSYCHIATRY FOR LAWYERS

5. Erikson, E. H., *Childhood and Society*. New York: W. W. Norton, 1950, pp. 76-81.
6. *Ibid.*, pp. 77-78.
7. *Ibid.*, pp. 222-224.
8. Erikson, E. H., *Young Man Luther*. New York: W. W. Norton, 1958.
9. *Ibid.*, pp. 220-222.
10. Fenichel, O., *The Psychoanalytic Theory of Neurosis*. New York: Norton, 1945, p. 73.
11. *Ibid.*
12. Frank, J., *Law and the Modern Mind*. New York: Tudor Publishing Company, 1936, p. 118.
13. *Ibid.*, p. 143.
14. Freedman, L. Z., Conformity and Nonconformity. In: *Psychiatry and the Law*, Ed. P. Hoch & J. Zubin. New York: Grune & Stratton, 1955, p. 45.
15. Freud, A. & Burlingham, D. T., *War and Children*. New York: International Universities Press, 1943, p. 75.
16. Freud, S., Character and Anal Erotism (1908). *Standard Edition*, 9:167-176. London: Hogarth Press, 1959.
17. Gerard, M. W., Emotional Disorders of Childhood. In: *Dynamic Psychiatry*. Chicago: University of Chicago Press, 1952, pp. 181-185.
18. Gesell, A. et al., *The First Five Years of Life: A Guide to the Study of the Preschool Child*. New York: Harper Bros., 1940.
19. *Ibid.*, pp. 26-27.
20. Hancock, M., Conflict, Drama and Magic in the Early English Law. *Ohio State Law J.*, 14:133, 1953.
21. Loewenstein, R. M., A Contribution to the Psychoanalytic Theory of Masochism. *J. Amer. Psychoanal. Assn.*, 5:197-234, 1957.
22. Lorenz, K., *On Aggression*. London: Methuen, 1966.
23. March, W., *The Bad Seed*. New York: Rinehart, 1954.
24. Newman, L. & Weitzer, L., Duress, Free Will and the Criminal Law. *So. Calif. Law Rev.*, 30:313-334, 1957.
25. Nord, M., The Mental Element in Crime. *Univ. Detroit Law J.*, 37:671-700, 1960.
26. *Philadelphia Sunday Bulletin*, Sec. 2, p. 1, Oct. 14, 1956.
27. Reynolds, Q., *Smooth and Deadly*. New York: Popular Library, 1953, pp. 27-28.
28. *Ibid.*, p. 60.
29. Ribble, M., *The Rights of Infants*. New York: Columbia University Press, 1943, pp. 56-59.
30. Roche, P. Q., Criminality and Mental Illness—Two Faces of the Same Coin. *Univ. Chicago Law Rev.*, 22:320-324, 1955.
31. Roche, P. Q., *The Criminal Mind*. New York: Farrar, Straus & Cudahy, 1958, pp. 1-29.
32. Sacher-Masoch, L. von, *Venus in Furs*. New York: Sylvan Press, 1947.
33. Sade, Marquis de, *Selections from His Writings and a Study by Simone de Beauvoir*. New York: Grove Press, 1953.
34. Saul, L. J., *Emotional Maturity*. Philadelphia: J. P. Lippincott, 1947, pp. 124-125.
35. Saul, L. J., *The Hostile Mind*. New York: Random House, 1956, pp. 76-99.

36. Spock, B., *Baby and Child Care*. New York: Pocket Books (Cardinal Edition), 1951, pp. 185-190.
37. Spock, B., Why I'm Rewriting My Baby Book. *Ladies Home Journal*, Sept. 1957, pp. 22-30.
38. Weihofen, H., *The Urge to Punish*. New York: Farrar, Straus & Cudahy, 1956, pp. 154-155.
39. Zilboorg, G., *The Psychology of the Criminal Act*. New York: Harcourt, Brace, 1954, pp. 82-88.

VII

The Phallic Period and the Oedipus Complex

Of all psychoanalytic concepts, the oedipus complex probably enjoys the widest popular knowledge and has aroused the most controversy. The oedipal (or phallic) period embraces the developmental events of the child's life from approximately four and a half to six years of age and is the point at which children for the first time truly turn their interest outward and begin to develop the capacity for "object love." They engage in their first love competition and emerge with certain conclusions which have a powerful influence on the subsequent status of conscience, ego, and the adaptive patterns by means of which they will adjust to society.

By the time a normal, healthy child has reached the age of four and a half, he has developed tremendous skill in using his body musculature, and almost all physical activities have an automatic quality. He no longer needs to learn how to use his body. He must discover now what one can do with it (16). As all who have lived with children of this age can testify, they are actively and aggressively intrusive toward their environment, and intrusiveness is the behavioral mode of this age. There are active attacks on others, talk and questions are aggressively loud, things are taken apart and put back together, there is constant poking, prying, and probing the frontiers of unknown surroundings.

While this may seem more like the behavior of boys than of girls to most of us, such activities are characteristic of both at this stage of development. It is just at this time, however, that society begins

190

to place strong prohibitions on behavior and to expect sexually linked behavior. Although it has been assumed that many activities are biologically related to masculinity or femininity, anthropological study reveals that there are very few characteristics of specifically masculine or feminine character, beyond the anatomical and physiological aspects of the genitals themselves. The so-called characteristics of masculinity and femininity appear to be determined largely by cultural factors, and they vary widely from culture to culture. Within any given culture, there is also variation in behavior which depends on the nature of each individual's specific conditioning (37).

Early psychoanalytic theory suffered from a strong though unconscious tendency to conform to the current social value judgments of masculine superiority. For example, in classical theory, the penis reigned supreme. Men were supposed to be overwhelmingly concerned with keeping their penises safe and were seen as hopelessly proud of this fine possession. Obviously, the most severe punishment which a man could suffer under such circumstances was the loss of his genital, while women, from their depreciated position, could only strive for symbolic masculinity and would anxiously seek to avoid any further "castration." A few years ago, Bruno Bettelheim proposed a theory which made the reverse value judgment (6). According to his theory (for which he had considerable archaeological and historical evidence as well as many clinical examples), the supreme human value is feminine fecundity. He describes men as striving to catch the potential of creativity which women possess, while women's motivation is directed toward maintaining their own superiority in this respect. The fact that his theory explains the dynamic facts so well, clearly illustrates the necessity of paying close regard to cultural value judgments when assaying "normal sex characteristics." However, we do live in a society which, at least in the past, has given cultural dominance to masculinity, and this value judgment has been incorporated into psychological functioning.

There is, nevertheless, a hard core of biological sex difference which no culture can surmount or alter. The "facts of life," the role of male and female in procreation, do not shift. Childbearing is irrevocably a female function and cultures must incorporate this fact to be successful. A sufficient number of women must bear children to insure the biological survival of the group. Also, some way must be found to secure the adequate growth and development of the off-spring, although actual child care responsibilities may be shifted from females to males, as is the case among the mountain Arapesh of New Guinea (38). In any event, each individual, according to the cultural setting of his childhood, must develop sensitivities and abilities which relate to the standards of his sexual role in his own group. The timing of much of this learning relates intimately to the oedipal period.

On reaching the age of four to five, a child is capable of genital sensation and begins to derive pleasure from masturbatory stimulation. Also, especially among boys, there is pleasure in the act of urination. Little boys commonly play competitive games around this function and hold contests to see who can "pee" the farthest. If children are made to feel guilty about these early sexual explorations, it may contribute to a sense of inadequacy and fear of competition in them as they grow up. Little boys at this early age have biologically based urges to "push into" things, while little girls have some vague and nondifferentiated desires to "be pushed into or to receive." Sexual games of one sort or another are universal. It might be supposed that these activities are reflections of observations children have made of their elders, but there are indications to the contrary. Anna Freud reports that children go through the motions of copulation under circumstances in which there is absolutely no possibility of their having observed or even heard about adult sexuality (21). Her observations were made on very young children, and they lend support to the idea of inner biological determination for the differences in sexual activity in males and females.[1] There is ample evidence, however, that the degree of physical activity is not specifically linked with one sex or the other.

The most significant aspect of the oedipal phase is the emergence of love. Although younger children will *say,* "I like you" or "I love you" to their parents, this is clearly related to some manipulative effort to get something from the parent by "loving" him. While this maneuver forms the foundation for love, initially it is entirely a self-centered, receptive kind of emotion characteristic of the beginning of the oedipal period. With the onset of the oedipus complex, the child first turns his sensually oriented interest toward the one near-

[1] Lorenz, Tinbergen, and others have studied the inherited sexual behavior patterns in lower animals and find them to be species-specific (51).

est at hand—the parent of the opposite sex. An active courtship ensues. The little boy avidly avows love for his mother, and the little girl for her father, as they openly proclaim their intention to marry them as soon as they get big enough. There will be obvious efforts to get rid of the competing parent so as to enjoy the relationship with the loved one alone. This initiates a relationship in which the child is willing to actively give for the first time. Giving to the loved one is at first motivated by the desire to receive love in return.

This strong feeling of love coupled with an improved ability to perceive environmental reality makes the little boy aware that he is in active competition with the father, whom he also loves. While this does not deter him from competition for a time, it soon becomes apparent that the parental competitor has the inside track and is going to win (or at least should in a well-functioning family). This disquieting realization in combination with the inner fear that if the competitive impulses get out of hand they will bring on some kind of injury or deprivation, cause the boy to conclude that it might be best to give up his sexually tinged love for his mother. He resolves to become like father so that, when he grows up, he too will have the inside track with a woman who will be like mother. The sexual interest is blocked and split off. In short, the sexual instinct is inhibited and redirected toward some future object. At this point it is very important for father to be an adequate masculine model so that, by his example, he can teach his son how to become manly. This should include the capacity and willingness to love like a man. This move to identify with father facilitates love with inhibited sexual aim for mother, and it is the imposition of this inhibition (or, to put it another way, the mastery of a control device) which makes possible ongoing feelings of tenderness and affection for mother and ultimately for other women.

Both boys and girls get most emotionally involved at first with their mothers (or whoever performs the mothering function) because they are dependent on them for nourishment and security. A boy's feelings progress in a straight line from imagining himself and his mother as one, to discovering his separateness and his dependency, to valuing her as a person and wanting not only nourishment and security but also her undivided esteem and approval for his sexually developing self. To resolve oedipal competition with his father, with its imagined as well as real risks, he shifts his primary focus away from heterosexual interest in mother to a powerful identification with his own sex and with father. Girls, initially just as intensely involved with the nourishing supporting mother as boys, must move away from this major source of all security to develop heterosexual interest in father (and males). The resolution of her oedipal (or more specifically, Electra) complex involves moving back to the previously "slighted" mother to renew her identification with her and with feminine models (8).

The added hazard of this double shift makes girls especially vulnerable in certain ways. All infants need their mothers for survival. Shifting allegiance away from her and taking her on as a rival is a considerable risk. Any serious insecurity up to this point may cause the girl to decide not to take the chance. Also, after the risky experiment has been run, the shift back to an identification with the mother may easily be felt by the girl as a step backwards into former infantile dependency, rather than as a step forward toward having a man of her own. The chances for such a conclusion are greatly increased by the social expectation that women are to be childish and dependent. These characteristics are displayed as attractions by many women, some of whom use them as a socially acceptable screen for their power struggles. To a little girl, however, identification with the mother can seem to be childish and dependent. When girls can be aware of mother's strength, maturity, and sexual attractiveness, (assuming normal relationships all around) they are able to avoid these pitfalls and progress to identification with mother with a solid sense of worth and achievement.

One more general consideration affects the female child. In essence, our society expects that women shall act dependent but feel independent, act passively and receptively but be able to accept their own aggressiveness and to give to children unstintingly. The difficulty in making these fine adjustments tends to revitalize some of the psychological attributes of the early oral period and to make women vulnerable to the emotional conflicts stemming from that period. With the poorly delineated sexual roles now so characteristic in the American culture, this may necessitate marked reactions against aspects of the feminine role, creating an ultimate splitting in female sexual identity. We thus find many women who feel totally defeated and lost if they acquiesce to their own images of femininity. Much of the feminine protest against the female sexual role (though it unquestionably has some basis in reality) is a protest against the feeling that to be feminine is to be brought down to the infantile position of dependence and vulnerability.[2] Thus a vicious circle is set up in our culture. So many women are made childish and emotionally dependent that we consider it vaguely feminine and "normal." Because it is expected, it becomes all the more difficult for women to feel self-respecting as females without running the risk of being labeled as masculine.

Both boys and girls must work through the difficult problem of sexual attachment and sexual identification with the parent of the same sex in order to enjoy loving and being loved as adults. The groundwork for genuine "object interest" is accomplished in the normal resolution of the oedipus complex. Saul states:

> [Object interest] is also the essence of adult "love," using the term in its broadest sense—not something given in order to get something, but something given as an expression of regard for the person loved—even to the point of sacrifices for the beloved. Throughout childhood, it is of prime importance to *be* loved. Life depends upon it. But in adult life, one can be strong enough to diminish the need to *be* loved by others, and to develop the enjoyment of *loving*, others. This capacity to *enjoy* giving interest and love becomes the basic adult attitude toward the sexual partner, children, friends, profession, job, hobbies. The capacity for loving, for object interest, for the enjoyment of productive, responsible attitudes and activities—this is an attribute of maturity, an expression of the overflow in the adult of the biologic energies which have previously been devoted to his own growth and development [45].

A commonplace moral concept, stemming from Judeo-Christian tradition, is that the truly religious person serves others without regard to self-gratification. For example, there is the admonition that it is "better to give than to receive." While the psychiatrist would not disagree with the advantages of such manifest behavior, it does not fit the facts to see this behavior as being without any kind of self-satisfaction (24). What is the essential difference between *object love* and the child's primary motivation of self-interest which we called *primary narcissism?* In the successful resolution of the oedipal relationship, the child does not abandon his wish for a feeling of inner satisfaction. Rather, he learns to get his inner satisfaction

2 There is much of this theme in Simone de Beauvoir's extensive work on the feminine role, *The Second Sex* (7).

through giving pleasure to others. This we call *secondary narcissistic gratification*. This source of pleasure underlies all personal relationships, none of which can endure without some kind of gratification of either primary or secondary nature. To switch successfully from primary to secondary forms of narcissistic gratification, a person must learn to assume that he will get such pleasure in the end. Farsighted planning and the postponement of immediate pleasure gratification are only possible when there is an inner conviction that an ultimate gain of some kind will be made. This conviction is related to man's sense of justice, and the feeling that all should be treated alike.

The child's ego during the phallic period is well developed in many respects. Reality testing has reached a high degree of effectiveness, but judgment is still imperfect through lack of experience. Oedipal and postoedipal children need help in evaluating their experiences, given over a long period of time without excessive criticism or prohibition, in order to permit real growth in the powers of objective evaluation. With successful resolution of the oedipus conflict, an important step has been taken in changing from an existence of self-centered pleasure to one which closely attends to the problems and concerns of others, as well as self. Sexual impulses directed toward the parent have been inhibited in the face of reality, and the long-range wish to win a mate like the loved parent provides direction and goals for many of the learning activities during the next decade of life.

Before considering abnormal resolutions of the oedipus complex, let us emphasize the fact that during this period of maturation the child learns to perceive socially competitive relationships as they exist in a harmonious setting. This first "triangular relationship" becomes the master plan for the child's understanding of all social relationships outside of the family (29), since children initially view all extrafamily relationships as being like those within their own family.

One aspect of family life pertinent to many legal problems is that of family stability. Clearly, if a child is to resolve the oedipal conflict ideally, it is essential that both parents be present in the home.[3]

---

[3] Studies of children reared in the communal setting of the *kibbutzim* reveal that the process of identification can be modulated and shifted from natural parents to surrogates, but such identifications remain an essential part of the formation of character and identity (32, 43, 53).

Evolving an appropriate self-image necessitates both masculine and feminine models; mother and father are both needed (28, 39). For this reason, efforts should be made to resolve intrafamily problems at the first sign of stress. All necessary and available community and medical resources should be bent to the task of removing the cause of the disruptive stress. Decisions to remove or not to remove children from the home should be made as early as possible, and once made they should nearly always be permanent and irrevocable. Although there has been little systematic collection of data in this matter, clinical experience demonstrates that children who are moved about from one foster home to another during their formative years suffer massive damage to their sense of identity. This results often, if not always, in serious personal or interpersonal psychopathology. Poor parental models are easier to adapt to than ever-shifting ones, for in the latter case there is neither time nor opportunity to figure out standards, nor to learn how to cope with them in gratifying and socially effective ways. Thus the answers to such questions as temporary or permanent termination of parental rights, adoption, and the disposition of children in divorce actions should be responsive to these needs, which become extremely important during the oedipal period.

A crucial achievement of the oedipal period is the repression of the sexual drive, leaving tenderness and affection which can be expressed freely. This repression is absolutely necessary since children in our culture are not permitted to express their sexual impulses openly for at least another ten to fifteen years. Many psychiatrists believe that much of the so-called infantile amnesia (the forgetting of events prior to the age of five) results from this oedipal repression. Not uncommonly, during the course of psychotherapy, after oedipal feelings are once more brought to light, patients begin to "remember" some of their preoedipal experiences.

During adolescence, the oedipal struggle is revived. Adaptive techniques learned earlier are renovated and refined. Thus, the oedipal maturational step becomes a template from which initial adjustments of adolescence will be fashioned. Adolescence necessitates a split between sexual impulses and tenderness so far as family members are concerned, but they may, indeed must, be fused in feelings toward loved persons outside of the family. Happiness in interpersonal relationships is so heavily dependent upon the normal outcome of the oedipal struggle that it is easy to understand why its importance is so strongly emphasized by psychiatrists and child care experts (40).

Having outlined the normal resolution of the oedipus complex, let us examine some abnormal ones. We already know that if oedipal conflicts are not resolved adequately, the individual must resort to defensive maneuvers to restore a feeling of well-being. One cannot simply "put them out of mind." Conflicts must be solved, in one way or another.

The oedipal problem involves the psychological attitudes of the mother, the father, and the child. We may analyze the several failure patterns according to the manner in which the adults deal with their child, since the child is the more passive party to the transaction. We have described the ideal relationship as one in which both mother and father feel true love for the child and for each other and are relatively free of neurotic needs. It is important that parents recognize the child's wishes and respond with understanding warmth so that he has an opportunity to learn how to "make love." Early and insensitive rejection of the child's advances can only teach the child that his impulses are bad and dangerous.

Obviously, the possibility for freely expressing and "living out" the oedipal fantasy is virtually nil. Not only is it taboo in all societies, but also age differences make it biologically ridiculous. At any rate, any partial sexual success that may be enjoyed will be countered by strong social opposition. Such an illicit relationship, therefore, cannot be comfortable and satisfying and is bound to have profound social, psychological, and oftentimes legal repercussions. We should note that, although the incest taboo is universally one of the strongest, incest does occur. Court officers, social workers, and psychiatrists are all very familiar with such cases since they are not so uncommon as our unconscious defenses may lead us to believe.[4]

A child reared in a family with several children can displace much of the oedipal conflict onto the person of a sibling. This permits attenuation of intensity in the oedipal conflict, but at the same time it becomes a source of increased tension between the children. It simply contributes yet another vector of psychological force to the *sibling rivalry* which already encompasses competition for the family

---

[4] In his novel, *King's Row,* Bellaman describes the widespread reverberations that such relationships may have (5).

supply of food, love, security, and now sexual appreciation. With this complicated system of needs and gratification means, the number of alternative resolutions is enormous. Some of the family emotional turmoil which spills over into antisocial behavior may come from tension between siblings, which itself may emanate partially, or wholly, from oedipal conflicts. Often it pays off handsomely to explore such parental comments as, "I don't know why Joey has turned out this way—the other children have all done so well." This may tip off the fact that Joey has had to bear the brunt of displaced oedipal feelings and to play scapegoat for the unresolved conflicts of the whole family.

Sometimes, however, the parent of the opposite sex is overly seductive to the child because of incapacity to love and be loved on an adult level (29). Such adult seductiveness springs from parental need, not from love for the child, and may play into oedipal fantasies in a crippling way (31). For the child, this means that instead of coming to terms with social reality and relinquishing oedipal strivings, he is encouraged to imagine that he does possess the parent of the opposite sex and will someday enjoy a full relationship with this parent. The other parent is eliminated as a contender and is perceived as a failure, unworthy of respect. The child continues in a close and smothering relationship, unable to resist the seduction and unable to transform his wishes into social reality. He is stuck with his success. Because of the loss of status in the parent of the same sex, there is no motivation for identifying with him. Indeed, such identification engenders hostility due to the anxiety produced by the absence of aggressive competition. For a boy, this means that he will tarry too long as "mama's boy" and will be progressively unable to identify himself with other males. This initial success as a male tends to result in an ultimate loss of masculinity. For a girl, a similar pattern occurs. Lack of femininity is usually less obvious, for the female child attributes her success to characteristics not shared by the mother—in essence, her little-girl qualities. In later life, this may cause excessive narcissism and dependency, which make adult love relationships difficult if not impossible.

Active incest is not the usual outcome of too close oedipal relationships. More commonly, the child who fails to resolve this conflict has a close and continuing involvement with the loved parent and foregoes marriage and the usual social-sexual relationships of a family. An interesting *New Yorker* cover,[5] by Mary Petty, shows a middle-aged man and his white-haired mother sitting sedately at opposite ends of a very formal dinner table, he eating and she reading a book. In the background, over the mantel, is a large portrait of the beautiful young mother with her shy and loving son in a spotless sailor suit, snuggled up close to her side. One needs no caption or clinical description to understand the implications of this picture. It is simply the case of a woman holding her growing son too tightly and thus preventing his giving her up for another woman.

Another solution for the oedipal conflict is marriage to someone very similar in personality to the parent of the opposite sex (similar, in part at least, on an unconscious level). In such situations, because of an inability to differentiate clearly between the parent and the mate, active fears of incest are aroused by warmth, closeness, or sexuality, and may result in serious marital problems (12, 33). This is one of the causes for relative or absolute sexual impotence or frigidity suffered by a large number of people (35).

The last maladaptation of an overly close oedipal relationship which we shall discuss is adult homosexuality. To such men, all women are perceived as being mother, and are therefore forbidden. Other men are the only remaining human sexual objects. This trend is reinforced by a boy's normal partial identifications with his mother, so that he grows up feeling himself to have mostly female characteristics. If, therefore, he is to be loved, he must be loved as a woman by a man. Such homosexuality is less complicated by anger and aggression than other forms. Because they are not basically antisocial, these gentle and affectionate men often form relationships which are both enduring and enjoyable. This makes them extremely difficult to treat because they have very little conscious motivation to change.

The next variation in parental attitude to consider is that in which the parent of the opposite sex is excessively hostile toward the child. This kind of feeling causes a child to block off and bury his impulses to love and be loved by them. He passes through the oedipal period without ever experiencing the emotion of sensually tinged love or learning how to control and indulge these feelings in a social relationship. He feels angry and rejected and keeps at a psychologi-

[5] May 3, 1952.

cal distance from the frustrating parent. Although he has the desire to attack and retaliate, he is unable to do so. He cannot avoid sexual feelings, so that sexuality and anger become fused, which leads to ultimate confusion and guilt feelings for the love-anger reactions toward the parent.

In later life this creates various difficulties centered around marriage, sexuality and, to a lesser degree, relationships with all people. If the oedipal rejection has been too intense, there may be a tendency on the part of the man to see all women as the rejecting parent and none will appear "suitable" as potential partners; all women may be rejected. Likewise, conflicted women will deal similarly with men. However, with the increasing capacity for independence that comes with age, the angry, retaliative impulses may be expressed directly in sadistic promiscuity. The individual may, for instance, sexually "attack" many women as symbols of the hated mother. This appears to be the motivation of some crimes of aggressive sexuality. While no detailed studies have been carried out on the psychodynamics of rapists, it seems highly likely that this is the motivating drive in such individuals. They carry deep hatred for women and their aggressive impulses dominate their sexual impulses so that all sexual relationships are carried out in an atmosphere of violence (13).

Sexuality is an ideal camouflage for other kinds of impulses. This is true not only of disturbed persons, but also of normal individuals. It is not unusual for certain aggressive impulses to be incorporated within sexual fantasies. A common example of such fusion in normal women is the wish to have their masculine sexual partner aggressively overwhelm them during intercourse. Their gratification is incomplete without this occurrence (14). Some prostitutes carry out angry, aggressive impulses originally directed toward father but now aimed at all men (9). The impulse to destroy men by way of sex enjoys a place in most mythologies. During the Middle Ages it was not unusual for women who were both desired and feared sexually to be charged with witchcraft. They were imagined to be capable of "sucking men dry" and destroying their vital force. This concept represents a complicated condensation of women's impulses and men's fears (54). Whatever the sexual situation may be, the unconscious memories carried from the childhood resolution of the oedipal conflict are incorporated and insinuated into adult relationships.

Sexual impotence in men and frigidity in women may also be a result of residual emotional conflicts stemming from parental hostility. This may cause one to unconsciously identify and thus confuse parent with sex partner so that childhood fears of retaliation for anger and/or guilt and shame over sexual desires will be transferred to current relationships. Thus, the pleasure of sex (real or anticipated) will be felt as evil, and its object (i.e., the cause of it all) viewed as an enemy to be hated and feared. Such feeling undercurrents stifle sexual reactivity and freedom, and symptoms result. This creates the paradox where the partner who could provide pleasure becomes the agent for greater psychic pain, since such symptoms themselves cause "loss of face" (i.e., the self-image suffers damage—"I am no good as a man" or "As a woman I fail.") If such failure persists or if it is felt as a possibility, further psychological defense becomes necessary. One such defensive maneuver might be a retreat into homosexuality. This move would itself be reinforced by what we have called identification with the aggressor (20)—"if you can't beat 'em, join 'em." The boy becomes like his mother, a woman, rather than to be rebuffed by her as a man. The girl becomes like her rejecting father to avoid his attacks and his rejection of her femininity.

Let us consider next the situation where the like-sexed parent is overly seductive. In this situation, closeness develops between the father and the boy or the mother and the girl, and the child is unable to divert enough of his love-sex feelings to the parent of the opposite sex. This deprives the child of his opportunity to learn how to love and be loved in a heterosexual way. This causes the maturing child to wish to continue the relationship with the loved parent. Since this is (by definition) a homosexual object, subsequent love relationships will also tend to be homosexual. In the event that such a person does marry, or get involved heterosexually, the relationship is likely to be shallow, fraught with so much mutual frustration and hostility that separation becomes necessary. This form of homosexuality is very deep-seated and there is very little motivation to give it up. There is little hostility and considerable satisfaction so that these pairings are not usually socially disruptive. They do not get into social difficulties as do the group of angry homosexuals described above.

The last major constellation producing failure of oedipal resolution occurs when the like-sexed parent has an excessively hostile attitude toward the child. This means that when it is time to repress the oedipal strivings there is no suitable and acceptable object with whom to effect the all-important sexual identification. It just is not possible to maintain a loving wish to be like that kind of parent, nor to strive to outdo him at his own skills. As we have said before, parents cannot be exchanged so that the relationship must be continued and the identification with the like-sexed parent must be a hostile identification—or identification with the aggressor (20). Here there is emulation, but it is a hated one.[6] In this continuing atmosphere of anger and hostility, the superego builds up powerful needs to maintain the hated but unavoidable relationship. Guilt resulting in great self-depreciation is generated by the internalized hatred for the parental model.[7]

The principal effect of this type of identification is that it overwhelms its possessor with a sense of profound sexual and social inadequacy. He cannot help but hate what he is, just as he cannot help but identify with the parent who hated him. This produces poor heterosexual love relationships since the individual enters them with a sense of inadequacy and resents the person who causes him to be in such "love." In Tennessee Williams' *Cat on a Hot Tin Roof* (52), Brick's relationship to his powerful, insensitive, and unsympathetic father drives him to be *like* his father, but it also gave him the feeling that there is no possibility whatsoever of achieving such a goal. This stirs up latent conflicts about sexual identification and sexual role which cripple his marriage and interfere with his adult maturation.

Although this matter will be discussed more fully in Chapter X, it should be noted here that nearly all marriages provide exquisite examples of unconscious efforts by both parties to maintain that part of their self-image which resulted from the resolution of the oedipal conflict. This portion of psychodynamic motivation, in conjunction with a multitude of other motivational configurations, determines to

[6] It is equivalent to the small and powerless nation who allies with its large, powerful and aggressive neighbor. While there is an alliance with conformance to common goals, it is fraught with underlying resentment rather than rapport and mutuality. Just prior to World War II, Hitler evolved and stage-managed many such treaties, none of which was notable for signs of mutual admiration. Just as his allies despised Hitler, so he despised them for their weakness and compliance. All hostile identifications suffer the same fate.

[7] See problem one, Chapter VI.

a substantial degree the nature of marital adjustment as well as all adult relationships. Such family problems as divorce, child custody, will drafting and litigation, the devising of trusts, and the many acts of personal violence which may come to a lawyer's attention derive dynamic thrust from the success or failure of the resolution of the oedipus complex.

"What is homosexuality?" is a perplexing question (18, 19). By definition, it is simply (and yet not so simply) sexual feeling for a person of the same sex. This is quite properly a very broad definition and provides the only means for understanding the nature of such sexual impulses. It deliberately includes the feelings which a little boy has for his father when he kisses him, as well as those of the little girl for her mother. It stems from the physiological inevitability of such feelings and not from the shifting cultural judgments that are made about them. These "normal" homosexual impulses are the substrate from which pathological homosexuality will develop. Generally, in our culture, healthy emotional development leaves overt homosexual behavior far back in the wake of childhood or, at the latest, adolescence. Kinsey confirms this clinical proposition in his observation that most adult males have at one time or another indulged in some kind of homosexual practice (34).

There is one other motive which may lead a person to homosexuality; it relates to the way in which fantasy accompanies love and sex. An individual who is still gripped in narcissism aims his love impulses primarily toward himself. Such persons when "loving" or "making love" are able to identify themselves fully with the object of their attention. Such highly narcissistic individuals may choose homosexual partners and thus, in effect, be loving themselves (22). Those individuals who are most likely to be seen by others as "queer" tend to display this high degree of narcissism. Often they follow occupations, careers, and activities which exploit their need to pay attention to themselves. Among the ranks of actors, dancers, and some of the "body-beautiful" people, are fairly large numbers of homosexuals. (Note that there are *some* homosexuals in these groups. It hardly need be said that most are not.) These individuals epitomize exhibitionistic narcissism which they may carry into their sexual life. Interest in the partner is purely narcissistic; they are only loving themselves. Under these circumstances, their relationships tend to be transient, volatile, and fraught with much interpersonal difficulty. Infantile and not capable of loving others, they are difficult to treat because of their outer shell of self-satisfaction.

The individual who *needs* to love himself by way of homosexuality cannot give this up until he finds some substitute gratification. The person who is homosexually active out of hostility and anger, and who needs to attack others in this vicarious way, also depreciates himself and places himself in difficulties. He cannot give up this behavior until his ego and superego are more capable of dealing with aggressive impulses. Legal pressure or punishment may produce more secretiveness, but generally it does not alter the form of sexual outlet. In short, this kind of homosexual behavior is not deterrable; punishment only creates further individual and social problems. As most prison administrators know, this class of person is an anathema in the prison population and a source of great difficulty to them.

How should we deal with homosexuality as a social issue? Psychiatrists tend to feel that the main treatment goal with these persons is to help them bring their activities under more discreet control so that they do not disturb others and at the same time can be comfortable themselves. Homosexuality, because of its deep-rooted causes, is extremely difficult and sometimes, for practical reasons, impossible to cure. Should we punish these individuals? If so, for what purpose? If they are able to conduct their lives so as not to penalize or affect others against their will, there seems to be little excuse for punishment. So long as homosexual practice is confined to consensual adults, it represents a personal rather than a social problem. In the last version of the Model Penal Code, formulated by the American Law Institute, consensual homosexuality between adults is not defined as a crime (2). This would have a good effect all around since it would also remove one of the principal evils resulting from statutes making homosexuality a crime (3),[8] that is, the many forms of blackmail worked by citizens and law enforcement officers alike.

The ALI Code would continue to define as criminal, homosexual acts carried out by adults with children. This is highly appropriate because such sexual seduction of children by adults plays into their homosexual potential and prevents learning appropriate heterosexual

[8] This point is also discussed at some length in the Wolfenden report (47), submitted to the British Parliament in 1957. It became the law in England in 1967 (49).

social techniques. Statistics reveal that these adults are deeply disturbed, and while they must be isolated from the community and placed in a position where they cannot continue their seductive activities, they should be regarded as "sick individuals" (26). We should note in passing that the child who is seduced is very often an active party to the seduction. There is a growing feeling among psychiatrists who work with these matters that children who are seduced should be examined and efforts should be made to help them re-orient their sex drives (1, 31, 36, 42).

Last, under the topic of homosexuality, we should question the possible effect homosexuality may have as an example to others. In our culture, homosexuality represents a failure to achieve maturity which may severely limit social performance as well. The typical homosexual is inadequate in many kinds of personal relationships. Such inadequacy and limited development are apparent to more mature individuals and are hardly appealing to them. Those who are less mature—children and adults with infantile personalities—may be influenced to follow their example if they are already inclined in that direction.[9]

It is appropriate in the context of the oedipal period to make some observations about masturbation. Although most educated people intellectually accept the fact that masturbation is normal and not harmful, there is still an enormously strong undercurrent of feeling that it is dirty and dangerous. Even the authoritative Encyclopedia Britannica, through its 1947 edition, described at length how parents could control masturbation and "unhealthy thoughts" through judicious use of cold showers, long hikes, and non-irritating underclothing (15). What is the basis for this persistent and pernicious fear which can gnaw at the conscience and consciousness of even the sophisticated? First of all, this activity is *autoerotic*—it is self-given pleasure and it is of a sexual nature. But, this still does not explain why it should be so widely viewed as bad. As noted before, healthy infants of 12-14 months will fondle their genitals without compunction, and while this is not encouraged by most mothers it is not so openly feared. It is not until the fourth to sixth year that concern mounts. Significantly, at this time the child is con-

[9] Some of the fears expressed on this point would suggest that most people *might* become homosexual if seduced (50).

sciously concerned with oedipal feelings. They are openly stated, and the adults can thus easily surmise what the child is thinking about when he masturbates. All adults know about sexual thoughts, and their capacity to thus identify with the child brings them to "recall" their own childhood fantasies. They observe the child's self-conscious guilt and this sets them on the trail of what in fact their child is thinking. This parental perspicacity confirms the child's belief in his parents' omniscience and his own vulnerable transparency. Thus the pressure to masturbate must be somehow divested at least of forbidden fantasies and hopefully be eliminated altogether. Attendant guilt and shame provide the motive for repression. This pressure is also a function of parental concepts of control. To avoid the temptations of their own mobilized feelings they must "control" them by forcing the child to control his seductiveness. Since they cannot truly control thoughts, at least actions can be barred with the hope of eliminating forbidden fantasies. The former goal is gained to some degree, but the latter merely drives impulses to deeper levels of unconsciousness.

For these reasons, overt masturbation largely disappears between the oedipal years and adolescence. However, the upsurge of pubescence reactivates masturbatory behavior. During the latency years, emotionally healthy children, for the most part, limit sexual behavior to occasional adventures into "playing house" or "playing doctor," which serve to advance sexual-anatomical knowledge and to alleviate the pressures of sexual curiosity. Children who are burdened with emotional conflicts, however, may indulge in open and even public masturbation, precocious sexual curiosity, and sexual seductiveness toward hetero- or homosexual elders. Such behavior should nearly always be viewed as the harbinger of serious emotional illness and not as mere "badness." Although its impact on the public may be disturbing, it cannot be corrected by reformatory treatment. Indeed, public agencies and institutions increasingly show a gratifying awareness of the true nature of such displays.

By the end of the phallic-oedipal period of development, the healthy child achieves those skills and attitudes which make him capable of moving out into his environment on his own initiative. If excessive anxiety is produced during this period of active exploration and fantasies about parents, the child moves forward into subsequent developmental phases with an overwhelming sense of guilt. The alternative ego orientations to develop during this period are "initiative versus guilt" (17).

The ambulatory stage and that of infantile genitality add to the inventory of basic social modalities that of "making," first in the sense of "being on the make. . . ." The word suggests pleasure in attack and conquest. In the boy, the emphasis remains on the phallic-intrusive moods; in the girl, it turns to moods of "catching" in more aggressive forms of "snatching" and "bitchy" possessiveness, or in the milder form of making oneself attractive and endearing. The danger of this stage is a sense of guilt over the goals contemplated and the acts initiated in one's exuberant enjoyment of new locomotor and mental power: acts of aggressive manipulation and coercion which go far beyond the executive capacity of organism and mind, and therefore call for an energetic halt on one's contemplated initiative. While autonomy concentrates on keeping potential rivals out, it is therefore more an expression of jealous rage most often directed against encroachments by younger siblings, and initiative brings with it anticipatory rivalry with those who have been there first and may, therefore, occupy with their superior equipment the field toward which one's initiated in one's exuberant enjoyment of new locomotor and mental yet essentially futile attempts at demarcating a sphere of unquestioned privilege, now come to a climax in a final contest for a favored position with the mother; the inevitable failure leads to resignation, guilt, and anxiety. The child indulges in fantasies of being a giant and a tiger, but in his dreams he runs in fear for dear life. This, then, is the stage of the 'castration complex,' the fear of losing the (now energetically eroticized) genitals as a punishment for the fantasies attached to their excitements. Infantile sexuality and incest taboo, castration complex and superego all unite here to bring about that specifically human crisis during which the child must turn from an exclusive, pre-genital attachment to his parents, to the slow process of becoming a parent, a carrier of tradition. Here, the most fateful split and transformation in the emotional powerhouse occurs, a split between potential human glory and potential total destruction. For here the child becomes forever divided in himself. The instinct fragments which before had enhanced the growth of his infantile body and mind now become divided into an infantile set which perpetuates the exuberance of growth potentials, and a parental set which supports and increases self-observation, self-guidance, and self-punishment" [17].

In short, a successful resolution permits the child to be "on the make" and be willing to "stick his neck out." These ego qualities are complemented by superego attitudes of profound importance. The manner in which the competition is resolved, the way in which the child feels he may compete, and the parental attitudes which have been incorporated around the oedipal feelings become a very important part of the adult superego. Due to the precarious balance between instinct and control, which is still present at this age, the superego of the five-year-old tends to be markedly severe and uncompromising (23). It could hardly be otherwise and still permit a child to function effectively in relation to social demands. With continuing growth, development, and experience, this uncompromising structure should be progressively altered to evaluate realistically the basis for the various standards and values which are incorporated.

Many of the impulsive "crimes of passion" are really the result of a failure to modify and modulate too rigorous childhood standards. Small slights are denied and internal pressures mount with each accumulating affront. Finally, the last straw is added, the fragile controls are broken, and all of the pent-up violence bursts forth in murderous fury (46). After venting these feelings, such persons often recoil with guilty horror and then commit suicide. Nearly every daily paper carries at least one account of such an episode.

It is also important during this critical period of life that the parents have a constant and continuous relationship with the child. Shifting values held by the parents cause at least confusion, at worst islands of primitiveness in the child's conscience. Recent work on the conscience structure of some classes of adolescent delinquents clearly demonstrates that what appears to be absence of conscience is, in fact, a conscience with holes in it (30). Areas of impulsiveness remain which, instead of being prohibited by the parents, are allowed or even unconsciously encouraged by them. Also, when parental identifications are not lovingly and securely made, the rejection of part or all of the parental standards may occur. Antisocial attitudes may also be incorporated directly from parents. The devastating effect of this type of identification or lack of it, is clearly described by Redl and Wineman in their excellent study, *Children Who Hate* (44).

After reviewing this phase of child development, it is easy to understand why the clinical study of personality should have laid so much emphasis on the oedipus complex. The patterns which emerge from these first true object relationships become the precursors for all subsequent social capacities. In the oral period, attitudes about the self and the universe, trust or mistrust, are laid down. In the anal period, attitudes about the self and authority, autonomy or shame, are laid down. In the phallic period, attitudes about the self and social relationships, initiative or guilt, are achieved.

The sexual explorations carried out during the oedipal phase of development may be continued into later activities in various forms. Interest in masturbation and genital exploration is normally carried on into adult sexuality. "Dirty" jokes reflect unsatisfied interest in genital matters. In our society, full exploration of sexuality during childhood is generally impossible and is therefore the subject and focus for much adult activity.

Some of the sexual energy which comes under repression with the oedipal resolution emerges later on in romantic fantasies (for example in poetry where love is idealized) in which the partner is viewed as being godlike. In excessively severe repression, the impulses are often expressed by means of their opposites. For example, sexual interest and curiosity may be turned into puritanism or extreme sexual modesty.[10] These reversals produce various problems in sexual and social relationships later, when sexual desire is socially appropriate. Conflicts over sexuality may result in various forms of neuroses, psychoses, or character problems. When a person has developed successfully up to the period of genitality, there is usually no need to utilize such drastic defensive maneuvers as occur when trauma occurs at one of the earlier developmental stages. When conflicts center purely around genital sexuality, (i.e., the phallic phase) the neurosis usually takes the form of hysteria. In these syndromes, sexual repression produces various types of symptoms, which are relatively easily accessible to an individual's awareness.

The sexual curiosity derived from the phallic period may also produce a number of perversions such as narcissistic exhibitionism, voyeurism, and the excessive sexual activity described as nymphomania and satyriasis (48). These represent indirect efforts to satisfy

[10] This we have described as "reaction formation." (See Chapter IV.)

either curiosity or sexual expression, and to bypass the superego conflicts which the oedipal resolutions create. Prostitution may result from oedipal failure, representing not only the aggressive wish to achieve an oedipal victory symbolically, but also the masochistic self-punishment for having the oedipal wish. The relationship which prostitutes have with their "pimps" or "madams" is essentially a masochistic one. These individuals often take ruthless advantage of their "girls" (4, 25, 27, 41). The "girls" are in collusion with their persecutors as a guilt payment or punishment for the (unconscious) successes which they achieve symbolically (10).

Oedipal remnants are observable in milder forms of sexual oddity or failure and in occasional or periodic sexual promiscuity. The girl "in trouble," for example, is often acting out a masochistic need for punishment for her sexuality, assuming intelligence and social standards are average. In deciding how to deal with individuals who exhibit these traits, it is necessary to understand the motivation. When legal pressure is brought to bear, it is of the utmost importance that the sanctions work *with* the motivations if we wish to eliminate antisocial activities. In the Model Penal Code, the drafters wisely consider all consensual sexual activity among adults as noncriminal in nature. This is in keeping with the psychological implications of the activity, since to find criminality would not improve the situation nor prevent it in others.

We have considered a variety of specific outcomes of the oedipal situation and the psychological challenges of the phallic period. In describing a healthy resolution and achievement for this age, we have used the term "object love." To emerge from this period of development with a capacity for object love is of cardinal importance to subsequent personal and social maturation.

PROBLEMS

Example

You have been representing a married woman for the past four months, during which time you helped her to obtain a judicial separation on the grounds of cruelty. The wife received custody of the two children (a girl aged two, and a boy aged five) and the husband was given the usual "rights of visitation." Since the separation, the mother, wishing to facilitate some ongoing relationship with her husband, had acceded to his wish for the boy to spend an occasional weekend with him at his apartment. This has taken place on three or four occasions since the separation. When the wife arrives at your office for this appointment, she states at once that she is very upset and worried by what her son has been telling her about his visits with his father.

When you ask for elaboration, she tells you that, among other things, the child reports that he "sleeps snuggled up against father" in the same bed. Also, your client states that it appears to her that the husband devotes the entire weekend to indulging the boy's every whim, regardless of the standard of behavior allowed at home. She says that on several occasions she has tried to work out some agreement with her husband about these matters, but he responded "in the same insulting way he always spoke to me and would not cooperate in the least." (Though you expect your client to smooth over her own participation in the arguments, you feel that she is giving a more or less accurate picture.) She is quite upset about the effects of this behavior on her son and asks you what she should do about it.

The problem falls into two main parts: (1) How do you perceive the husband's behavior in terms of its possible harmful effects on the child? (2) What will you do to help your client answer the question of what she should do to alleviate the risks to the boy?

The first thing which should occur to counsel as he ponders this situation is that he is rapidly moving in between the horns of a dilemma. The boy does *need* a man with whom he can relate in order to learn how to be manly. However, this father appears to be acting so seductively toward the boy that it could have serious effects on the boy's development toward masculinity and independence. The seductiveness is occurring on two levels; the buying of favor with the child at the cost of his general need for discipline, and at the sexual level, with his excessively demonstrative behavior in regard to the sleeping arrangements. Both of these situations need remedy. Awareness of the psychological implications of such behavior should help counsel feel more sure of himself as he proceeds to do something about it. (I assume that most lawyers, even without benefit of special psychological knowledge, would "know" that there is something wrong with the father's behavior toward his son. However, because they might not be able to make explicit what the defects are, it might make them hesitant to act. They might adopt the ostrich's head-in-the-sand technique of waiting in the hope that "maybe he'll change if we give him a little time.")

In all cases like this, the first questions considered should relate to *why* the father behaves as he does? Part of the answer to this question must inevitably go back to the relationship between the man and his wife. Since his current behavior must give him some satisfaction (recalling our principle that all behavior has adaptive utility), the question is what satisfaction? We know that the man's separation from his wife and children probably deprives him of necessary sources of gratification. This places him on a deficit emotional budget as it were. Clearly, he is trying to get emotional gratifications from his son, which would be more appropriately gotten from his wife or some other adult-to-adult relationship. Did he know how to get these gratifications from his wife in the first place? Does his current relationship to his son give some insight into the difficulties the husband and wife were having? Is there any possibility for remedial action about such problems at this time? Have the husband and wife ever sought help for those problems? Is there any hope for working out some corrective solution for them which would permit them both to get what they need from each other? (We should not forget the psychological proposition that mates choose each other *because* they have the capacity to fulfill each other's needs, whatever they may be, *provided* they can learn to acknowledge those needs in themselves.[11]) One thing is certain, unless the husband is able to "refinance" his emotional life somehow, it can be readily predicted that he will fight vigorously to continue his current behavior. This is not because he is disinterested in his son's welfare. Rather, it reflects the sink-or-swim behavior of a person using the only survival means at his disposal. He cannot and will not give it up until he has a better means for floating.

These ideas should all occur to a lawyer who is familiar with the psychological concepts presented in this volume. Obviously, they will not take the explicit shape or detailed formulation which might be obtained from psychiatric consultation. Perhaps, before moving to a remedy, counsel might wish to get consultative assistance with some of the questions suggested above in order to help him select the proper target and to sharpen his legal aim upon it.

Whether assistance is obtained or not, there are several possible strategies to be considered. All should turn upon an estimate of the father's (and to some extent the mother's) capacity to understand consciously what effect his behavior is having on the boy. One consideration is the husband's willingness to listen to his own attorney's discussion of how he must, for the good of the child, behave differently. Indeed, it is also proper to consider whether the husband's attorney understands the matter. Regrettably, one cannot assume such knowledge in lawyers since

---

[11] See Chapter X for a discussion of this topic.

their training does not usually embrace such professionally important information.

Ideally, this matter should be handled by correcting the cause for the father's behavior, since it is only rarely possible to force a remedy by judicial means. The most a court can do in a case like this is to bar the father's access to his son, which would deprive the child of needed contact with men. However, if there is no way to bring about change in the father, some such course may have to be taken. (Here we should note that the present law of divorce, as well as some canons of ethics, place barriers before the ideal procedure which would be joint conferences with all parties concerned.)

In the end, the lawyer's goal in this case should be to get the father into a position where he can continue to see his son but in ways which are not so potentially harmful to the boy. The first approach should be to carry this out informally, perhaps with help from a psychiatrist or a marriage guidance counsellor. The intention should always be to help the father learn how to get alternative satisfactions in place of those for which he is now using the boy. In the event this does not work, then and only then should judicial intervention be used. In the latter event, counsel must then remember that he has the duty to prove to the court that the father's behavior is in fact detrimental to the child's proper development. To do this he should rely on information about the normal growth process and needs of a child as he resolves the oedipal conflict by shifting love objects and identifications.

If the latter course develops, strategy must be used, and counsel surely will need a psychiatric consultation. Then he must be sure that he follows the procedures previously discussed about the proper use of the expert, the ways to assure that only relevant testimony will be presented, how to make it comprehensible, and how to relate it to adequate corroborating material from other witnesses. Finally, it should never be taken until all other choices have been exhausted. This course of action will itself provoke great stress in the family. If it fails to achieve its goal, the boy will be the one to suffer the major consequence, since he will be caught in the middle.

1. In *Carter v. U.S.* (252 F.2d 608 [1956]) the following historical data on Carter appeared in the decision:

Born illegitimate, Carter spent the first seven or eight years of his life with his father's sister, a blind woman. Shortly before his eighth birthday he was hit by a car. He was taken to Freedman's Hospital, where his symptoms were described as a comatose condition, convulsive seizures, and grinding of the teeth. Hemorrhage was noted from the right ear, and there were lacerations on the forehead. His father testified that after the accident, "Sometimes he would answer people when people wouldn't be calling him, and then get out and you could call him and he wouldn't answer at all." And further, in response to the question, "Was he still jolly and playful?" his father answered, "Not much after that. He wouldn't do much talking after that."

A year after the accident Carter's aunt released him to the Child Welfare Division of the Department of Public Welfare. He was forced to leave his first foster home. After six months at a second foster home he was placed with a Mr. and Mrs. Reed, with whom he stayed almost four years. The Reeds found him extremely difficult. He relieved himself in his clothing and bed-clothing "just as regularly as if it were the right thing." He often struck smaller children without provocation; he was extremely cruel to animals—put a cat in a sewer and tried to strangle a dog; and he stole food. It was not uncommon for him to stay out all night, and on occasion he left home for as much as eight or ten days. At these times he slept in pool halls, garages, and the neighboring woods.

Carter left the Reeds in August, 1949, and went to the Industrial Home School at Blue Plains. While there he forced a child into an act of sodomy, threw a knife at another child, and was in the habit of fighting with smaller children who would not give him their possessions. His behavior there was characterized as aggressive and hostile. Upon reaching the age of sixteen (in December, 1952) Carter was placed in another foster home. He stayed there only a short time and then went to live with a Mrs. Gordon, who requested the authorities to remove him from her home after he masturbated in her presence.

Thereafter Carter moved to still another foster home for about one month, after which he was again placed in yet another foster home where he remained for three days and then ran away. He was found seventeen days later sleeping in a garage and was removed to the Receiving Home for Children. He subsequently left the Receiving Home to live with his father, remaining there about one month. His father testified that Carter absconded with a hundred dollars. He was apprehended on a complaint charging "disorderly conduct or peeping tom" and was sent back to the Receiving Home. By this time Carter had grown to be a large physical specimen. While at the Receiving Home he picked up another boy bodily and threw him on the floor, causing injuries serious enough to require hospitalization. His explanation was that the boy had been looking at him. His nature had become so vicious that he required constant supervision.

On June 21, 1954, when he was about seventeen and a half years old, Carter was sent to Gallinger Hospital by the Department of Public Welfare for a determination as to whether he was at that time of unsound mind. While there he was given an I.Q. test on which he scored 74—"borderline intelligence." The report, if there was one, of the psychiatric examination was not put in the record, and there is no testimony by a doctor as to the results of such an examination at that time. The social worker testified, however, that as a result of the report from Gallinger the Department filed a "beyond control petition" with the Juvenile Court. The petition stated that Carter had "a considerable amount of aggressive hostility," that he "acted impulsively," and that "we felt he would perhaps get into some difficulty because of his mental abilities—his inability to make use of community resources, his inability to plan for himself." The social worker testified; "And there were no other relatives who showed any interest in him whatsoever and we did not believe that he should be continued in the community. We felt that he should be placed in an institution." The petition to the Juvenile Court stated further that the difficulties Carter had been in and his behavior indicated that perhaps there was a mental illness. The petition was denied on the basis that Carter "should be able to go out into the community and learn to take care of himself even though [the Department] did not feel that he was able to do this."

Carter stayed at the Receiving Home until his eighteenth birthday, December 30, 1954, when the commitment to the Department of Public Welfare automatically expired. After his eighteenth birthday a social worker, knowing that Carter had no place to live, helped him find a place in the Municipal Lodging House, where he lived for about two and a half weeks. The social worker discussed with Carter the possibility of an army career, and Carter attempted to enlist. He was unable to pass the mental examination, however, and was rejected.

He was seen in April, 1955, by the social worker who had had much to do with him and by one of his former foster parents. He was disheveled and appeared confused. "He looked terrible. Glassy-eyed and staring, starry-eyed—I don't know—it was an expression of a person that when I left him I said to myself, 'I wonder if he had been using dope. . . .' And I said to myself, 'Nuts,' because that is just the way he looked." In June, 1955, he was indicted for murder in the first degree.

> (a) With this knowledge, what kind of psychological problems would you think this boy might have had in relation to his "oedipal development?"

2. In the case above, four doctors testified as experts.

The psychiatrists were presented as government witnesses on rebuttal. The examinations of three doctors had been made at the District Jail after Carter was indicted. One of them testified the electroencephalogram was negative; it showed no abnormal findings; there was no neurological damage. "The intelligence tests showed this man to be a person of dull, normal to average intellectual ability. It was with an intelligence quotient of 83 . . . dull normal . . . definitely within the normal area but below average." The doctor observed no evidence of psychotic behavior, no unusual mannerisms; Carter's emotional reaction "was appropriate to the situation and did not show any abnormality"; there was no evidence of hallucinations or delusions; he "was precisely oriented in all spheres"; his memory showed no impairment. The doctor found in Carter no "mental disease, psychosis" and no evidence of mental defect. The testimony of two other doctors was similar to the foregoing. One said, "I felt he was what we call a schizoid personality . . . a sort of lonely, withdrawn fellow who keeps pretty much to himself."

One doctor had examined Carter for a few minutes at the Receiving Home in December, 1954. He cautioned that his examination was not a thorough psychiatric evaluation but said that he saw nothing which would lead him to believe Carter was of unsound mind; he felt Carter was "extremely aggressive, hostile."

(a) How do you explain these psychiatric conclusions?

(b) If you had to deal with this rebuttal testimony, how would you proceed?

3. In *Carter v. U.S.* (252 F.2d 608, 617 [1956]) the court states:

Mental "disease" means mental illness. Mental illnesses are of many sorts and have many characteristics. They, like physical illnesses, are the subject matter of medical science. They differ widely in origin, in characteristics, and in their effects on a person's mental processes, his abilities, and his behavior. To make a reasonable inference concerning the relationship between a disease and a certain act, the trier of the facts must be informed with some particularity. This must be done by testimony. Unexplained medical labels—schizophrenia, paranoia, psychosis, neurosis, psychopathy—are not enough. Description and explanation of the origin, development and manifestations of the alleged disease are the chief functions of the expert witness. The chief value of an expert's testimony in this field, as in all other fields, rests upon the material from which his opinion is fashioned and the reasoning by which he progresses from his material to his conclusion; in the explanation of the disease and its dynamics, that is, how it occurred, developed, and affected the mental and emotional processes of the defendant; it does not lie in his mere expression of conclusion. The ultimate inferences *vel non* of relationship, of cause and effect, are for the trier of the facts.

Durham was intended to restrict to their proper medical function the part played by the medical experts. Many psychiatrists had come to understand there was a "legal insanity" different from any clinical mental illness. That of course was not true in a juridical sense. The law has no separate concept of a legally acceptable ailment which *per se* excuses the sufferer from criminal liability. The problems of the law in these cases are whether a person who has committed a specific criminal act—murder, assault, arson, or what not—was suffering from a mental disease, that is, from a medically recognized illness of the mind; whether there was a relationship between that specific disease and the specific alleged criminal act; and whether that relationship was such as to justify a reasonable inference that the accused would not have committed the act if he had not had the disease. The law wants from the medical experts medical diagnostic testimony as to a mental illness, if any, and expert medical opinion as to the relationship, if any, between the disease and the act of which the prisoner is accused. The conclusions, the inferences from the facts are for the trier of the facts. All this *Smith v. United States* implied and *Durham* was meant to bring about.

In discussing, as we have, expert medical testimony, we have not overlooked the admissibility of lay testimony. Lay witnesses may testify upon observed symptoms of mental disease, because mental illness is characterized by departures from normal conduct. Normal conduct and abnormal conduct are matters of common knowledge, and so lay persons may conclude from observation that certain observed conduct is abnormal. Such witnesses may testify only upon the basis of facts known to them. They may testify as to their own observations and may then express an opinion based upon those observations. Of course the testimony of a lay witness with training in this or related fields may have more value than the testimony of a witness with no such training. Also obvious upon a moment's reflection is the fact that, while a lay witness's observation of abnormal acts by an accused may be of great value as evidence, a statement that the witness never observed an abnormal act on the part of the accused is of value if, but only if, the witness had prolonged and intimate contact with the accused.

    (a) In the light of this statement by the court, if you were to defend Carter in a retrial, what kind of psychiatric testimony would you expect to present?

4. Following is a published case history of an impulse murderer (11).

In a jealous rage, a 30-year old man had found an ax, and in the presence of neighbors he had killed his former sweetheart. Originally, he had seduced her away from his brother, when the latter went to Europe on military duty.

    This man, second of six children, was the target for the most violent un-controlled brutality on the part of the father who, although he had a good job as a shop foreman, was a philandering alcoholic and a physical and mental sadist in his relationships with the prisoner's mother. The father's wild beatings of the boy were so frightening that neighbor men often interceded. The mother said she continued to live with the father only "to be sure he did not kill one of the boys," while at the same time her husband doted on the older daughter, of whom the prisoner was violently jealous. The father often beat and choked the mother in the children's presence. He shouted that she was a whore and a wanton and that he would kill her someday. From the age of 3 years, the mother said, the prisoner recurrently ran away from home because he was so terrified of the father. From the time the boy was 14 years old, his father accused him of vicious sexual practices with girls, a charge which was not true at the time. The mother said that the father constantly "spoke evilly about other people's sex lives" in the presence of the children. At no time did the father ever accept any responsibility for his brutal acts, and he never expressed any remorse. The boy never dared to bring a young friend into the home.

    The mother offered no protection to the child against the father's attacks, but she did console him afterward. She never called the police to protect the boy. She and the prisoner leaned on each other emotionally, and apparently he was always tender with her. At no time did the mother express any guilt or responsibility for having kept the boy in such a savage environment, and at the time we saw her the next oldest son was experiencing a similar life with the father. The prisoner said that without her warmth and comfort he would have killed himself long ago. He cried and moaned about his love for her for 15 minutes when she was first mentioned in the interview. He could not recall any conscious hostility toward his mother.

    He always felt that his fiancee was better than he and above him socially. He made no protests when she had promiscuous affairs with others and left him. Later, for a time, he tried to win her back after she had married. How-ever, he began to live with a woman 10 years his senior, an occurrence which prompted his former fiancee to divorce her husband and to attempt to woo him back, promising marriage. As a result of this, he abandoned the

woman with whom he had been living, whereupon the former fiancee began
to go out with other men. The prisoner found an ax and killed her.

(a) How would you relate this behavior to the oedipal period?
(b) If you were to defend such a person, how would you present
    the psychiatric testimony in a "McNaughton" jurisdiction? In
    a "Durham" jurisdiction?

REFERENCES

1. Abraham, K., The Experiencing of Sexual Traumas as a Form of Sexual
   Activity (1907). In: *Selected Papers of Karl Abraham*. London: Hogarth
   Press, 1949, pp. 47-63.
2. American Law Institute, *Model Penal Code: Tentative Draft No. 4*. Philadelphia: American Law Institute, April 25, 1955, pp. 278-281.
3. *Ibid.*, p. 281.
4. Anonymous, *Streetwalker*. New York: Viking Press, 1960, pp. 64-126.
5. Bellaman, H., *King's Row*. New York: Simon & Schuster, 1940.
6. Bettelheim, B., *Symbolic Wounds: Puberty Rites and the Envious Male*.
   Glencoe, Ill.: Free Press, 1954.
7. de Beauvoir, S., *The Second Sex*. New York: Alfred A. Knopf, 1953.
8. Deutsch, H., *The Psychology of Women*, 1:1-23. New York: Grune &
   Stratton, 1944.
9. *Ibid.*, pp. 262-267.
10. *Ibid.*, pp. 267-268.
11. Duncan, G. M. et al., Psychogenetic Determinants in Murder: Study of
    Six Prisoners Convicted of First-Degree Murder and Their Parents.
    J.A.M.A., 168:1755, 1958.
12. Eidelberg, L. Neurotic Choice of a Mate. In: *Neurotic Interaction in Mar-
    riage*, Ed. V. W. Eisenstein. New York: Basic Books, 1956, pp. 59-61.
13. Eisenstein, V. W., Sexual Problems in Marriage. In: *Neurotic Interaction
    in Marriage*. New York: Basic Books, 1956, p. 115.
14. *Ibid.*, p. 116.
15. *Encyclopedia Britannica*, 1:176. Chicago: Encyclopedia Britannica, 1947.
16. Erikson, E. H., *Childhood and Society*. New York: W. W. Norton, 1950,
    p. 51.
17. Ibid., pp. 224-226.
18. Fenichel, O., *The Psychoanalytic Theory of Neurosis*. New York: W. W.
    Norton, 1945.
19. Ferenczi, S., The Nosology of Male Homosexuality. In: *Sex and Psycho-
    analysis*. New York: Basic Books, 1950.
20. Freud, A., The Ego and the Mechanisms of Defense (1936). *The Writings
    of Anna Freud*, 2. New York: International Universities Press, 1967.
21. Freud, A., Observations on Child Development. *The Psychoanalytic Study
    of the Child*, 6:18-30. New York: International Universities Press, 1951.
22. Freud, S., On Narcissism: An Introduction (1914). *Standard Edition*,
    14:73-102. London: Hogarth Press, 1957.
23. Freud, S., The Dissolution of the Oedipus Complex (1924). *Standard
    Edition*, 19:173-179. London: Hogarth Press, 1961.

24. Fromm, E., *The Art of Loving.* New York: Harper Bros., 1956, pp. 38-46.
25. Greenwald, H., *The Call Girl.* New York: Ballantine Books, 1958, pp. 147-159.
26. Guttmacher, M. S., The Homosexual in Court. *Amer. J. Psychiat.*, 112:591-598, 1956.
27. Harris, S., *They Sell Sex.* Greenwich, Conn.: Fawcett, 1960, pp. 74-93.
28. Illsley, R. & Thompson, B., Women from Broken Homes. *Sociol. Rev.*, 9:27-54, 1961.
29. Jackson, D., Some Factors Influencing the Oedipus Complex. *Psychoanal. Quart.*, 23:566-581, 1954.
30. Johnson, A., Sanctions for Superego Lacunae of Adolescents. In: *Searchlights on Delinquency*, Ed. K. R. Eissler. New York: International Universities Press, 1949, pp. 225-245.
31. Johnson, A. & Robinson, D., The Sexual Deviant—Causes, Treatment, and Prevention. *J.A.M.A.*, 164:1559-1565, 1957.
32. Kaffman, M., Evaluation of Emotional Disturbance in 403 Israeli Kibbutz Children. *Amer. J. Psychiat.*, 117:732-738, 1961.
33. Kinsey, A. C. et al., *Sexual Behavior in the Human Male.* Philadelphia: W. B. Saunders, 1948, pp. 376-391.
34. *Ibid.*, pp. 623-636.
35. Kinsey, A. C. et al., *Sexual Behavior in the Human Female.* Philadelphia: W. B. Saunders, 1953, pp. 376-391.
36. Loewenstein, R. M., A Contribution to Psychoanalytic Theory of Masochism. *J. Amer. Psychoanal. Assn.*, 5:215, 1957.
37. Mead, M., *Male and Female.* New York: William Morrow, 1949, p. 142.
38. *Ibid.*, pp. 100-104.
39. Meiss, M. L., The Oedipal Problem of a Fatherless Child. *The Psychoanalytic Study of the Child*, 7:216-229. New York: International Universities Press, 1952.
40. Mullahy, P., *Oedipus Myth and Complex.* New York: Hermitage Press, 1948, pp. 23-28.
41. Murtagh, J. M. & Harris, S., *Cast the First Stone.* New York: McGraw-Hill, 1957, pp. 147-168.
42. Overholser, W., *The Psychiatrist and the Law.* New York: Harcourt, Brace, 1953, pp. 51-55.
43. Rabin, A. I., Some Psychosexual Differences Between Kibbutz and Non-Kibbutz Israeli Boys. *J. Proj. Tech.*, 22:328-332, 1958.
44. Redl, F. & Wineman, D., *Children Who Hate.* Glencoe, Ill.: Free Press, 1951.
45. Saul, L. J., *Emotional Maturity.* Philadelphia: J. P. Lippincott, 1947, p. 127.
46. Satten, J., Menninger, K., Rosen, I. & Mayman, M., Murder Without Apparent Motive: A Study in Personality Disorganization. *Amer. J. Psychiat.*, 117:52-53, 1960.
47. Secretary of State for Home Department, Committee on Homosexual Offenses and Prostitution, *Report of the Committee on Homosexual Offenses and Prostitution.* London: Her Majesty's Stationery Office, Nov. 15, 1956.
48. Sperling, O., Psychodynamics of Group Perversions. *Psychoanal. Quart.*, 25:56-64, 1956.

49. *Times,* Sexual Offenses Bill Goes Through Without Vote. London: *The Times,* Dec. 20, 1966, p. 5.
50. *Times,* Seaman's Corruption Fever. London: *The Times,* Dec. 19, 1966, p. 7.
51. Tinbergen, N., The Evolution of Behavior in Gulls. *Sci. Amer.,* 203:118-130, Dec. 1960.
52. Williams, T., *Cat on a Hot Tin Roof.* New York: New Directions, 1955.
53. Winograd, M., The Development of the Young Child in a Collective Settlement. *Amer. J. Orthopsychiat.,* 28:557-562, 1958.
54. Zilboorg, G. & Henry, G., *A History of Medical Psychology.* New York: W. W. Norton, 1941, pp. 161-174.

VIII

The Period of Rapid
Acculturation: Latency

The years between age six and thirteen have been designated the "latency period." This name derives from an analytic theory which held that children of this age have no active sexual interests, and hence are sexually latent. Subsequent observation has displaced this theory, and while the name is still used, we no longer consider this a period devoid of sensual or sexual activity. There is ample evidence that children of this age do have sexual interest and curiosity, and that it is actively exploited, though not so openly as during the oedipal period.

Latency children are physically well developed and possess all of the motor skills and neurological capacities to accomplish almost any task. All they lack is social training and experience. To gain these is the principal psychosocial goal of the period. After settling the relationship to family, children turn eagerly toward the environment of school and community and, as if to slake a great thirst, they seek knowledge and experience in the ways of the world. With the decision to grow up and become like mother or father, there comes a loosening of the emotional ties to parents which permits and facilitates the formation of identifications with persons outside of the family. During this process, knowledge and experience are gained from a broader cultural base than that represented by immediate relatives. Those skills which were learned previously, and those ego qualities which were developed during the first six years of life, are now applied to the complexities of the social group in which the child lives. There is active interest in others and a strong wish to relate and identify with them. There is open competition with peers and concomitant stimulation to increase skill and cultural facility. At the same time, widening horizons make it necessary to learn standards, values, and morals of the larger and more complex social group (2, 8, 9).

Society and parents are extremely interested in "the company he keeps." This recognizes the fact that latency children are perhaps the most vulnerable to social influence. The very fact that a child is mature enough to turn a little away from his parents, and the fact that there is a simultaneous wish to form identifications and ties with persons outside of the family, not only lays him open to the positive and beneficial aspects of such relationships, but also to their potential dangers. There are good reasons to have close control over the activities of children in this age range, and deterrence still has psychological effectiveness for enforcing behavioral conformity.

As ego techniques for handling these new situations evolve, there is increased control and mastery over self and the environment. Impulses of hostility are controlled and conformed to group standards and values, which initially have less personal meaning and importance to the child than family standards. Likewise, impulses to be the center of attention, and narcissistic striving for dominance, meet with harsh rebuff. There is a strong reality necessity to learn how to deal with narcissistic frustration and to get along with less tolerance and love than existed in the family setting. Learning and sublimation advance at a rapid pace during this period (25). Identifications are formed with social ideals and social values (24). Such concepts as racial identity and other group labels come strongly to the fore during this period. Social issues such as school segregation are very important because of the effect they produce upon the child's internal conception (and thus the "reality") of "democracy," "fairness," "equality under the law," and "the brotherhood of man" (20). Without tangible experience, such value concepts are at most intellectualizations, which will not stand up under real social pressure. To embrace truly and to act according to these values, experience and participation in them is essential.

At the beginning of the latency period, the child starts school. This early introduction to the institution of the school colors all subsequent development in regard to learning (31). This is a challenging period of life which merits considerable social attention. Some of the most profound and important influences in the formation of a child's social patterning occur during the first few years of school experience. Our society, although strongly committed to the value and importance of the public school system, is insufficiently aware of the importance of the teacher. All too frequently, the learning function is viewed as a purely intellectual operation (10, 19). *For the child to be able to identify with the teacher is at least as important as the teacher's intellectual attributes.* A brilliant teacher, well schooled in all of the latest pedagogical methods, may not succeed half so well as one who has the ability to make the child wish to be like him.

We should not forget that each child, according to his sex, has just moved away from oedipal attachments and wishes to move toward identifications with persons of the same sex. Yet, in the first kindergarten year, children are met by a female teacher who often possesses all of the qualities of a good mother, and will rekindle the residual problems of the oedipal struggle. Children meet such a psychological threat by taking appropriate steps to relieve their anxiety. As early as this, "learning problems" develop. For example, a small boy, still unsure of his capacity to function as a male, may find the warmth of the kindergarten teacher all too seductive. This will force him not only to reject her, but what she stands for as well—education.

In order to retain his masculine identification under such circumstances, a boy must wall himself off from the learning process. Starting school also confronts him with a multitude of value judgments, many of which may not conform with his social and family background. A child with courage and strong identification with family values is hard-pressed to do anything but to reject the new values. Instead of learning, "Dick ran up the hill. Jane saw Dick. See the rose, Dick? Oh, how pretty!" a boy may need to reject such materials as being "sissy," because they are in such sharp contrast to his own background values. Instead of learning to read these strange words, he develops avoidance techniques in order to keep comfortable. The high correlation between poor reading and delinquency and between truancy and delinquency suggests that more is at stake during early school years than mere intellectual development (35).

The reason for these correlations is not well settled, but it seems clear that at least part of the problem stems from the difficulty that children from some social groups have in identifying with the strange new materials in the school setting (1, 29). Teachers and society at large should be aware of this identification difficulty. It is one of those points at which social values and individual psychological development interact with each other.

This kind of problem also arises on those occasions when children are removed from their own family settings and placed in institutions. If the child is to be successfully integrated into not only the new setting, but also into subsequent social relationships, his "identification background" must be taken into consideration. The child uprooted from one set of identifications cannot pick up and accept a new set without a great deal of help (37). Adaptation does not occur simply. Many children who have been reared in institutional settings sadly lack what we have called an identity. They have adjusted to the strange new setting either by extreme passivity and a failure to develop any aggressive personality characteristics, or else they have fought back (a more healthy ego solution) and in their resistance to learning new ways, have become "delinquents." These events are initiated and largely developed during the period of latency, when the child's hunger to learn about his own corner of the world is most intense. He will learn readily and he is easily indoctrinated, but if placed in extreme conflict he will learn "not to learn" with equal intensity (30).

Quite often, latency children will bring nonscholastic problems into the area of school behavior. Various family power struggles can be carried on in the context of educational activities. One result may be "school phobia" (6). In these situations the child is usually fighting to control a sector of the family's decision-making and implements this by refusing to go to school in the guise of being terrified about some aspect of it. He *is* terrified, but not of school. The real terror stems from his inner awareness of the power confrontation with which he is apparently getting away. What a responsibility for a small child! The parents acquiesce to the refusal, stating that they do not wish to harm their child by forcing him to do such a frightening thing.

This particular problem may be interesting to lawyers because its proper psychological treatment involves "forcing" the child back to school (15). Since the child is inevitably playing out a resistance role which one or both parents approve, it is occasionally necessary for a school to take legal action to bring about his return. When such a course is recommended by the psychiatrist, its prompt legal implementation is of vital importance to the treatment of the child and his family. At such a juncture, the court may be asked to assume temporary custody of the child in order to carry out the community's goal of compulsory education for all children. Only when this issue is faced squarely, can the underlying psychological conflicts between the parents, the child, and the school be unraveled. The child's terror is real, but the cause is obscure. Parental concern is genuine, but its focus is inaccurate. The school's concern is legitimate, and it is important to resolve the problem. Only determination of the underlying psychodynamics and motivational patterns can resolve these conflicts of interest.[1]

The child's sensual pleasure interest during latency does not, for obvious reasons, have any new or different organ site. Rather, latency is a period in which new integrations and shifts of emphasis occur. This process varies widely, according to the culture in which the child is reared (38). These variations are closely related to the form of the culture, and the nature of its major goals as they relate to character adaptation. Old pleasure sources are denied, others are sublimated, and some are turned into opposites (14). For example, in our culture, any pleasure interest in anality is heavily repressed and blocked. Anal interest must emerge in sublimation or reaction formation and, as we described earlier, this is expressed in various character traits having to do with control, neatness, and precision. Our culture makes good use of these sublimations. In the very process of education, we tend to underscore them by pressing the child to learn and to accept control and regimentation. He is not encouraged to exploit his own imagination in control techniques.

During latency, the principal method of dealing with sexuality is repression. The child learns that he must not express genital-sensual impulses toward his parents, and during this period of life there is marked sublimation (27). He may not demonstrate overt

---

[1] Curiously, this particular syndrome is a product of contemporary interest in children's "feelings." A few generations ago, a child could not get away with such behavior; he was forced back to school and he went. The same parent-child conflict may have existed and emerged in some other form of emotional disturbance.

genital activity but, at the same time, he may secretly play games which have sexual undertones. The doctor-nurse or mother-father games are very common and very normal.

As barriers to sexual expression become more stringent with increasing age and with the important impact of oedipal repression, latency children generally tend to have like-sexed playmates (18). There is some tendency to regard the opposite sex as inferior and undesirable. In our culture, little boys will have little to do with little girls and vice versa, and those who break this pattern are generally regarded as "tomboys" or "sissies." This tendency of latency children to form friendships with peers of the same sex is reinforced by the adults who not only fear any manifestation of sexuality, but criticize and discourage the expression of any attribute which they view as belonging to the opposite sex. Thus little boys should be physically active while little girls "naturally" are quiet and gentle. These characteristics are assumed to be related to the innate biological equipment of each sex. In fact, this is not the case; each sex has the capacity and need for both passive and aggressive expression. To place too great pressure on latency children to give up either passive or aggressive impulses is to force them to form identification patterns which may raise sexual difficulties later on (11, 28).

With the greater interest of latency children in social activity, there is less need for autoerotic activity. With the vast amount of learning which goes on, always in a social frame of reference, various ego traits derived from previous developmental stages are elaborated in very specific ways and in socially oriented terms (12). The ego, during these years, is extensively invested in social reality testing, and skills are progressively developed for evaluating and judging social realities for oneself. These are integrated with various social value judgments which are also being learned.

Latency children are not free thinkers. They do not thrive in an environment which gives them much freedom of choice. Fifty years have passed since the origination of many of Freud's theories, and nearly the same length of time since John Dewey first introduced his ideas about education (4). We have had ample opportunity to evaluate the results of "freedom" in education. In fact, a rather large number of children reared in educational systems based on complete freedom of choice have now passed through the analyst's consultation room. According to "theory" (which was from the outset a distortion of both Freud's and Dewey's ideas), they should have been capable of audacious expeditions across intellectual frontiers, untrammeled by the dead hand of authority. In fact, such children turned out to be among the most deeply inhibited persons whom analysts have treated (22). Why did this occur in the face of brilliant theory and optimistic hopes? A penetrating understanding of ego functioning clarifies this apparent enigma. While the latency child has a great desire to identify and explore, his social reality-testing capacity is, as yet, limited. Placed in a setting with unlimited choice, he is overwhelmed by the vastness of possibilities (17). It would be similar to expecting a law student on his first day in class to brief a complex antitrust issue by turning him loose in the law library. The enormity of the problem, the complexity of the issues involved, as well as his feeling about the importance of the outcome, would frustrate, frighten, and probably paralyze him. Many would quit then and there. Some would make an attempt, but everyone would be aware of failure. If real success were a vital issue, even the most capable would feel despair. This is what happens to most children faced with the excessive freedom of some "progressive" schools.

During this period of intensive learning, conflicts are principally dealt with by repression, and repression is an excellent technique for avoiding anxiety. What better solution than to take the frightening issues of the environment and hide them behind the walls of repression?

Since social reality testing is one of the principal learning goals of this period of life, how do we put these two apparently contradictory statements together? As a child gains more and more skill in coping with new situations, he must be permitted to look more closely into the forbidden areas which were previously hidden from him. He must slowly learn his capacity for anger, love, sexuality, dependency, and the other important emotions. These must become familiar, and he must develop the capacity to deal with them more or less consciously if he is to become a successful adult. The ideal environment for the latency child, then, provides him with sufficient help with problems of social judgment, but also gives him progressively increasing freedom to experiment and learn what he may and may not do with his feelings (13, 16b, 21).

We noted above that during latency the child elaborates his character and personality. Character is a word which we use in many different contexts, sometimes in a moralistic sense, sometimes referring to courage and tenacity, and sometimes meaning personality. Psychoanalysts use the word "character" almost as loosely. The technical literature reveals no consistent definition of the word; each author infuses slightly different ideas into his definition. For the purposes of our study, we will define character as "the basic traits of a personality." These identifying traits represent the end product of several different psychological processes as well as the evolved techniques for dealing with inner impulses and external realities. Each individual's experience, in some subtle way, is different from that of everyone else, and the ego structure developed to deal with these differing experiences is character. Reich (34) points out that this aspect of ego development is derived from three general processes: (1) From identification with the frustrating reality,[2] specifically the principal person who represents such reality through setting its standards and defining its limits. (2) From the aggressive impulses stimulated by such frustration which are turned back inside of the person, thus limiting their direct expression. Thus character has the function of inhibition which helps in adapting to aggression-provoking situations.[3] (3) Energies derived from sexual reactions which cannot be permitted expression are split off, repressed, and then emerge in character manifestations. These adaptive reactions taken together, produce the character of a person.

Character, as the analyst describes it, represents one aspect of the ego and the manner in which it deals with inner impulses and the external, structuring environment. It is an internalized, specific set of behavioral characteristics, which are used automatically and with great psychological efficiency, to adapt to environmental circumstances (3). The concept of the repetition compulsion is not dissimilar to the concept of character, in that both represent conditioned techniques for meeting stress and resolving it, and are part of the basis of predictability in human behavior.[4]

In keeping with the colloquial meaning, the type of "character" a person develops has important implications for his social behavior.

---

[2] See Chapter IV.

[3] The economics and the dynamics of this process are discussed in Chapter III.

[4] Questions of prediction are discussed in more detail in Chapter XI.

This fact is reflected in legislation regarding school systems, social activities among juveniles, and in efforts to control what may be read and viewed by children in movies, television, and various literary forms. This is a legitimate interest, and every society, either consciously or unconsciously, attempts to regulate these forces, knowing full well that they have an impact on the ultimate character of the social group.[5] Communities control the curriculum of their school systems, attempt to regulate questions of religious influence, and more recently, racial relationships and their impact on character have been considered a public social responsibility.

Examination of various cultures makes it clear that there is a wide variation in the types of character which each group evolves. Detailed knowledge in this field is just beginning to accumulate. However, it appears that it will ultimately be possible to correlate the child rearing practices and techniques of social indoctrination with the character structure of individuals in a specific group, as well as with the cultural style of that group. The recent and current struggle between democratic and totalitarian societies has sharpened our awareness of the importance and the difficulty of attainment of our social and character ideals. We are more aware than ever of the need to rear our children in such a way that they will develop the capacity to function effectively and happily in a democratic community. A democratic society demands skill in social interaction without undue dependence, cooperation without excessive conformity, and individual initiative without inappropriate rebelliousness. All of these capabilities must be placed in the perspective of long- and short-term social goals. The frequency of large-scale wars makes it obvious that as a race of animals we have not come terribly far in learning how to live together effectively and cooperatively. Also, the high crime rate and the evidence of other antisocial behavior illustrate that our ideals are far from being integrated into our character development (5, 36). Ralph Linton has aptly said, "We are, in fact, anthropoid apes trying to live like termites and, as any philosophic observer can attest, not doing too well at it" (26).

Some recent reports from Russia note the emphasis which is being placed on "character" building in their educational programs (23). This training is directed toward the inculcation of a value system

[5] The psychiatrist who has written most in this field, though I do not agree with many of his conclusions (39), is Frederick Wertham (40).

which places community and state over individual and family. It stresses such things as protection of public property, pride in civic buildings, and a sense of personal responsibility for them.[6] While such indoctrination has many serious political, social, and psychological implications, it nevertheless should arouse our curiosity. The wanton and "meaningless" destruction of public and private property as well as human life, so frequently described in the daily press, is indication of mounting disregard felt by a substantial segment of our population for the values we hold in highest regard.

The concept of character has important implications for problems of treatment. Behavior derived from character is drawn from unconscious resolutions of conflicts in past experiences. Such behavior is neither fraught with neurotic anxiety nor associated with painful symptoms and conflicts. Rather, it fits in perfectly with conscious value judgments and ideals—the person feels right and good about what he is doing. Character traits are *ego-syntonic*. Therefore, when criminal activity is grounded in the individual's character, there is no internal motivation for change. Many of those referred to as "hardened criminals," fall within the category of "character disorders." These individuals are usually regarded as being hopelessly fixed in their criminal behavioral patterns, but recent studies report some therapeutic success with this kind of problem (32).

From the foregoing, it should be apparent that there are two important aspects of character development which have great importance for any legal system which would rationally approach the treatment of persons with character problems. First, if we really care to alter the future behavior of those with character problems, we must handle their treatment in ways which will modify their psychological structure (i.e., their ego). Neither good will on the part of society, conscientiousness of patients/prisoners, nor the use of the most efficient "security" confinement, will in themselves change character structure. In fact, traditional procedures such as imprisonment, state hospital commitment, and even decisions to give or not give psychotherapy are often doomed to failure because they ignore the nature of character defenses and often even play into their unconscious and neurotic purposes.

Second, it is highly important to go to whatever lengths necessary

6 These comments are drawn partially from anecdotes related by colleagues recently returned from visits to Russia.

to assure that the latency child has the maximum opportunity to develop a character which will be efficient and adaptive in terms of our social and cultural ideals. This involves providing the kinds of experiences in which these ideals may be perceived and practiced and at the same time avoiding those in which temptations for deviation are too strong. Hopefully, there will also be latitude for progressive exploration of varying kinds of reality in order that the concept of experimentation (reality testing) itself, will become an integrated part of the child's developing character. This latter capacity is the difficult-to-attain essential for the mature and effective personality in a democratic society where individual decision-making in the context of social responsibility is a cherished value.

While the latency child accomplishes the massive task of learning the language and style of his culture, if he is relatively healthy in his capacity to relate to people, he tends to cling to chosen identification objects with an intense, enthusiastic, and uncritical idealism. This idealism can be oriented toward either socially valuable or antisocial goals.[7]

All conflicts from the past and their end resolutions which we have described before, are now fitted into a broader social application. The latency years should be the period of broadest intellectual advance. Ideas and concepts are tried out and tested against wider social realities. Attitudes and views from the past must be updated and integrated into current reality. Trust must be extended from immediate family relationships to society at large in a realistic manner. Initiative must be capable of social extension. There must be integration of all emotional modalities with realistic application of them to life situations to (a) incorporate materials (oral), (b) digest and expel the nonvaluable (anal), and (c) put out constructive work (phallic) in such a way as (d) to include within the concept of the self (ego boundaries) tools and techniques which can provide pleasure and productivity. Success gives a sense of achievement and a feeling of mastery; failure brings inferiority and inadequacy. The latter may be due to parental overprotection of the child stemming from the family's inability or reluctance to prepare the child for the wider experience of school and the outside world. It may result from the use of rearing techniques which fail to sustain

[7] For example, Redl and Wineman vividly describe the *Children Who Hate* (33).

progressive growth, such as excessive punishment, inadequate love and gratification, or forcing the child into identifications which are ego-alien. Any of these lacks can divert valuable psychic energy from the industrious pursuit of growth and maturation, thereby increasing the sense of inferiority as pubescence approaches.

Latency children, in an environment of relative security, constancy, and gratification potential, go through this period with ease and smoothness. They are usually likeable and easy to get along with since, if reasonably well-adjusted, they are all-too-eager to identify themselves with the social and individual goals encountered in their surroundings. This smoothness and pleasantness comes sharply to a close with the physiological upheaval of pubescence. The ego which has reached reasonably effective integration suddenly runs into new and disquieting energy sources with great potential for disequilibrium.

The physiological process which marks the attainment of physical sexual maturity is accompanied by a stimulation of the instinctual processes, which is carried over into the psychic sphere in the form of an influx of libido. The relation established between the forces of the ego and the id is destroyed, the painfully achieved psychic balance is upset, with the result that the inner conflicts between the two institutions blaze up afresh [16a].

PROBLEMS

Example

Late one afternoon you get an urgent call from the younger partner of a flourishing father-son company which you serve as counsel. This young man (whom you prefer to avoid because of his prudish solemnity about things) requests a conference with you at once, to which he wishes to bring his wife. Although you had hoped to get away from the office early that afternoon for a serious conference with your golf foursome, you set the appointment for one hour later. (What else *can* you do with a client who is responsible for a tidy part of your income each year?)

A few minutes before the appointment time, the young couple arrives, looking very distressed. You usher them into your office and attempt to put them at ease with a few casual remarks about matters of common knowledge. The wife looks apprehensively at her husband, and he forthwith says that he would like to get down to the problem that brought them. You invite him to tell you about it, and he proceeds, obviously under great emotional strain.

You learn that the couple has a seven-year-old daughter, Mary, who is their only child. It appears that Mary, for the past several days, has stopped off on her way home from school to play with her friend Sue. On this particular afternoon, her mother happened to ask her about what they played. She thought she sensed withdrawal in Mary and wondered what it meant. Reluctantly, and only because of mother's "firm pressure," the little girl revealed they had been playing "doctor and nurse" with Sue's 10-year-old brother, Robert. Finally, "feeling very ashamed of herself," Sue described the sexual explorations the children had performed on each other in the context of their game. The mother, "not knowing what to do about such a terrible thing," immediately called up her husband. He, in turn, promptly got in touch with you. "I decided we should do something about that little sex maniac at once." He sounded like he wanted you to get hold of the police, the public prosecutor, and the local League for Disturbed Children, post-haste. Instead of a brisk nine holes of golf, you now have this problem on your hands. What *will* you do?

Being a comfortable person yourself, so that you remember back to childhood without undue restlessness, and being forearmed with some knowledge about child development, you recognize at once that the main problem here will be to counsel this pair of unhappy and frightened parents. Their fears and anxieties are probably the only things which must be handled. That makes the problem none the less serious however, and you know that you must somehow "get to them" or they will in fact turn to the law for relief. As always, the first issue is to get them to put into words what it is that they really fear. After acknowledging that you can see they are very upset by this, you may ask them to tell you more about what they fear is happening to Mary. What do they think she knows about sexual matters, and what should she know about them at her age? How do they think "normal children" find out about sex? (As this line of exploration proceeds, they no doubt will become somewhat uneasy. A good tactic for relieving such tension, is the simple expedient of acknowledging it. "This is a pretty uncomfortable topic even for us adults to discuss, isn't it? Well, we're all brought up to be a little afraid of such an exciting topic as sex." This kind of remark [or "interpretation" if you will] is truly reassuring, because it tells your clients that you understand what they are *feeling*. This is in contrast to the nonreassuring effect of "Now don't worry about a thing. We'll take care of everything." In the first place, you show you don't even know what "everything" is since you demonstrate you do not know how they are feeling or why they feel it.) Hopefully, such a tack will bring them to acknowledge, either covertly or overtly, that their little girl's behavior is stirring up some of their own childhood fears.[8] When you get to that point, you are half-way to the golf course.

Of course, another thing you will wish to ascertain is whether or not the behavior *is* part of the normal sexual explorations of childhood. How often has it happened? What exactly do the children do? How widespread is Robert's behavior? Has he done anything like this before? Have any other parents complained? (The chances are very high they have not, or Mary would likely have been forbidden to play with Sue.) The purpose of all of these questions, in addition to settling the point of "normality," is to help the parents lower their sensitivity and vulnerability to Mary's behavior. You will be trying to help them educate Mary to the "facts of life," even while they teach her how to regulate her behavior to appropriate standards of social behavior. Once you ask the question of how much and where children will, can, or should have such learning experiences, the difficulties of such judgments appear. Here will be solid ground upon which you can join the parents in their anxiety. Such questions of degree are very difficult of resolution and one *always* fears children might go too far sometime—whatever that may mean.

In the event you think there might be some abnormality in the play (and it would appear from the data set forth here that such is not the case), it would be well to help them arrive at the decision to have a conference with the other parents, and to see it as a problem to explore further with assistance from an expert in child development. As counsel, your crucial goal throughout is to help make them more comfortable with their own feelings so that they can be more objective in their handling of the matter—more objectively subjective, as it were. We know the parents' reaction is a reflection of their own sexual feelings. Beyond a doubt, they will either have to resolve some of this conflict or be kept hanging by their thumbs during their daughter's growing up (if she is lucky and resists their too prudish pressure upon her). Otherwise, they may cause her to deny and withdraw from her own sexual maturation and experience in ways which will be harmful to her. (This, of course, assumes that it is desirable for children to grow up so that they may enjoy an intimate and a sensually satisfying relationship with a loved person of the opposite sex.) Since one can assume that these parents *will* have this kind of conscious concern for their child, this concern can be mobilized to help them deal with the anxiety of watching their child

[8] For a discussion of this phenomenon, see Chapter X.

face the risks of mastering sexual knowledge, with its potential for happiness or misery. It would be very useful to say something like, "Kids sure put you over the jumps as they grow up, don't they? It's practically like going through childhood all over again yourself." This comment is absolutely true, and it *may* help this couple gain a bit more sexual freedom themselves.

To suggest that counsel carry out an interview of this sort will strike many as being extraneous to the proper function of lawyers. We must not overlook the fact that this problem *was* brought to a lawyer, and he must do *something* with it. He could brusquely send the parents away and tell them they are being foolish (if he knows the behavior is normal). This would cause him to lose, or at least alienate, his client. To proceed along the lines of contacting police or juvenile authorities would be to commit not only a serious error of judgment, but would make counsel look (and perhaps feel) foolish. This leaves only one alternative—that of doing the appropriate thing. Such a course of action as suggested above is not only a good solution for a workaday lawyer's problem, but it is also a highly desirable mental health procedure. When people are in acute emotional stress (such as this family was in), it is terribly important to do the right thing at the right time. Lawyers, because of the nature of their professional role, are in a good strategic position to make such moves.

1. A boy of eight took piano lessons from a young and pretty teacher. He was gifted, industrious, and made good progress, and her affection and respect made her slightly indulgent. The boy reciprocated this affection to the point of adoration.

One day, the teacher observed that some coins were missing from a box on the table in the lesson room. It did not even occur to her to suspect the beloved pupil. But the thefts were repeated, and it struck her that money was always missing just after this boy's lessons. Although she dreaded the disappointment of such a revelation, she could not disregard the facts and decided to watch the boy closely. Indeed, she soon had the opportunity of seeing that the moment he was alone in the room, the boy approached the box and removed a number of coins. She was distressed and shocked, but what followed increased her astonishment, for the boy did not go home with the money. Instead, he went into the garden, where he dug a hole and buried it. The teacher decided to say nothing but to watch the boy further, and the performance was repeated at the next lesson. She finally called the boy to account in a cautious and inoffensive manner. The lad confessed with tears, went into the garden, dug up the money, and gave it all back. When he was questioned as to why he had done it, he gave the following strange reply: "I wanted to have something of yours, I do love you so" (41).

(a) How do you understand this incident?
(b) How should such a behavior be treated?
(c) How might this relate to the behavior of the person we label as a "kleptomaniac"?
(d) How should kleptomaniacs be treated by the law?

2. The second case pertains to a girl of fifteen who was committed to an institution for delinquent girls for stealing. Her stealing was compulsive and showed the earmarks of a sadistic perversion, the fantasy behind it being that she killed her mother in the act of stealing. She was a completely isolated individual who suffered from excessive conscious guilt feelings, unusual in delinquents, and who could not tolerate being separated from her mother. The father had deserted the family when the girl was about four years old; there was a brother, a few years her senior, whom the mother delegated to punish the patient by severe beatings for her misdemeanors. The patient's mother, who lived in strained financial circumstances, was a peculiarly infantile personality with shallow affects and a superficial cheerfulness quite inappropriate to her real situation. She professed concern for the daughter and was willing to make the greatest sacrifices in order to have her treated. The sacrifices were not accepted, but the child started treatment after her discharge from the institution. As long as the child declined to see the psychiatrist or resisted any help, the mother insisted on her treatment. But after a while, the first signs of a positive transference showed, and the youngster improved temporarily—i.e., she ceased stealing. The mother immediately interfered by insisting that the patient wanted a job. She promised that she would call the analyst at once if there was the slightest sign of trouble. The next I learned was that, through the mother's provocation, the girl had had a temper tantrum and the mother had called the police and had the daughter confined to the State Hospital. She notified neither the analyst nor the social worker. She took the child back soon and, although she complained to the social worker and the police, she nevertheless seemed to be satisfied to have her daughter continue to steal (7).

(a) How should this pathological family relationship be dealt with by the law, assuming it were diagnosed?
(b) How far would you be willing to intervene with the parents, and how would you do it?

3. In a news item on page 35 of *The Philadelphia Inquirer* of October 30, 1957, the death of an infant due to parental neglect is reported. The final two paragraphs are as follows:

Detective George L. Barkley told how the child was taken to Pennsylvania Hospital and pronounced dead, and the body removed to the morgue. He said the apartment in which the parents were then living, at 11th and Pine Streets, was vermin-infested and filthy; that the father had been drinking, and that the mother told him she had fed the child pineapple juice upon getting home that morning, and a bottle of milk at 3:15 that afternoon.

The judge, pointing out that the reports before him did not indicate a definite cause of death, said he was "unable to do any more than hold these two on a charge of neglect of child." He also directed that they be subjected to examination and their elder daughter, Barbara, 3, be taken from them as unfit parents and placed for adoption by the Municipal Court.

    (a) What do you think of this solution to this situation?

    (b) How would you decide the question of when to remove a child from its parents?

    (c) If the older child were eight years old, would this alter your opinion? Would the age of the child change the psychological situation in any significant way?

4. In a recent case in the mid-West, a teacher-mother insisted on her right to educate her daughter at home. This resulted in a protracted legal battle.

    (a) What psychological considerations should be raised in order to settle this question optimally?

    (b) Would you permit this mother to educate her daughter in the way which she wished?

REFERENCES

1. Blanchard, P., Psychoanalytic Contributions to the Problems of Reading Disabilities. *The Psychoanalytic Study of the Child*, 2:163-187. New York: International Universities Press, 1947.
2. Bornstein, B., On Latency. *The Psychoanalytic Study of the Child*, 6:279-285. New York: International Universities Press, 1951.
3. Bromberg, W., The Treatability of the Psychopath. *Amer. J. Psychiat.*, 110:604, 1954.
4. Dewey, J., *The Child and the Curriculum, the School and Society*. Chicago: University of Chicago Press, 1956.
5. Dublin, L., *The Facts of Life: From Birth to Death*. New York: Macmillan, 1951, p. 324.
6. Eisenberg, L., School Phobia: A Study in the Communication of Anxiety. *Amer. J. Psychiat.*, 114:712-718, 1958.

7. Eissler, R. S., Scapegoats of Society. In: *Searchlights on Delinquency*, Ed. K. R. Eissler. New York: International Universities Press, 1955, p. 291.
8. English, O. S. & Finch, S. M., *Introduction to Psychiatry*. New York: W. W. Norton, 1954, pp. 25-26.
9. English, O. S. & Pearson, G. H. S., *Emotional Problems of Living*. New York: W. W. Norton, 1955, pp. 145-152.
10. *Ibid.*, pp. 155-158.
11. *Ibid.*, pp. 152-154.
12. *Ibid.*, pp. 158-162.
13. Erikson, E. H., Psychoanalysis and the Future of Education. *Psychoanal. Quart.*, 4:59-64, 1935.
14. Ferenczi, S., On Obscene Words. In: *Sex in Psychoanalysis*. New York: Basic Books, 1950.
15. Finch, S. M. & Burks, H. L., Early Psychotherapeutic Management of the School Phobia. *Post-Grad. Med.*, 27:146-147, 1960.
16a. Freud, A., The Ego and the Mechanisms of Defense (1936). *The Writings of Anna Freud*, 2:145. New York: International Universities Press, 1966.
16b. Freud, A., Psychoanalysis and the Training of the Young Child. *Psychoanal. Quart.*, 4:15-24, 1935.
17. Freud, A., *The Psychoanalytical Treatment of Children*. New York: International Universities Press, 1946.
18. Freud, S., Family Romances (1909). *Standard Edition*, 9:235-241. London: Hogarth Press, 1959.
19. Glover, E., Unconscious Functions of Education. In: *On the Early Development of Mind*. New York: International Universities Press, 1956.
20. Group for the Advancement of Psychiatry, Committee on Social Issues, *Psychiatric Aspects of School Desegregation*. New York: G.A.P., Report #37, 1957.
21. Hartmann, H., Kris, E. & Loewenstein, R. M., Comments on the Formation of Psychic Structure. *The Psychoanalytic Study of the Child*, 2:29-30. New York: International Universities Press, 1947.
22. Jackson, E. B. et al., Panel Discussion: The Use and Abuse of Psychoanalytic Concepts in Education. *Bull. Amer. Psychoanal. Assn.*, 8:226, 1952.
23. Kardiner, A., When the State Brings Up the Child. *Saturday Rev.*, 47:9-11, Aug. 26, 1961.
24. Kluckhohn, F. & Spiegel, J. P., *Integration and Conflict in Family Behavior*. Topeka, Kan.: Committee on the Family, Group for the Advancement of Psychiatry, Report #27, Aug. 1954, pp. 8-12.
25. Kris, E., On Psychoanalysis and Education. *Amer. J. Orthopsychiat.*, 18:622, 1948.
26. Linton, R., *The Tree of Culture*. New York: Alfred A. Knopf, 1955, p. 11.
27. Mahler, M. S. & Rabinovitch, R., The Effects of Marital Conflict on Child Development. In: *Neurotic Interaction in Marriage*, Ed. V. Eisenstein. New York: Basic Books, 1956, pp. 51-55.
28. Mead, M., *Male and Female*. New York: W. Morrow, 1949, p. 95.
29. Pearson, G. H. S., *Emotional Disorders of Children*. New York: Norton, 1949, pp. 113-118.
30. Pearson, G. H. S., A Survey of Learning Difficulties in Children. *The*

Psychoanalytic Study of the Child, 7:322-386. New York: International Universities Press, 1952.

31. Peller, L. E., The School's Role in Promoting Sublimation. *The Psychoanalytic Study of the Child,* 11:437-499. New York: International Universities Press, 1956.
32. Persons, R. W. & Bruning, H. L., Instrumental Learning with Sociopaths. *J. Abnorm. Psychol.,* 71:165-168, 1966.
33. Redl, F. & Wineman, D., *Children Who Hate.* Glencoe, Ill.: The Free Press, 1951.
34. Reich, W., *Character Analysis.* New York: Orgone Institute Press, 1949, p. 147.
35. Roman, M., Margolin, J. B. & Harari, C., Reading Retardation and Delinquency. *NPPA J.,* 1:107, 1955.
36. Saul, L. J., *Emotional Maturity.* Philadelphia: J. P. Lippincott, 1947, p. 19.
37. Schrager, J., Observations on the Loss of a Housemother. *Soc. Casework,* 37:120-126, 1956.
38. Soddy, K., *Mental Health and Infant Development,* Vols. 1 & 2. New York: Basic Books, 1956.
39. Watson, A. S., Book Review: *A Sign for Cain,* by F. Wertham. *J. Crim. Law, Criminol. & Police Sci.,* 58:247-248, 1967.
40. Wertham, F., *Seduction of the Innocent.* New York: Rinehart, 1954.
41. Woolf, M., The Child's Moral Development. In: *Searchlights on Delinquency,* Ed. K. R. Eissler. New York: International Universities Press, 1955, p. 271.

IX

Adolescence: The Giant Step from Childhood to Maturity

During adolescence the child becomes the adult, and the last opportunity for basic remodeling of the personality through normal growth-maturational processes is largely expended. When this period of life draws to a close, the basic structure of the personality is fixed to a considerable extent and, with but few exceptions, will change little during the balance of life.

Let us review the psychological events leading up to adolescence. We have traced the growth and development of the child from the helpless dependency of the newborn to the gangling restlessness of the 11- or 12-year-old. What has been happening during these intervening years?

The newborn, for the most part, is little more than a collection of vague, poorly circumscribed, ill-directed "instincts" which are aimed solely at satisfying his biological needs. There is no knowledge, judgment, motor skill, nor integrative capacity with which to achieve satisfaction. He must *depend* upon his environment and the persons in it for his satisfaction. We have detailed the manner in which these early need gratifications begin to structure the ego, and how automatic patterns of response are evolved in relation to these needs. We saw that the five-year-old child was capable of meeting his basic need patterns with well-integrated motor responses. He could control his inner impulses (id) reasonably well without excessive anxiety, and derive adequate pleasure. We have seen how his conscience developed and became well-structured by this age, and how the broad foundations of conscience values were laid down. For example, the five-year-old normally has a sense of justice and "trust" that justice will occur. An ability to feel guilt and responsibility for his actions is well established. Around these general attitudes, the specific shaping of his conscience takes place.

We described how most of the above events take place within the confines of the immediate home situation. With the arrival of school age, broader community attitudes impinge on the child and his personality. The emotionally healthy school child is ready, willing, and able to deal with the socializing processes of latency. His eagerness to learn is used to mold his behavior into well-integrated, socially effective patterns. During the five or six preadolescent years, huge strides are made in this socializing process. The healthy preadolescent is a well integrated, goal-directed, essentially happy individual. The main characteristics which he lacks are those of sexual maturity and social and psychological independence. The development of these is the task to be accomplished during adolescence.

In discussing the concept of psychodynamics, we have used some analogies from energy mechanics to describe it partially. Preadolescent development is predicated on a system with a more-or-less fixed quantity of available instinctual energy. In other words, the latency child has built his psychological system around a rather constant energy source, and his defenses deal with a nonfluctuating amount of aggressive and sexual energy (38). Suddenly, a momentous event occurs—pubescence.

Physical Maturation

What is pubescence? Simply stated, it is the maturation of the reproductive endocrine system (the hormone-producing sex organs, i.e., the ovaries and the testes, which are called gonads), a physiological event with far-reaching psychological and physical effects. By analogy, it is like installing a Cadillac engine in a Model-T Ford chassis—something has to give, and so it does. As you would need to change the braking and transmission systems in the car, so the personality must change to cope with the energies which pubescence unleashes. Using past knowledge and the skill derived from dealing with the Model-T, the new problem of utilizing the Cadillac's power is approached. To make this changeover is not easy, and the process causes much grinding of gears—the turmoil of adolescence.

For the first two or three years of life, there was an extremely rapid growth rate, followed by a period of gradual growth during latency. Now, at pubescence, there is again an upsurge in the growth rate, and body size increases greatly. However, there are some new variables and, for the first time, there are major qualitative differences which are sex-determined. Up to now, physical differences between boys and girls was limited largely to the genitals. Pubescence brings with it full development of the "secondary sex characteristics." In males, this includes growth of body and pubic hair, coarsening of the beard, lowering of voice pitch, and broadening of the shoulder girdle in relation to the pelvic girdle. These changes result from the effect of the male's testicular hormones (androgens) on the body. They are the hallmarks of physical masculinity, although they vary in degree in the races of Man. Secondary changes in the female bring a relative widening of the pelvic girdle, the breasts mature, and there is a general rounding of body contours. There is some body hair growth, but this is usually limited to the pubis and the armpits. These changes are controlled by the female estrogenic hormones produced by the ovaries. When these changes have occurred, the child-man is capable for the first time of fulfilling *all* of the biological functions, including procreation. This potential is signaled in females by the onset of menstruation (menarche), and in the male by nocturnal emissions of seminal fluid. Sexual maturation is complete.

Psychological Changes

An important psychological effect of the pubescent physical changes is the impact they produce on the "body image." We have noted before the ego's task of conceptualizing a picture of "the self," the "I," and during preadolescence a self-image evolved slowly. Now, as a result of body changes, the former image must be altered, re-evaluated and reconstituted. The manner in which this is carried out has much to do with subsequent social behavior, psychological effectiveness, and with some "criminal" activities.

There is a universal need to feel adequate in order to feel secure. Adequacy relates to the feeling of being able to do necessary tasks as well as most others can do them. To feel adequate, one must see oneself (the "I") as being physically and emotionally equipped to meet demands. If the energy potential unleashed by pubescence, with all of its new physical capabilities, is not systematically and effectively integrated into the self-image, confusion and anxiety result, and a compensatory maneuver is necessary to restore the ego's integrity. Much delinquent and criminal activity is related to such a compensatory process. The man who sees himself as being physically small and inferior, even though he may be larger physically than the average, can compensate for this sense of inferiority by doing "big things." The criminal who can pull "a big caper" may be able to see himself restored to equality—for a time. Unfortunately (or perhaps fortunately), in reality terms the compensating maneuver places him in greater danger and thus increases anxiety and necessitates further adjustment. This need may become the motive for the next "caper."

The same adjustment process may be manifested in various forms of sexual activity. For example, Don Juans and Casanovas are often struggling with a self-image which makes them constant prey to feelings of inadequacy. To compensate, a new sex partner nightly proves "manliness." Unfortunately, since the relationship is devoid of any love, it does not give security but instead increases anxiety. Similarly, many prostitutes try to prove their effectiveness as women, as well as their disdain for men (5). The motive of some homosexuals is to destroy the strength and power of their masculine partners, and thus devalue them in order to prove that they are as big as other men by comparison (26).

Insofar as such persons use criminal behavior as a neurotic compensation for depreciated body images, the law may unwittingly support their neuroses when it invokes its sanctions. Deterrence or rehabilitation, if it is to operate for these individuals, should deny them the use of crime as a means for becoming "big shots." To label them as neurotic "punks" would be more effective, and might force them into different channels of expression, which may be more accessible to change than is criminality (3).

Psychological Goals

What are the essential psychological problems which must be resolved during this period of life? The three principal ones, according to Erikson (6), are (1) to reconcile love and sexuality; (2) to reconcile genital orgasm and extragenital sexual needs; and (3) to reconcile sex, procreation, and work-productive patterns. Let us consider each of these separately.

As stated before, "love" is a relationship with another person in which one's concern and interest for the other is essentially on the same level as one's concern and interest for oneself. Where does this concept come into conflict with sex? When the psychosocial patterns of the 4-to-6-year-old were discussed, we mentioned sexual attraction to and interest in the parent of the opposite sex. We said this was desirable, since it provides the prototype experience for later sexual love. However, during that phase of growth and maturation, in order to manage the sexual interests and drives, the child tends to split them off from the love feelings directed toward the parents. Part of this is accomplished by sublimation (socially acceptable *diversions* of instinctual energies), and part by repression, often associated with a sense of guilt. When the endocrine stimulation of pubescence revives such sexual activity as masturbation (with its attendant fantasies) the old fears, concerns, and attitudes about sex are again forced into awareness. The individual finds himself in his former dilemma. Adolescence, with the maturing sexual drives, induces a desire for social and (ultimately) sexual relationships with persons of the opposite sex. How is this desire to be satisfied?

The adolescent's search for sexual knowledge and understanding is disturbing both to himself and to society. While he has little "official" sanction for his search, we are all well aware of the fact that sexual experimentation is commonplace (33). Kinsey's studies force us to accept once and for all the fact that all individuals carry on some form of sexual experimentation (16, 18). However, since this activity must be carried on without open social acceptance, it is fraught with conflict and guilt. To evaluate properly a specific individual's sexual behavior, we must understand the general nature of the sex learning process. In our culture(s), it appears terribly easy to misapprehend and overreact to the sexual activity which occurs during adolescence. Let us review the nature of these experiments and explorations.

Generally, the adolescent's initial learning about sex takes place with members of his own sex. In his peer group, it is possible to find *some* answer for the perplexing questions about sex and, all too often, better and more accurate information is not available elsewhere. Groups of boys debate and discuss the still mysterious matters of sexuality. Their activities may include masturbatory "games" and sexual acts of a "homosexual" nature. However, to regard this as pathological homosexuality is erroneous, and to treat it as such is nothing short of catastrophic for the individuals involved, since this is a common introduction to sex among young males in our society. Such experiences lead to knowledge, desire, and the ability to shift to heterosexual orientation.

Another form of sexual exploration common at this age is reading pornography. This form of sex information is often all that is available and is a substitute for "the real thing." One can speculate that so long as a society hides and denies its sexual activities from the young, the need to read and study pornography will remain. Probably the intense reactions of many adults toward this type of material is related to their own guilty interest and experimentation with it during youth. The question is asked whether this material has any potential danger or degrading effect to the individuals who read it. It seems likely that, if normal maturational potential exists in an adolescent, he will largely "outgrow" his interest in pornographic literature, since it will prove less than satisfying. We must remember that the more infantile an activity is, the less satisfying it is as an ultimate outlet to an adult, *provided* there is opportunity for a more mature form of gratification (22). Stimulation by visual or fantasy means is only a forerunner to genital activity. When more mature sexual relationships and outlets are available, these forms of stimulation have only passing interest.

There has been much discussion about the possible dangers of pornography producing criminal sexual activity. While there have been statements that such reading does produce criminal or immoral activity (36, 37), there appears to be little concrete evidence that this is so. In fact, it would appear that delinquents have, as a group, a very marked reading disability which would tend to lessen their interest in reading of any sort. They may look at "filthy pictures," but they most certainly will not tackle Joyce's *Ulysses* or Lawrence's *Lady Chatterley's Lover* (25). While there may be conceivably some correlation between reading some types of "comics" and various criminal acts, it appears unlikely that this is a cause-effect relationship. For the reasons given above, it would seem unwise to over-react to adolescents who are found to possess these materials. While it is highly desirable to keep pornographic materials from children in the latency period, adolescents are able to deal with these matters themselves if they have reached appropriate maturity, and therefore it seems wise to place control standards on a liberal basis. As Learned Hand said in *U. S. v. Kennerley* (209 F.2d 119, 121 [1913]): "To put thought in leash to the average conscience of the time is perhaps tolerable, but to fetter it by the necessities of the lowest and least capable seems a fatal policy." It is safe to say that those individuals who continue to manifest an inordinate amount of interest in pornographic literature, are manifesting a symptom of immaturity.

After his tentative, roundabout explorations into sexuality, the adolescent is ready to move toward heterosexual relationships and dating begins. Ideally, this should be motivated by the adolescent's own desires to meet and relate to members of the opposite sex. Social pressures often prematurely urge activities with which the individual is not ready to cope. Today, one has the impression that dating activities begin at an earlier age than that which represents true sexual maturity. These first dates normally arouse anxieties about adequacy, acceptability, and competency, and necessitate revision of the self-image to include concepts of sexual maturity and such adult sexual roles as husband, wife, mother or father. This larger and more demanding role concept must be integrated into his identity if successful maturation is to continue.

Because adolescent sexual relationships arouse the once forbidden childhood sexual wishes, much of the guilt and shame which surrounded these childhood desires is also re-aroused. This may result in the old need to separate love from sex—love and sex may not share the same bed. This is a common problem of men and women who can only enjoy sensuality with a person toward whom they feel no love or tenderness. The need to keep feelings of love and sex separate is markedly influenced by the manner in which sexual explorations are carried out. If sexual integration is successful, by the time the adolescent reaches maturity and is ready for marriage, sexual pleasure, love, and tenderness should be compatible.

The second problem to be resolved relates to the developmental shift of emphasis in the sites of sensory pleasure. The newborn child tends to get pleasure from the mouth through sucking. Also, in a totally passive manner, he "takes in" pleasant sounds, sights, and skin sensations, and utilizes these for part of his instinctual gratification. With growth, he gains pleasure through mastering muscular control, and through increased motility. Still later, pleasure is derived through genital masturbation. Now, in adolescence, powerful heterosexual desire arises. How are these varied sources of pleasure synthesized and integrated into adult sexuality?

We saw that, at each step of this psychosexual development, certain frustrating influences occurred. They resulted in anger, hostility, and aggression which were dealt with by repression and a sense of guilt.[1] Sensory pleasures which were blocked (e.g., sucking is frustrated by weaning) were coupled with a sense of guilt. Any subsequent stimulation of these pleasure sources arouses guilt, are perceived as forbidden, and the tendency is to block them from awareness. Yet in the process of courtship and love making, normal, biological reactions bring forth these originally infantile expressions. Most courtships begin with a pleasure-producing glance ("love at first sight"). Next may come pleasure-producing touching contacts. Finally, under appropriate circumstances, this will culminate in a mutually satisfying object-love relationship with genital orgasm. In other words, the love act of adults, with its normal sexual foreplay and forepleasure, goes through all the stages of the development of sensory pleasure characteristic of individual growth and development. (Biologically speaking, this is not unlike the concept that "Ontogeny recapitulates phylogeny": the development of the individual repeats the development of the race.)

What happens when some of these part-pleasures (technically "partial instincts") are surrounded with excessive guilt or shame? Can they be cancelled out or eliminated? Parents often believe that, if infantile sensual impulses are severely enough criticized and prohibited, they will, in fact, be eliminated. This is *not true;* the

---

[1] For a description of the various ways in which hostility may be handled, see Chapter 5 in Leon J. Saul's *The Hostile Mind* (27).

result is rather to magnify and emphasize the conflict around them. This means that when there is a possibility for expressing such feelings, severe conscience prohibitions necessitate that they be excluded from action, so that displacement takes place. Instead of pleasure being associated with the loved partner, guilt is aroused and perhaps a secret resentment for the imagined deprivation (2). It is frequent in such circumstances for the person to be convinced that the partner "wouldn't like" the foreplay activity. More often than not this is a projection of conscience, and there is surprise at the discovery of interest and pleasure capacity in the partner, once the initial qualms are overcome. The many marriage manuals stress these facts.[2]

When there is a failure to work out these unexpressed wishes, and when there is pent-up frustration and anger and guilt around them, it can only result in a loss of sexual freedom. The sexual relationship becomes strained and unsatisfying, and the impulse to seek satisfaction elsewhere arises. Will such alternative outlets resolve the tension? Not likely, since conscience goes along. Mounting anxiety can necessitate some alternative outlet, and this pressure may cause some of the "sex crimes" (39). For example, the male who enjoys looking at nude women may be ashamed of his impulse and may fear acknowledging it with his wife or sweetheart. As anxiety mounts, he may ultimately need to do some "peeping," and one day "Tom" will be caught in the act of satisfying his desire to look. To eliminate this problem, he must eliminate the cause of his fear so that an easier and more legitimate outlet may be had. He could even go to a burlesque show; at least that would not be unlawful. The existence in many people of a deep and continued wish to look, seems to be corroborated by the widespread use of advertisements with men and women in various stages of undress. Such techniques are used because they are useful; they answer a need in the observer. Such ads would have little appeal to the Balinese, where the body is freely exposed and the impulse to look is amply satisfied.

When these partial instincts are integrated appropriately, they become part of the pleasure-giving foreplay of the normal sex act. It might be well to note that, although all authorities regard such

2 For a good example, see: Van de Velde, *The Ideal Marriage* (32).

activities as normal (17), they are heavily stigmatized by social mores, and even come under the sanction of the law in many jurisdictions. This disparity between social attitude and biological fact can only result in greater emotional confusion, and in the end, serves no useful social purpose. In fact, one occasional result is a form of legal "blackmail" when such matters are brought up during divorce litigation.

It is interesting to note that even while we call these normal sensual derivatives "childish" or "infantile," there is the connotation of disapproval. To accurately describe their psychological appropriateness necessitates much verbal elaboration. We have no English words, apparently, to denote "activity, appropriate in adults under certain circumstances, which arose in childhood." This surely represents a negative cultural attitude. In German, this matter is readily handled with the words *kindisch*, meaning inappropriate childishness, and *kindlich*, denoting the appropriate (21).

The third major task of adolescence is to bring into a balanced, harmonious relationship the patterns of sexual need, procreative functions, and work-productive demands. It has been said that civilization and culture "advance" in proportion to the degree to which the members of the society succeed in redirecting and sublimating instinctual energy (13, 15, 30). In other words, energy which once would have been aimed directly toward impulse gratification must be redirected toward a more socially useful goal. This means that, to some degree, there will be instinctual frustration. To illustrate: A caged animal, which is regularly fed to satiety, does not develop much skill in exploring its environment. However, the same animal, unfed for a time, driven by hunger, is motivated to explore its surroundings fully. It is forced to extend its horizon of comprehension. If it is frustrated too long, however, confusion and/or lethargy appear and the learning process ceases. Humans react in a similar manner. To achieve adult effectiveness and productiveness, there must be some frustration of instinctual drives. Adulthood requires the assumption of the parental role of mainly "giving," and this must become a pleasure-producing role. Such a change takes one far from the passive-receptive-dependent gratifications of childhood. How are these changes effected? How is this all-important shift brought about, emotionally and culturally?

Means of Achieving the Goals of Adolescence

As outlined in Chapter III, the most effective learning stems from direct experience. It is the sign of a healthy ego for a person to carry on a continuous process of intelligent experimentation. The latency child slowly and methodically stores up experience and knowledge. Much of this learning, however, is within a relatively dependent situation, in which the direction and nature of learning are closely controlled from without. With the advent of pubescence, this trend is markedly affected by a more powerful striving toward self-sufficiency and independence. There is a strong wish for self-determination in behavior, and it is no longer felt desirable for direction to come mainly from outside the self. How does this change in behavior manifest itself?

Many persons have said that adolescent behavior, seen at any other time of life, would be evidence of psychosis. This observation alludes to the tempestuous swings in behavior and attitude which the adolescent exhibits. One day he is an idealist and the next an out-and-out antisocial rebel. How can a "normal" person show such wide vacillation of behavior? It simply reflects a grand experiment directed toward producing an answer to the question: "What kind of person am I?" What factors effect the nature of each person's adolescent experimentation? How should we regard these experiments from the social standpoint, and what should be allowed and disallowed in regard to them? The answers to these questions are of great moment to law as it relates to this age group.

When the resolution of the oedipal conflict was discussed, we said that the manner in which that resolution was achieved would later be used as a template for the adolescent experimentation. In other words, when the stress of the pubertal changes are felt, the maturing child resorts to techniques used "successfully" before. However, this technique is a two-edged sword. What worked well in the family may be totally inappropriate for other relationships since other people are different. This seemingly obvious fact, if it goes unnoticed, can result in a failure to solve the problems of adolescence. The ability to see people as they really are is a critical skill to learn. All persons are *not* replicas of parents, to be responded to and treated in the same way. However, we may say that to fall back on "prototype" procedures as an initial effort makes for an economical beginning.

During adolescence the child has available for the first time the advantages of wide access to new persons, new situations, and new frames of reference. If the reality-testing function of his ego has been reasonably well developed, failure patterns can be dropped and new techniques, as well as old, can be continually re-evaluated.

Another technique the adolescent initially utilizes to avoid some of the stress created by the new sexual energy is to attempt a psychological retreat—i.e., deny any interest in persons of the opposite sex. Much of his social activity is carried on with members of his own sex, and results in some of the "crushes" and friendships which young people experience. In these intimate associations, there is much "boy and girl talk" of an exploratory nature, which lays the groundwork for the first dating ventures. It is important to appreciate the nature of adolescent "homosexual" orientation, because occasionally it results in overt homosexual behavior. Moral pressures or sanction of the law serve no useful social purpose and may be permanently injurious. Such punitive treatment may assure, once and for all, that no further advance toward socially desirable heterosexual relationships will be made.

We may see a good example of a young man with such a problem, if we refer again to the character of Brick in Tennessee Williams's play, *Cat on a Hot Tin Roof*. The somewhat immature Brick has a very intimate "buddy-buddy" relationship with an old college football team-mate. Their closeness arouses the jealousy of Brick's wife. She suspects and accuses the two of being homosexuals. Although she has ample grounds for complaint in her marriage, her accusation is untrue. However, massive guilt over the latent homosexual feelings was aroused, and the result was a lasting disability for Brick, to the detriment of the marriage.[3] During early struggles with feelings about masculinity, he had utilized the commonplace means of coping by turning to a "buddy" relationship. His wife's accusation afforded him the defense of "righteous" martyrdom, and this permitted him to avoid his real inner problems involving fear of masculine competition with his father.

[3] By this we mean that Brick used pseudo masculinity to cover up his wish to surrender to his fearsome father and thus *not* be a male competitor. It is the identification with the aggressor which results in open homosexuality in some boys.

After an adolescent has gained enough "courage" and knowhow to make a start, dating begins. At times, this dating is associated with peer group prestige, since there may be no group status until dating (and at times even sexual experimentation) has begun. This provides an artificial cultural stimulus to behave in a manner which is, as yet, without a purely biological basis. (It is the psychological equivalent of "sending a boy to do a man's work," and there will be little likelihood of success.) Once the dating pattern has been established, the well-adjusted adolescent's social life centers around heterosexual social activities. This does not exclude participation in sports, hobbies, and "homosexual" peer groups such as clubs, fraternities, and sororities continue to flourish.

Another characteristic of adolescent behavior which frequently and forcibly comes to our attention is that of group activity. It is a rare day without a news item describing some "juvenile gang war," "youthful hoodlumism," or some other form of delinquent juvenile group activity. From the pinnacle of our place in the adult world, there is a strong inclination to look on this "herd" activity as grossly abnormal. Such a judgment disregards the universal need of adolescents to have group activities as a setting from which to work out new and potentially more mature social relationships (24). It is a time when there is a normal tendency to move away from the patterns, activities, and values of the family and to test and experiment with new techniques for living. Normal children do not undertake this frightening experiment alone. They turn to age-mates and others who can satisfy their powerful psychological need for support and empathic understanding. In a neighborhood where the only group activities to be found are gangs with an antisocial bent, they have little choice but to ally themselves with such groups (29). It would almost be a sign of abnormality if they did otherwise. In neighborhoods with more secure social and economic status, these same groups are known as clubs or fraternities, or they reflect some hobby orientation. The type of group that an adolescent joins is more often than not purely a function of availability. Whatever the group represents, the adolescent member uses it to gain the security he needs to develop his own concepts, images, and ideas about himself. Without such an opportunity, psychological isolation and withdrawal are likely to occur. All societies, taking advantage of the psychological needs of this stage of development, inculcate in the young the ideologies and characteristics which the group deems important to its survival. Thus, we find organizations such as churches, Y.M.C.A.'s, Boy Scouts, and a multitude of others making their greatest efforts with this age group.

In recognition of the importance of this period of development and of its strong impact on each individual's subsequent social adjustment, it is dealt with culturally through a variety of initiation rites (7). In addition to their symbolic meanings, these rites always mark the child's entrance into the group as a full-fledged adult member. Often, they deal with the idea of sexual maturity and, in primitive societies, may be accompanied by ritual circumcision or defloration. After the ceremony, the initiate not only is permitted to function as an adult, but is expected to do so. Although some of these ceremonies may seem cruel, they may be less so than our adolescents' painful, groping search for acceptable adult behavior standards. The sharply defined, readily tangible roles which primitive societies introduce ritually, provide security and support for their adolescent members. Both solutions are directed to the same problem. Although we are not inclined to utilize primitive techniques, clinical psychiatric experience confirms that our young people have serious difficulty in finding their adult identities, and a large number fail entirely in this effort. That failure creates a multitude of social and medical problems.

Each young member of every social group, endeavors to take out of the past those significant attitudes and ideas which he can build into his own character and take as his own standard. "Ideologies seem to provide meaningful combinations of the oldest and the newest in a group's ideals. They thus channel the forceful earnestness, the sincere asceticism, and the eager indignation of youth toward that social frontier where the struggle between conservatism and radicalism is most alive. On that frontier, fanatic ideologists do their busy work and psychopathic leaders their dirty work; but there, also, true leaders create significant solidarities" (9).[4]

As adolescent experimentation proceeds, a strong personal drive

[4] *Time Magazine* recently published a journalistic analysis of contemporary adolescence in the United States. It presents quite an interesting and balanced account of how middle-class American adolescents are experimenting with and establishing their value systems and aims in life (31).

for real independence develops. When successful, this sense of free-dom becomes associated with the group from which the strength to experiment was derived. The individual learns to "belong" to the group and to evaluate simultaneously his feelings toward that group in a critical, objective way. Successful adolescents see themselves as an integral part of their group, with the right, and even the responsi-bility, for each to be an individual unto himself.

POTENTIAL BARRIERS TO SUCCESSFUL MATURATION

Side by side with the adolescent's growing sense of independence is the ever-present and disquieting sensation that it would be better to remain a child, dependent upon the group's leaders and the par-ents. The task of functioning independently seems an impossible and dangerous one. Hence, each person harbors a hidden wish and a variable potential for returning to his dependent relationships of the past. In well-adjusted and well-integrated persons, the wish never becomes dominant, but may be reflected in exploitation of situations where dependency is not only permissible, but highly gratifying. There are also many adults who, because of marked inner fear of this wish, need to overextend themselves in the direction of independence, and cannot permit any indulgence of dependency whatever. To avoid the anxiety elicited by their dependent longings, they need to participate in activities which reassure them of their strength and independence. Much of the criminal's sarcastic and derisive sneering that the law-abiding citizen is "chicken" or "a sucker" reflects his almost desperate effort to cover up his own feelings of vulnerability and weakness.

Delinquent and criminal behavior may be motivated by de-pendency needs. Wattenberg et al. describe a group of young auto thieves. Most of the boys came from middle-class families, tended to be physically larger than their age-mates, and seemed to feel considerable anxiety and uneasiness about their size. One could speculate that this forced them to "act" more maturely than they were capable of being. Their protest took the form of wanton anti-social behavior, and they usually referred to other boys of their age as "a bunch of babies" (35). Society, in dealing with such individu-als through the law, might well utilize this motivational conflict to force a change in their identity patterns. Punitive measures may well result in further rebellion. This is the point at which we must learn to disarm these individuals of their antisocial defense against their regressive wishes (19).

One of the characteristics of the adolescent period, is the frequent shifting of identification patterns and the great variety of heroes and heroines which are chosen for emulation. Much emotion is invested in these identifications, and they often have a strong romantic flavor. Whatever their character, they always represent the groping, trial-and-error search for identity. Many adults, forgetting their own youth, are greatly disturbed by this inconsistent behavior, and they feel certain it can lead only to difficulty. This is not the case and, in fact, too much interference with this searching process may result in pathology—intrapsychic retreat or delinquent acting-out behavior. These are important considerations in dealing with adolescent offenders.

Occasionally, in some social and economic settings, well-known criminals are used as models for identification. If they are the only available persons of prestige in that setting, the choice is almost inevitable and *necessary*. We cannot eliminate the emulative process; we can *only* provide the possibility of a better choice of persons to emulate. This is a critical diagnostic problem, and a mistake here may cause the young mimic permanently to identify himself with crime. The question of whether or not the offender should be publicly acknowledged and identified is related to the motive of the criminal act. If it was in the service of a search for identity, publicity might well solidify the criminal identifications. If the criminal character is well established, however, then full acknowledgment, which serves notice on the ego that "you can't get away with it," may have a salutary effect. This is a matter that ideally should *not* be handled on a blanket-rule basis. There is probably no other age group where individualization of laws and law enforcement is so important.[5] To play unwittingly into some neurotic defense maneuver, which would tend to distort the person's social behavior permanently, certainly runs counter to all of the goals of the law (34).

[5] For an excellent discussion of juvenile court legal problems which soundly utilizes psychological principles, see Paulsen's, "Fairness to the Juvenile Offender" (23).

IDENTITY: A SENSE OF SELF-VALUE

If an adolescent is successful in his development, the reconciliation of love, sex, orgasm, extragenital sensory needs, procreation, and work are effected, and a real sense of identity exists. The concept of identity encompasses these reconciliations. Erikson states, "The final identity, then, as fixed at the end of adolescence is superordinated to any single identification with individuals of the past: it includes all significant identifications, but it also alters them in order to make a unique and reasonably coherent whole of them" (10). From this a "new" person evolves with a "self" which is unique.

Included in this identity is a firm and appropriate conviction of sexual role. The young man should be committed to a primarily "phallic-aggressive" orientation (8). He should be able to "push out into" his environment constructively with comfort and pleasure, and without much sense of conflict. The young woman should be able to enjoy a state of "oral receptiveness" sufficiently to make her sexual role satisfying, and yet be aggressive enough to seek a mate and acquire the things she needs for happiness. Both of these sexual roles should be modulated to the primarily "giving" orientation of the adult—i.e., the adult's ability to enjoy giving, versus the child's need to receive. Thus, in the young adult, there is a solid psychological basis for the Biblical admonition that "it is better to give than receive." *Both*—giving and receiving—are pleasurable and gratifying.

It has been noted that the primary emphasis in masculinity is "activity," while in femininity it is "passivity." We must realize, however, that active and passive traits are common to both sexes and must be melded comfortably. This is expressed in the ancient Chinese symbol of Yang and Yin. This symbol, a circle internally divided in half by an S-curve, represents, among other things, the coexistence of active and passive, male and female traits within the personality (20). Robert Anderson's play, "Tea and Sympathy" sensitively portrays an adolescent's struggle to reconcile these traits in the context of masculine identity (1). The young man's problem lay in the difficulty posed by social pressures which attempted to force him into a particular masculine stereotype. In his peer group, "masculinity" seemed strictly limited to being the rugged athletic type. His interest in music and literature was regarded as "queer," and jeopardized his status. This sharp definition of qualities as "male" or "female" placed him in deep conflict, since many of his interests fell into what the group defined as feminine. The author also skillfully portrays the defensive quality of pseudo masculinity in some of the male characters. In order to hide from their much-feared passive and (by their own constructive definition) feminine wishes, they *had* to be aggressive and could not express any passivity whatsoever. Thus, some of the adult men in the play were really only chronic adolescents with "boy-scout" superegos and unintegrated ego identities. In many ways, these men were in more desperate straits than the principal character. They suffered from a failure to achieve a well-integrated sense of ego identity, or "role diffusion" (7).

An excellent description of a young girl's growing awareness of herself as a woman may be seen in the poignant and moving tale of Anne Frank: *The Diary of a Young Girl* (14). Here one sees how successful maturing occurs even in desperately trying emotional circumstances. This young Jewish girl, hiding away in a warehouse loft from German occupation forces, describes with penetrating insight her experiences and experiments with approaching womanhood, how she felt toward her family, and how she began to see them from an adult's vantage-point. She describes her sexual feelings and her fantasies about love and marriage. She began to imagine herself in the role of a professional person, and was well on her way toward implementing this desired role, with real skills and training. One gets a strong impression that, during the time encompassed by the diary, she actually accomplished these goals insofar as her age and the circumstances permitted. The reader has a deep feeling of loss when he realizes that this talented young lady "disappeared" into one of the German concentration camps during the Nazis' determined effort to destroy the "identity" of the Jew.

Examples of identity "failure," or what Erikson has called "identity diffusion" are manifold. The student who becomes what is colloquially called a "grind," tries to gain a sense of identity through the exclusive emphasis of scholarship. But this is only one of the adult roles which must be achieved. It is not inappropriate to invest a great deal of energy and attention in study and training at this time of life. In fact, *not* to work hard enough for a vocational goal is often evidence of neurotic conflict. In a healthy identity-acquiring process, work patterns, as all other skills will be *integrated* with the other identity goals.

The group of adolescents who utilize a delinquent or criminal identity is of special interest to lawyers (28). One of the crucial problems in dealing with adolescent delinquents is to diagnose *correctly* the psychological nature of the criminal activity. To achieve *some* identity is an absolute necessity without which the ego is thrown into great jeopardy and excessive anxiety is produced. This anxiety *must* be dealt with by acquiring some identity or identification. The chosen identity may be antisocial in nature. It is not unusual or necessarily pathological for adolescents to toy with some "criminal" activity, but it is imperative that society not *assist* in the choice of a negative identity. To quote Erikson again:

> The adolescent's leaning out over any number of precipices is normally an experimentation with experiences which are thus becoming more amenable to ego control, provided they can be somehow communicated to other adolescents in one of those strange codes established for just such experiences—*and provided they are not prematurely responded to with fatal seriousness by overeager or neurotic adults.*[6] The same must be said of the adolescent's "fluidity of defenses," which so often causes raised eyebrows on the part of the worried clinician. Much of this fluidity is anything but pathological; for adolescence is a crisis in which only fluid defense can overcome a sense of victimization by inner and outer demands, and in which only trial and error can lead to the most felicitous avenues of action and self-expression [11].

Discussing the same question, Bromberg points out that criminality is a "creative" effort to establish self-esteem (4). He suggests that if our knowledge of this fact were used educatively in television and other mass communications media, it might be possible to devalue crime as a "creative" outlet for identification, and thus force the search for self-esteem into more socially constructive channels (3). He notes that such use of communication media for changing underlying attitudes has been effective for other social problems such as venereal disease.

[6] Italics added.

To summarize the adolescent's goals, then, we may say that:

Man, to take his place in society must acquire a "conflict-free," habitual use of a dominant *faculty*, to be elaborated in an *occupation;* a limitless *resource*, a feedback as it were, from the immediate *exercise* of this occupation, from the *companionship* it provides, and from its *tradition;* and, finally, an intelligible *theory* of the processes of life which the old atheist [referring to George Bernard Shaw], eager to shock to the last, calls a religion [12].

PROBLEMS

Example

The widowed mother of a nineteen-year-old boy comes into your office in an acute state of distress. She has just heard from the Dean of Men at her son's college that he was arrested on a charge of burglary. She "cannot understand" why "Pete" committed this act, because she "gave him everything he wanted." Apparently, when the police arrested him and searched his apartment (he had been living alone recently, although she tells you he moved in and out of her house three times during the past two years), they found many items stolen in prior robberies to which he confessed. Some of these items he used in his apartment, while others were stacked around carelessly. The mother went to his apartment after his arrest (he is now out on bail) and he could give no explanation for his behavior. In fact, any effort on her part to find out made him surly and silent. She is very upset by these events and pleads with you to help with her son's problem. "He's all I have that matters in this world." Although you do not do much criminal work, you agree to take the case because she came to you through an old friend of your family's.

After checking with the police regarding the charges against him, you call Peter in for an interview. His mother drives him to the office but waits for him outside in the car (she has "some shopping to do"). He did not drive himself because he lost his driver's license following an accident for which he was charged with careless and reckless driving. He appears for his appointment neatly and conservatively dressed, looking much like the Ivy Leaguer, which he is not. He seats himself in a very proper manner, asks if he may smoke, and then leans back in a most comfortable way, making it clear that he leaves the initiative for the interview to you. He readily admits the alleged crimes and says he is surprised at not having been caught earlier, since he has been "doing this sort of thing for the past three years." What are you going to do to prepare to represent the boy as his lawyer? What more will you want to know about him before you proceed? What strategy do you intend to follow for handling the case, and how will you implement it?

First, Peter's motive for committing these acts must be established. Until you know this, there can be no logical work on the case beyond mechanical preparation and responding to the moves of the Prosecutor. We want to take the initiative and *personalize* the defense to reflect Peter's interests and needs. (This does not imply such needs will be at odds with the law.) We are interested, at least, in his *mens rea* (and when sentence is approached, information about his motivation will not only be useful for Peter, but crucial to the court's decision).

Since Peter's mother is in the vicinity, counsel may have her come in to discuss matters in the presence of the boy. (He will have noted the somewhat "strange" situation in which the mother brings the boy to the meeting, but at the same time, is not present except in spirit.) Peter could easily have come by public transportation, but he did not. Why? What is the meaning of the moves in and out of his mother's house during the past few years? In short, what is the relationship between Peter and his mother? The best evidence in relation to these questions may be gained by means of a joint interview. In addition to their words, it may provide important emotional and behavioral cues which demonstrate what really lies between them.

Counsel's suggestion to have his mother come in for part of the interview elicits a very visible but fleeting fear reaction in Peter. (His eyes widen and even dilate, and he becomes very restless. He asks, "Why?" in a weak and croaky voice.) Immediately following this reaction, he becomes very annoyed and slightly flushed. He says that he does not see why she should come in: "After all, I've done enough to hurt her already. There's no reason why she should be subjected to more pain, is there?" With some pressure, he acquiesces, and you have the feeling that he wants to have her there.

While the boy is out looking for his mother, counsel should be wondering about the meaning of his reactions. What is he afraid of? Why did he get angry at the suggestion of bringing his mother in? Why was there a sense of relief when it was settled that she was coming? All of these apparently disparate pieces must be fitted together with the considerable data yet to come, into a *single*, all-encompassing explanation for his behavior. While we know that he may have several contradictory motives, we must put them all together into a logical *psychological* formulation. Peter's reactions, his words, as well as his "explanations" of them, must fit together.

When the boy returns after about fifteen minutes, it is clear that the behavior of both Peter and his mother, is different than it had been when you saw each of them alone. They seem shy and uneasy like a pair of timid young lovers. There is no more vigorous protest from mother, and Peter seems less poised. You open by asking the mother what she thinks has caused her son to behave *criminally*. (This word is deliberately chosen to put pressure on them both in order to reveal the underlying relationship between them. You know your remark will make them at least slightly angry, but you also want to see how they will handle their anger between them. In short, you send out a kind of emotional scouting party to obtain *direct* information about how they react in relation to one of the cardinal emotions—hostility. Peter, in fact, has been *acting* with hostility toward his victims, and probably toward his mother too, since he caused her to suffer because of his behavior.)

The mother's first response is to say in a soft and too sympathetic voice: "My son isn't a criminal. He may have done these things but he isn't a criminal." The rejoiner to this is (still keeping the heat on), "But doing these things in fact *makes* him a criminal, once the court decides he did them [and he did confess]. How can you say that?" Her answer is, "Oh you know what I mean. He's not a bad boy."

When you glance over at Peter, somewhat to your surprise, he does not appear very happy about his mother's comment and attitude. So, you ask intuitively, "What do you say about that, Pete?" His mildly irritated answer is, "I wish my mother wouldn't say things like that. So far as the judge is concerned, I will be a criminal." You pick up the lead again and reply, "you sound a bit irritated." Peter's retort is, "Well, I am. *She never takes me seriously.*" Now you have really struck pay dirt. Very significant elements of the relationship are coming to light, because *you* know that this is a serious matter and the court will see it so, even if the mother doesn't. In fact, in this situation, the mother will ultimately *have to take Peter's behavior seriously.* Now we may have a substantial cue of why Peter committed the burglaries. Recalling that all behavior is purposive, we should ask ourselves at this point if he might not have committed these acts in order to *make* his mother take him seriously.

Since we still know very little about the background of Peter and his mother, it is a perfect time to say rather quietly (in a very different tone from the "hostile" pressure of the earlier foray), "I don't know very much about you people. Why doesn't one of you tell me something about the way things have been between you at home." (Again, note the non-directive nature of the question. It forces them to take the initiative and *demonstrate* what the relationship is like, rather than to tell what they think it is like. They will inevitably do the latter anyhow, thus enabling you to compare what they *say* it is like with what it *is* like from what you've seen. This is making use of the transference again.)

Peter seems about to speak, but before he can get started, his mother takes the matter in hand with, "Why don't I start. After all I've seen more of it than you have, Pete." While this is perfectly true at one level of significance, it also demonstrates that she feels her presentation to be the more important—very close to Peter's allegation that his mother does not take him seriously.

Perhaps, at this point, the reader is beginning to feel that it is all well and good for a psychoanalyst or a psychiatrist to draw inferences like these, but is it not a bit dangerous for a "mere" lawyer to do so? My answer to this question is that mere lawyers, and everyone else for that matter, *will* draw precisely the same conclusions, but without necessarily being aware that they are doing so. They might notice only a vague, puzzling feeling (especially if they were "lawyer-type" men) of dislike for the mother. They would then probably devote considerable energy to keeping their "neutrality," and thus would miss the whole point in the mother-son relationship. I would emphatically and unequivocally state that lawyers can and should learn to become aware of interpersonal psychological undercurrents. It is crucial if they are to understand and accomplish what they seek for their clients.

If you as counsel have picked up any or all of these cues from Peter and his mother, you might now properly decide that there is much likelihood that important psychological factors are causing this boy's criminal behavior. Since you will not likely have them well enough in hand to plan your strategy, it is a good point at which to seek a consultation with a psychiatrist, clinical psychologist, or social worker.[7] You must then raise the matter with your clients, using the ideas you have derived during the interview to explain and justify your intention. (In the vast majority of cases, clients will not object if you explain your reasons. After all, they already "know" that there is something wrong themselves. They have had to live with the consequences of their problems! Now they even have a rationalization to buffer the matter some—seeing a psychiatrist in order to help counsel.)

Although your question about the family situation was answered in more detail the same material came up with the psychiatrist and was included in his report. He noted that, following the death of Peter's father when the boy was six, the mother spent a fair amount of time working, in order to supplement the rather small estate left by her husband. However, she had been fully aware of the child's needs, and she

---

[7] For full discussion of this matter, see Chapter XI.

had always sacrificed income and, indeed, her own pleasure to the things which she "knew a boy needed." She emphasized how it was "rather difficult to be both father and mother to a growing son." The consultant noted that she was still a very attractive woman, and inquired if she had ever given any thought to remarriage? This brought forth the very interesting observations by her that, in fact, she had almost married a couple of times. Peter had kicked up such a fuss about the prospects of "going somewhere else to live," that she had put the marriage off. Then, rather sadly, she stated: "I guess I put it off too long, and the men got tired of waiting."

During most of the years, and until Peter was nearly ready to go to college, they "got along very well together and were very happy." It was only then that they began to have arguments (always conducted in a low emotional key). They generally started with his complaints that she never let him make up his own mind about things and was always arranging things so "they would turn out for his own good." Peter had remarked to the psychiatrist, "after a while you wish you could make a few mistakes as long as you did it on your own."

The consultant concluded that in his opinion the burglaries had the following significance: (1) They had the underlying and unconscious purpose of forcibly getting out from under his mother's influence. (Needless to say, Peter also wished for his mother's full attention, but put the wish aside in order to avoid frustration. If he surrendered to his mother's unwitting pampering, he would lose all of his masculine initiative.) (2) They were also a means for getting even with her for depriving him of the opportunities to learn masculine independence (by being so nice to him and making him "want" to stay). Thus he sought to make her feel bad, ashamed, and guilty, for the way he has turned out. (This is a hostile gesture toward her. It was this impulse that he feared when counsel proposed seeing them together. It was bound to come out if the matter was explored.) (3) It was a self-punishing maneuver, to make up for his hostility toward his mother as well as his forbidden oedipal desire to keep her all to himself. (He *had* gotten away with driving off her suitors. Of course, as a child, he could not know that it is a mother's "duty" to resist her son's seductive efforts and to go ahead and have her man. To properly understand the relationship in its full perspective, we should also like to know why the mother did *not* act on her own desire to remarry. It probably reflects some conflict she had with her late husband, something from her own childhood, or more likely both. No effort was made to ascertain this since it was deemed irrelevant at the time.)

The psychiatrist, after setting out these explanations for Peter's behavior, and the historical and interview material to back up his hypotheses, suggested that Peter (and perhaps his mother too) should have some kind of therapy to enable *him* to come to understand the reasons for his behavior. He noted that he thought the boy would be quite responsive to such treatment. He felt reasonably sure that if Peter were under a probation order which required treatment, there would be little likelihood of further burglaries. He also stated that the boy should not be permitted to live at home with his mother under any circumstances so long as the present problem existed between them. He went on to say that, perhaps as treatment progressed, this proscription could be removed.

Armed with the psychiatric report and your own impressions of the case, you decide to recommend a plea of guilty to the charges, and to put the psychiatrist on the stand to testify in relation to sentencing. You decide to argue for a suspended sentence and probation, one of the terms of probation to be treatment. (Peter and his mother are both eager to cooperate, not only to avoid a jail sentence, but because they have caught a glimpse of some of their problems in the course of their consultations—a good prognostic sign in itself.) The judge is pleased to follow your recommendations for "this nice family."

This case clearly involves a middle-class family, which the lawyer, psychiatrist, and the judge alike can relate to easily, since they come from approximately the same backgrounds. It is to be hoped that counsel and other participants in the case will not forget that the same kinds of problems exist in poor families as well, even though they may appear different. Unfortunately, they do not often walk into lawyers' offices. Perhaps by seeing and understanding the dynamics in cases such as Peter's, lawyers will become more venturesome in the application of psychological principles to the poor and disadvantaged members of society, who need the help quite as badly.

1. What is the central developmental problem which adolescents must solve to gain maturity? How does this affect the question of treatment of the adolescent offender?

2. On page 25 of *The Philadelphia Inquirer* for July 18, 1956, there is an article captioned "Brigade Cadet Corps Lists 2000 Boys and Girls in Ranks." It describes an organization set up along military lines in a very poor Negro slum. Members used surplus U.S. Army uniforms and equipment. "Enlistment" seemed to have been spontaneous and enthusiastic. Training consisted of military drill instructions, and the corps even boasted its own Military Police Unit. The unit's goal, as stated by its organizer, was "to encourage citizenship and character building through military training." The unit was brought to official attention when one of

its leaders was arrested for passing a bad check (very small, a typical transient overdraft. A middle-class white person in the same circumstances would have been requested to "please make up the balance" in a polite letter). Needless to say, this organization created considerable concern in the minds of the police and juvenile authorities.

  (a) How do you understand this episode of a manifestation of adolescent psychology?
  (b) How do you think the authorities should handle such a situation? Justify your conclusions psychologically.
  (c) Are there any clues in this episode to suggest possible methods for dealing with the "juvenile delinquency problem?"

3. Typically, the proceedings in a delinquency hearing are closed to the public and receive no publicity. How does this fact relate to the personality dynamics of the adolescent period? Outline these dynamics and explain them.

4. (a) Referring back to the quotation from *Gregoire v. State*,[8] how should this homosexual event be viewed in relationship to the boy's adolescent status, and how should he be treated by the court?
  (b) If this boy had actively solicited the sexual contact described, how would you suggest he be treated by the court? Give the psychological justification for your view.

5. In recent years a great deal of attention has been directed toward narcotics addiction, especially in the high-school age adolescent.

  (a) What factors in the psychological development of adolescents, might make them tend to be more vulnerable to this threat?
  (b) What might be done to aid this age group in resisting this potential threat?

6. (a) Frequently there is great clamor in the public press about the dangers posed by the exposure of adolescents to pornography and obscene materials. What do you think about the psychological validity of this claim?
  (b) If, as a judge, you were confronted with the problem of deciding what to do with a group of adolescents who had been picked up by the police for having and exchanging a number of pornographic photographs, what would you do? State the psychological concepts upon which you would base your decision.

[8] See Chapter IV.

REFERENCES

1. Anderson, R., *Tea and Sympathy*. New York: Signet Books, 1956.
2. Benedict, R., Sex in Primitive Society. *Amer. J. Orthopsychiat.*, 9:570-573, 1939.
3. Bromberg, W., Crime—Is There a Cause or Remedy? *Arch. Criminal Psychodynam.*, 1:341, 1955.
4. *Ibid.*, p. 336.
5. Deutsch, H., *The Psychology of Women*, Vol. I. New York: Grune & Stratton, 1944, pp. 260-265.
6. Erikson, E. H., *Childhood and Society*. New York: Norton, 1950, p. 87.
7. *Ibid.*, p. 228.
8. *Ibid.*, p. 88.
9. Erikson, E. H., The Problem of Ego Identity. *J. Amer. Psychoanal. Assn.*, 4:114, 1956.
10. *Ibid.*, p. 68.
11. *Ibid.*, pp. 72-73.
12. *Ibid.*, p. 65.
13. Ferenczi, S., A Lecture for Judges and Barristers (1913). In: *Further Contributions to the Theory and Technique of Psychoanalysis,* ed. J. Rickman. New York: Basic Books, 1952, p. 432.
14. Frank, A., *The Diary of a Young Girl*. New York: Doubleday, 1952.
15. Freud, S., Civilization and Its Discontents (1930). *Standard Edition*, 21:57-146. London: Hogarth Press, 1961.
16. Kinsey, A. et al., *Sexual Behavior in the Human Male*. Philadelphia: W. B. Saunders, 1948.
17. *Ibid.*, p. 510.
18. Kinsey, A. et al., *Sexual Behavior in the Human Female*. Philadelphia: W. B. Saunders, 1953.
19. Lindner, R., *Rebel Without a Cause*. New York: Grune & Stratton, 1948.
20. Linton, R., *The Tree of Culture*. New York: Alfred A. Knopf, 1955, pp. 548-549.
21. Muret-Sanders, *English-German and German-English Dictionary*. Berlin: Schoneberg (Rev. Ed.), p. 1198.
22. Murphy, E. F., *The Value of Pornography*. *Wayne Univ. Law Rev.*, 10:655-680, 1964.
23. Paulsen, M. G., Fairness to the Juvenile Offender. *Minn. Law Rev.*, 41:547-576, 1957.
24. Redl, F., The Psychology of Gang Formation and the Treatment of Juvenile Delinquents. *The Psychoanalytic Study of the Child*, 1:367-377. New York: International Universities Press, 1947.
25. Roman, M., Margolin, J. B. & Harari, C., Reading Retardation and Delinquents. *NPPA*, 1:1-7, 1955.
26. Saul, L. J., *Emotional Maturity*. Philadelphia: J. P. Lippincott, 1947, pp. 125-148.
27. Saul, L. J., *The Hostile Mind*. New York: Random House, 1956.
28. *Ibid.*, p. 21.
29. Scharr, J. H., Violence in Juvenile Gangs, Some Notes and a Few Analogies. *Amer. J. Orthopsychiat.*, 33:29-37, 1963.

30. Sherfey, M. J., The Evolution and Nature of Female Sexuality in Relation to Psychoanalytic Theory. *J. Amer. Psychoanal. Assn.*, 14:118-125, 1966.
31. *Time*, The Inheritor. *Time Magazine* (Internat. Ed.), Jan. 6, 1967, pp. 14-19.
32. Van de Velde, T. H., *The Ideal Marriage*. New York: Random House, 1930.
33. Walters, P. A., Promiscuity in Adolescence. *Amer. J. Orthopsychiat.*, 35:670-675, 1965.
34. Watson, A. S., A Critique of the Legal Approach to Crime and Correction. *Law and Contemp. Probl.*, 23:614-622, 1958.
35. Wattenberg, W. W., Franlon, J. I. & Quiroz, I., Clinical Psychologic Studies of Auto Thieves. *J. Clin. & Exper. Psychopath.*, 16:289-299, 1955.
36. Wertham, F., *Seduction of the Innocent*. New York: Rinehart & Co., 1954, p. 164.
37. Wertham, F., *A Sign for Cain*. New York: Macmillan, 1966, pp. 193-228.
38. Wittenberg, R., On the Superego in Adolescence. *Psychoanal. Rev.*, 42:271-279, 1955.
39. Wortis, J., Sex Taboos, Sex Offenders and the Law. *Amer. J. Orthopsychiat.*, 9:554-564, 1939.

X

Adulthood and Aging

Although we have laid great stress on the impact of childhood experiences on all subsequent behavior, still the experiences of later years are not without effect. Because childhood experiences create the lens through which all subsequent experience is colored and distorted (as well as accurately perceived), it *must* receive a great deal of attention in any therapeutic or diagnostic work. Some distortion is inevitable even in the healthiest personality, but it must be recognized and analyzed if we are to understand current behavior.

The tendency to repeat past techniques for solving present problems (repetition compulsion) is another source of adult distortion stemming from early experience. This efficient mechanism of the psyche greatly facilitates learning and maturing and, because it is automatic and largely unconscious, it frees energy to deal with new problems. It also makes it possible for a man to make the same mistake over and over for a lifetime, without ever grasping the fact that he is doing so. It cannot be too strongly emphasized that these personality manifestations are automatic, unconscious and inaccessible to the person's own immediate insight and understanding. Realistic legal concepts about man's behavior, must consider this automaticity and lack of conscious control in relation to motivation as well as behavior.

The goals, ideals, and fantasies of earlier years have a powerful effect on the behavior and perceptions of later life. A growing child is sensitively aware of the adults around him and, by identifying with them, incorporates their ideals into his own ego ideal. Positive identifications with successful persons usually stand the test of time.

Negative identifications or "reaction formations" (the determination to be the opposite of the person identified with) are shaky because unconscious conflicts prevent successful and appropriate actions. Early memories stored in the unconscious remain capable of providing strong motives for action.

Since part of the capacity for successful aging rests in the hope of achieving certain goals, these goals must be consistent and achievable. Each year of growth and aging should provide manifest evidence of closer approximation to goals (64). Without progressive success, hope dies, and aging becomes a constant, tormenting reminder of failure.

The values placed on aging and the aged by the society we live in, as well as the attitudes we assimilate in childhood from our own family, strongly affect our image of what maturity will mean for us. Long before aging is perceived as a reality, the advantages and desirability of maturity come under question. It is commonplace for some adults in our society to say to adolescents, "Go ahead, have a good time. These are the best years of your life. Soon enough you will have to face the problems of being grown up." Such a shocking admission of failure and such a blatant cry for sympathy are certainly pitiable, but it is hard to imagine why they should be taken for granted. Children with parents like these will be most reluctant to "grow up." Aldous Huxley said, twenty years ago, that the American idea of heaven was a perpetual dinner party where all the guests were 21—an idea that suffocated him with boredom.

Margaret Mead has written extensively about the emasculating effect of a security-dominated culture. She suggests that the emphasis on the child-centered home, the overweaning influence of "family" is turning men into children (46). The corollary question is, can children be turned into men in such an environment? Children must see demonstrated, the gratifying opportunities of maturity, the pleasures of adult achievement, intimacy, freedom, and the rewards of aging, if they are to strive for them and if they are fully to enjoy three quarters of their lives.

Popularizations of dynamic psychiatry may have unwittingly added to the dismal picture of old age that the advertising and entertainment industries have so feelingly reflected. To be giving, responsible, independent, and mature spells grim, sounds grim, and is grim. Enjoyable maturity includes freshness, spontaneity, interdependency and, in fact, the joys of childhood plus the joys of adulthood.

The problems of aging must not be isolated from the surroundings and social patterns relating to this process. Every culture develops its own concepts of value for the aged. In some, age is associated with wisdom, honor, and increased prestige. In others, for example some of the Eskimo societies, age means loss of usefulness to the community, and the cultural expectation is that the aged person will commit suicide by whichever method the group utilizes (53).

Our culture is presently struggling with a massive problem of how to deal with aging. In the past, it was frequently expected that a person would retire at age sixty, regardless of his physical and mental state. Now, more and more, this is viewed as wasteful and frustrating. In our complicated society, persons are often just reaching the peak of their usefulness and productivity at this time, and to cast them off is to forego the value of their years of experience and their wealth of knowledge. We also are learning that people, if they are to continue healthy and happy, must feel themselves to be valuable, and retirement hardly demonstrates that point. Also, advances in medical science have eliminated many of the causes of death in earlier years, and we have a progressively larger segment of the population reaching the age where physical deterioration is the major cause of disability. This is in sharp contrast to past generations, where acute illnesses and childbirth tended to cause death at earlier ages. The concurrence of these several factors has resulted in a progressively aging population and creates many social problems which demand solutions in the near future (34). It will be well to take into account the psychology of aging if we are to manage the problem wisely. We emphasize again that the end products of behavior, insofar as each individual is concerned, come from a summation of cultural attitudes and individual attitudes, and from these, each person must develop his own philosophy for growing old.

We may appropriately divide adulthood into three periods: young adulthood, maturity, and old age. These somewhat arbitrary divisions relate to cultural patterns and reflect psychic development.

Young Adulthood

The early postadolescent years in our society are years of great activity. They are invested in establishing family, social, and vocational roles, which should last and be developed during the balance of life. This period roughly spans the ages of eighteen or nineteen until twenty-five or twenty-six. When he reaches young adulthood, a mature person has achieved competent ego control and integration; all of the routes of gratification are reasonably successfully meshed with the realities of the external world. Such a person has a comfortable and complete image of himself, a solidly established identity. He is able to form close and friendly relations with peers, and sees his family much as others see them. He has a capacity for appropriate and pleasurable heterosexual experience. In Erikson's words, the mature individual during early adulthood achieves "mutuality of orgasm with a loved partner of the other sex with whom one is able and willing to share a mutual trust, and with whom one is able and willing to regulate cycles of work, procreation, recreation, so as to secure to the offspring, too, a satisfactory development" (17).

To achieve orgasm, one must be able to abandon oneself completely to powerful sensations which sweep away everyday perceptions of reality. To insecure people, far from being a pleasant experience, this can only be compared with the sense of "going insane." The intense fear it evokes is frequently manifested in impotence, frigidity, and other sexual abberrations (48). The cause of these symptoms is not some biological deviation, but rather the fear of trusting oneself to this powerful experience with another person. "A human being should be potentially able to accomplish mutuality of genital orgasm, but should be also so constituted as to bear frustration in the matter without undue regression wherever conditions of reality and loyalty call for it" (20).

The mature person has the capacity to gauge appropriately a free use of physical aggression. While violence is not a solution for social problems, it is occasionally a social necessity. It should be within the power of the mature personality to recognize this necessity and take physical action. During the recent wars there were many individuals whose ego and superego structure was such that they were unable to meet this demand, and they were forced into adaptations which were less appropriate (57).

Finally, an adult should be capable of abandoning himself to inspiration and intuition. These ill-defined capacities to perceive and sense what is going on under the surface and between the lines, and to draw these perceptions together into new and different constellations, make change possible and are the source of creativity (5). Since this represents casting off some of the patterns of the past, an insecure person may regard this form of activity as being a dangerous adventure into the unknown, where only trouble may ensue. It is impossible, however, to stand still. Without change and creativity only withdrawal and stagnation can occur. Many years ago, Freud was asked what he considered to be an appropriate standard for living. His answer was simple and short: *"Lieben und arbeiten"*—to love and to work (21).

During the years of young adulthood, one of the basic steps taken is that of seeking a mate and consummating a marriage. While adequate and happy adjustments may be made outside of marriage, it is more common to solve most of life's problems within this institution (23). Erich Fromm, in somewhat different language, states that a goal of all human beings is to overcome the sense of isolation and aloneness by achieving a sense of *unity* by means of *productive work, orgiastic fusion, conformity,* or *love* (26). He goes on to state, brilliantly, "The unity achieved in productive work is not interpersonal; the unity achieved in orgiastic fusion is transitory; the unity achieved by conformity is only pseudo unity. Hence they are only partial answers to the problem of existence. The full answer lies in the achievement of interpersonal union, of fusion with another person in love" (27).

To put these considerations in yet another way, marriage provides (in our culture) the *social* opportunity to enter into a relationship where fantasies of the past can be brought into present reality. All of the exciting sexual reveries of childhood can now be mutually explored, indulged, and reciprocated with the beloved partner. Each, with a sense of personal risk and incipient shame, may expose, express, and indulge the acts which before were the subject of dreams and imagination. Tentatively at first, but with increasing satisfaction as mutual pleasure grows, such sexual "play" cuts across the whole spectrum of sensual development. Because this experience is undertaken with an ominous sense of psychological jeopardy (the product of all of the real and imagined proscriptions of the past), it creates a kind of mutual satisfaction which is extremely personal and virtually impossible of easy replication. It builds a bond of mutual tenderness and understanding, excitement and love, which can carry the love partners through all kinds of difficult or painful circumstances. Such a union comes to be recognized by the partners as well as others, as a movingly intimate, powerfully satisfying, deeply loving relationship of equal, interdependent, independent adults. They are joined in an exquisite companionship which can face and resolve mutual problems and needs in the best possible way, come what will.[1] Obviously this kind of involvement can only develop with time and following a great deal of living together. It involves the assumption of risks, some very creative gambling, and much plain hard work.

We readily see that, in order to get married, both the man and woman involved must be able to be freely aggressive to seek out an appropriate mate. Previous discussions may provide us with explanations for failure in this area. In order to have a good marriage, the partners must be willing and able to resolve differences, which usually means "fighting some things out." Happy marriages are not made in heaven; rather, they are a product of active struggle and adaptation by the individuals involved.[2] Various irrational and neurotic fears, which can inhibit this process, may preclude the possibility of achieving marital happiness. Failures in marriages result in much pain and unhappiness for the partners and their children. While it is easy to say that, if one or the other of the partners had married a different spouse, they would have no difficulties, this does not appear to be the case (11, 39, 63). All too often, individuals who fail in one marriage will fail in another, due to their unerring ability to choose another mate exactly like the first. The problem that first caused failure in selection or failure to arrive at happy agreement must still be resolved no matter how many

[1] It has always seemed to this author that this is the concept which D. H. Lawrence explored in most of his novels and which he brought to its culmination in *Lady Chatterley's Lover* (40). Far from being obscene, it is a sensitive, candid, and highly artistic presentation of this process.

[2] For a short and very readable book on the practical aspects of "working out" a marriage, see Levy, J. & Monroe, R., *The Happy Family* (42). This might be a useful book to suggest to clients who are struggling with marriage problems and want some help on a *method* for approaching their problems.

partners are tried. For this reason, an opportunity to resolve the basic underlying problems is more often indicated than divorce. The lawyer's professional role gives him an opportunity to throw his weight toward the constructive or the disruptive approach to a marriage problem (66).

While the lawyer's primary skill and service lies in dealing with legal problems, the overriding point of importance, is his client's welfare. Mere knowledge that marriage problems frequently indicate severe emotional disturbances in the participants may facilitate the lawyer's making a wise decision in relation to his client (28, 65). Counsel can help his client discover that he has more basic problems than the marital ones. With this understanding, the client may then seek help which can assist both marriage partners to resolve their difficulties (1). Practicing psychiatrists frequently see marriage problems which might possibly have worked out successfully had it not been for the ill-timed and inappropriate invoking of some legal procedure. While such a concept may collide with many lawyers' personal attitudes about their practice, if they have their clients' interests at heart, the intention must be to preserve rather than disrupt marriages whenever it is appropriate. Legal intervention should be the last, rather than the first kind of professional service offered to unhappy married couples.

In the past, marital difficulties were looked upon as something to be endured, because of the moral judgment that marriage must not be dissolved as well as the legal and economic difficulties of doing so (44). Social mores and religious attitudes have changed, and today the incidence of divorce has greatly increased. Dublin, in 1951, noted that there were "almost 400,000 divorces and annulments" granted each year, with a peak of 629,000 in 1946 (9). This is about 10.5 divorces per 1000 married couples (10). There are some statistics to indicate that remarriages tend to endure, but there is no way of knowing whether this means that the individuals made a more adequate adjustment or merely gave up their hopes of successful marriage, and so stayed married (6, 32).[3]

[3] This author clearly accepts what Lady Barbara Wootton has called the "utilitarian" view of divorce: "Whom man hath joined together, man may put asunder—but only with due consideration for the interests of the helpless." (Quoted by McGregor [45].) A Committee appointed by the Archbishop of Canterbury recently recommended a broadening of divorce grounds to recognize the reality of "marital breakdown" (3).

Under "ideal" circumstances, relatively soon after marriage the family embarks upon child-rearing functions with all of its personal and social implications. By this time of life, mature individuals have resolved "give-get" emotional problems, and are ready to enjoy intense satisfaction from giving to their offspring and the younger generation.[4] The psychic reservoir has been filled generously enough to permit free giving without dissolution of the ego. Not only is this primarily giving or love orientation efficient for the psychic economy, but it is also intensely gratifying. Unlike giving motivated primarily by the desire to please, or to be "a good child," it is done with full awareness and with a full reaction of pleasure to the act of giving. This capacity has been applauded in all ethical religions and philosophies, although it is often debased in practice through lack of adequate emotional strength and maturity.

Young adults then, find themselves at the crossroads of *intimacy* versus *isolation* (19). What of those unfortunate individuals who fail to make the grade into full adulthood? Rather than to draw closer with peers, family, and friends in warm and intimate relationships, they are driven to withdraw more and more into themselves and develop a greater and greater sense of isolation. Isolation, often masquerading as pseudo independence, can frustrate basic emotional needs for all age groups. It may be compensated for by massive investment in job, scholarship, or avocational pleasures, but in the end it only adds up to loneliness. It is a shaking experience to apprehend the numbers of drifting, lonely, people in the heart of a large metropolis. Loneliness is so common as to be a major emotional characteristic of our complex urban society (55). It is paradoxical that in the midst of masses of people, isolation should exist so frequently. In rural societies, where a relatively homogeneous cultural pattern facilitates a sense of identity, individuals more easily draw together and form warm, intimate, bonds of friendship, even though they may be geographically more isolated than their city brothers. This is not to say that rural societies per se are more healthy than urban ones. Especially today, there is evidence that value conflicts of the urban versus rural life are making heavy in-

---

[4] The role of the mother in child rearing has often been described. For a fine discussion of the paternal role, well suited for general reading, see English and Foster, *Fathers are Parents Too* (15).

roads into the emotional security and tranquility ordinarily attributed to rural populations.[5]

We should also note that the need to avoid isolation may cause some to identify with groups which may have primarily antisocial orientation. One need only read some of the autobiographical accounts of prisoners and criminals to see how powerful is their need to cling to their criminally oriented group in order to insure their sense of identity (54). Efforts at rehabilitation and reorienting such a group must, above all else, provide some suitable alternative with which these persons may readily identify. This lies at the core of the rehabilitation problem.

Early adulthood should be a highly productive stage of life. As in all previous stages of development, failure to achieve adequate adaptation here, introduces a chronological lag which can only compound adjustment difficulties with the passage of time. Failure to have some goal in life by this age is usually indicative of serious difficulty. With success, there is an increasing sense of belonging to the group and society, and a real closeness to others. Failure necessitates withdrawal and isolation, with a need to compensate somehow for the loss. Compensation may be manifested variously in antisocial behavior, or neurotic or social disability. The meaning is constant, however; the individual is alone and isolated and is struggling for restitution (29).

YEARS OF MATURITY

Between the ages of twenty-five and fifty, mature adults become deeply involved in the various productive activities of their respective cultures, and a great deal of this productivity is channeled into the institution of the family. As we have previously indicated, with the achievement of psychological and biological maturity, the human organism has surplus energy which it may invest in the maturing process of the growing children (13).

[5] For example, in a study of suicide rates among urban and rural populations in the State of Michigan, the rural suicide rate was found to be almost double that of the urban. In their conclusion, the authors postulate that: ". . . As urban values and ideals become more widely disseminated in rural areas, the conflict in rural and urban values becomes more intense. This conflict offers greater possibilities for maladjustment and personal disorganization among rural people. Second, the data that has been presented . . . indicate that the majority of rural white males who commit suicide are engaged in occupations which are characteristic of urbanite groups" (58).

Sociologists and anthropologists have given us good descriptions of the cultural function of the family unit. Some of these concepts have been incorporated into psychiatric thinking only recently.[6] Within the structure of the family, the adult participants, by virtue of the social role which they occupy in that family and in that culture, automatically accumulate around themselves various unspoken symbols, which are a function of their role. These roles impose certain responsibilities and pressures on the adults, as well as provide them with various advantages and privileges. The mature person is able to integrate these pressures in a predominantly satisfying way, which facilitates his own further maturation and the development of his offspring.

We should also note that as adults rear children they are forced, whether they wish it or not, to re-experience vicariously all of their own childhood. A mother nursing her child will "relive" all over again, the pleasures of sucking as she watches and "feels" her baby suck. A father watching his son's angry attack on his pestering younger brother will "enjoy" the attack. These kinds of empathic experiences occur at *every* step of the child's growth. Each provides an opportunity for the parent to re-examine old attitudes from the perspective of adulthood, to *change* those attitudes. While child-rearing activities do present options for change, they also create possibilities for reinforcing old and conflicted resolutions. (Is it "bad" to get angry at the pestering? Or is it merely that one must learn to modulate appropriately the impulse to kill "the little bastard?" Do you need to give up all of that good sucking? Or do you merely shift where and how you do it?) Instead of seeing old impulses in a new light, the previously "accepted" attitudes can be hardened. The oldest son is "very bad" for attacking his brother and he must be punished (and the punishment is meted out with anxiety-evoked anger, too). One certainly must not enjoy sucking—it is "so babyish." The latter conclusions represent an unfortunate loss of opportunity: the chance to be helped to maturity by one's children—a partial parental *quid* for the *quo* of all the hard work.[7]

Adult roles, by their very nature, lead a person out into his com-

[6] For an excellent description of the psychological aspects of the family and the integration of the sociological concepts of *role,* and *value orientation,* see Report No. 24 of the Group for the Advancement of Psychiatry (35).

[7] Therese Benedek beautifully outlines this in her classic paper, "Parenthood as a Developmental Phase" (4).

munity where he may further invest himself in such activities as bear relevantly on his social, political, vocational, and recreational relationships. Erikson describes the ego potentials of this phase of life as *generativity*, which results from success in meeting these demands, or *stagnation*, which results from failure to achieve integration at this level (18). We have already described the manifestations of generativity. The ultimate in stagnation can be seen in those sad individuals who inhabit the skid rows of large urban centers across the land. This is social integration (or rather disintegration) at a level of absolute nonproductivity; whatever potential these individuals possessed, and is achieving no realization whatsoever. True intimacy is wanting and is substituted for by the pseudo intimacy of these groups of physically and psychologically debilitated men. Investigation into the personalities and pasts of these men often reveals great social and intellectual potential. Failure to achieve an adequate level of integration has forced them back into a primitive, merely vegetative mode of existence. They are bitter, hostile, and lost; they look out into the desolate world around them with a sense of utter hopelessness. Other persons solve similar problems by way of mental illness and overt antisocial behavior.

It is not too difficult to find less striking examples of adult integrative failure in the "normal" population. Boredom, restlessness, and a sense of futility and emptiness are the symptoms of unproductive adulthood. Our culture provides many ways of investing oneself but, by its very complexity and specialization, tends to penalize anyone unlucky enough not to get on the right line at the right time and place (38).

Women in our culture face difficulties in finding a productive social role, which are somewhat different from those facing men. Men, in general, have trouble in shifting from a job role, with its kind of rewards, to successful intimacy and creativity in intense personal relationships. Women are favored in that they are productive and creative in their biological role as mother and in the social acceptance of their investment in close personal relationships. This initial advantage creates some difficulty later, since complete investment in family tends to isolate a woman from the larger community. As both children and husband become more and more self-sufficient, their emotional need for her form of creativity is greatly reduced. (She may also have severe conflicts between family roles and choices in work or profession. Our society has not yet found easy ways to integrate these divergent goals.) At this point the specialization and masculine orientation of many community institutions make it difficult for her to move comfortably and successfully out into other equally valued roles (50).

Social attitudes may result from adaptive failures, which produce powerful desires for some form of external support and stability. Failure to accomplish a sense of strength through solid productivity may necessitate turning to some outside source for security. Such strength and support may be demanded from various governmental or social agencies, including those designed to provide security in one's old age. At least some of the motivation for the erection of the paternalisitic state is derived from this origin (51).

Another fairly common manifestation of maladaptation to aging occurs in the sweeping debilitation which may arise from minor injuries and in which the injured party sues for financial relief (41, 47, 52, 59, 60). We commented earlier about the theory of secondary gain. Emotional insecurity about one's productive capacity may also play powerfully into this reaction, necessitating clear-cut and final resolution of the legal question of damages, if the individual's future adaptive capacity is not to be curtailed.

Many of the difficulties surrounding menopause in both men and women have their source in the emotions related to ideas of self-worth (8, 14, 16, 49). In the past these difficulties have been attributed primarily to the hormonal impact of the "change of life." However, more recent study shows that loss of reproductive ability carries with it a feeling of diminished individual value. Thus, the shift from what Linden calls "evanescence" to senescence, is quite as much a psychological readjustment as it is a hormonal one (43). The "menopausal syndrome" therefore, is mainly an adaptational technique to deal with the anxiety produced by the biological events of this phase of life.

OLD AGE

The later years of life, although they include the period during which there is actual physiological senescence, should provide the individual with the ultimate opportunities to visualize himself in relation to his life experience and the philosophical and historical past of his culture.[8] Hopefully, he should have achieved the satisfactions of a large share of his potential capacity and integrated them thoroughly into a philosophy of life.

According to Erikson, the ego values relating to this period are *integrity* versus *despair*. The individual with ego integrity becomes part of the psychological bulwark of the community and may become, for the newest members of the group, a person "to trust." Erikson defines trust as the "assured reliance upon another's integrity . . ." (67). This brings us full circle through the life span with the mature status of the group's oldest members providing the solid foundation for the growth and development of its newest members (22). The infant's need to trust is directed to the integrity of the community's elders.

When ego integrity is not achieved, the individual must face the waning of his life and his oncoming death with a sense of despair. It has been observed by both philosophers and clinicians that the problem of facing death is always intimately related with the manner in which that individual has dealt with living. Those who have not been able to enjoy a satisfying, productive life visualize the arrival of death as a frightening, annihilating experience. On the other hand, those who have led a full and productive life are commonly observed to face death with a philosophic attitude.[9] Indeed, if there is any manner in which we may test out the idea that there is a survival after death, it must lie in our observations that the mature and productive individual always leaves as a legacy to succeeding generations, the fruits of his experience. In a very real sense, the advance of culture and civilization is nothing more than the slow and painful accumulation of the fruits which individual lives have borne. Those who have failed in life and have not achieved full ego integration, when faced with the progressive loss of their physical powers, quite commonly revert to infantile techniques to reassure themselves that they still have security. This accounts for the regressive and childish behavior of many aging people (24, 61).

Recent clinical experience amply demonstrates that permitting an individual to continue productively and usefully in relation to his

[8] For a good summary of these goals and how to meet them, directed to the aged person himself, see "Looking Forward to the Later Years" (62).

[9] Here again, a reference to Camus' *The Plague* is in order (7).

surroundings may forestall and limit his psychological regression (12, 30). The *need* to regress, among other things, may include sexual regression (especially in men), and reverting to prepubertal techniques for gratification (31). Thus, the aged sexual offender should not be looked upon by the community as a person to punish, but rather as one in need of assistance. Guttmacher and others have demonstrated that these individuals do not usually need to be incarcerated, but may be easily dealt with within their own family surroundings (36, 37). This again points up the desirability of looking to the offender's motivation when dealing with antisocial activity. Since the aged often function on the psychological level of childhood, the law quite wisely treats such behavior as though the individual were, in fact, a child.

Several of the complex problems the law faces in dealing with the aged involve issues of competency. Quite appropriately, there is no definition of competency which embraces all circumstances. For example, the capacity to execute a will is, and should be, different from the capacity to enter into a contract. It is not our intention here to attempt to deal with this problem in detail. Suffice it to say that the amount of ego capacity a person can muster in the service of judgment and intellectual activity changes according to his emotional and physical state.

Physical factors become progressively more important with advancing age. Adequate circulation to the brain is often lost with the implacable changes of senescence. While, quite obviously, these changes vary widely, there is inevitably some loss of cerebral vascular efficiency, and a concomitant loss of intellectual capacity. These alterations are usually noticeable to those familiar with the person's behavior, but their exact importance in the issue of competency is a matter for expert evaluation. Difficult to assay at best, the precise distortion-producing potential which these changes represent is easy to mistake. Perhaps in no other age group are there such wide variations in intellectual capacity. Proper evaluation of such capacity for any given time or situation is a job for a skilled clinician. It should be added that there is a great need for empirical research on these problems if we are to obtain answers upon which reasonable reliance may be placed.

Old age is truly a time for sagacity and philosophizing on the nature of life.[10] A mature individual can see himself in his surroundings with a real sense of order and a spiritual unity with the past and the future (25). His experience creates a sense of values worth defending, and it becomes the appropriate role of the aged to provide a conservative brake on society. From the broad experience of a total life, held against the longer perspective of the past, newer ideas and concepts for change may be judged effectively (2). The individual arriving at this period of his life should have little or no identification conflict to cause vacillation and indecisiveness. The elder should be a leader in the truest sense, providing an example for the young derived from his own successful experiences in learning from the elders whom he emulated. Many of our great judges and justices afford beautiful examples of this capacity to serve.

PROBLEMS

Example

You are counsel for the First Rate Insurance Company, which specializes in workman's compensation insurance. Your company is being sued by Mr. Timothy McCoy because his claim for total disability, following a rear-end collision with his truck while working, was disallowed. Following the accident, he was hospitalized for weeks, during which he was treated for "traumatic strain of the lower lumbar region." He received daily physiotherapy for his back-pain during that period and, when released from hospital, was placed on a course of exercises. Although Mr. McCoy still complained of some pain when he was discharged, the doctor signing him out stated that "the pain was ultimately diagnosed to be psychosomatic, since there was no evidence of any residual physical disability. There is no reason why the patient should not return to work."

Mr. McCoy did return to work, but immediately complained of back pain when he drove his truck. Although he was tried on a variety of other jobs, he could not perform them either because of the pain. He was sent to the industrial medicine clinic several times, and their findings did not differ from the discharge report. In the end, Mr. McCoy left work and applied for total disability pension. Under the terms of the company's policy, he was entitled to compensation during treatment for job-incurred injuries for the duration of the injury. In the event of total disability, he could receive a lump sum settlement.

[10] For an interesting account of a well-known scholar's personal search, see Goodenough's *Toward a Mature Faith* (33).

After reading the medical file on Mr. McCoy, you realize that the critical issues in the suit are: (1) Is the residual back pain which is said to be "psychosomatic," attributable to the accident? (2) Is the condition treatable so that Mr. McCoy will be able to return to work? (3) In the event the accident "triggered" the psychosomatic condition, what part of the condition could be said to pre-exist? (4) What is the prognosis for Mr. McCoy? You contact a psychiatric consultant and put these questions to him. You ask him to answer them and to detail the basis of his findings. (As you embark upon this step, you also know that the psychiatrist's report must be shared with plaintiff's counsel as a condition of examination.) Two weeks later, the following psychiatric report arrives at your office as follows:

PSYCHIATRIC REPORT ON MR. TIMOTHY McCoy

Mr. Timothy McCoy was referred for psychiatric examination by Mr. James P. Trueblood, Esq., in connection with an impending lawsuit. He arrived at my office promptly for his appointment and did everything he was able to do to cooperate during the examination. It was immediately apparent that he was very depressed. He looked extremely sad, his responses, for the most part, were rather flat, emotionless, except as noted below. When initially asked how he was feeling, he referred at once to his back pain and would have gone on about that at great length if permitted. He was then asked to describe the accident, his background, and his work history.

Mr. McCoy, 54 years old and widowed for six years, has been living with his youngest son, Robert, in the family home. He has four children, all married except Robert. He was, himself, the youngest of five children. He grew up in a home in which the father was an occasional laborer when he was not involved in bouts of drunkenness, often accompanied by physical brutality to his wife and children. His mother, who worked in a laundry to keep the family alive, was too preoccupied and too harassed to have much attention left over for her youngest child. Most of the attention he received came from an older sister who was not very happy with her own role in the family.

Always small for his age, Mr. McCoy early developed a rather pugnacious character which made him extremely competent in the sandlot games of his community. Because he dropped out of school in order to help out with the family economy, he never participated in any school-centered athletics, "though I was good enough to do it if I had gone." He did every kind of work imaginable, including jobs "that you'd never guess I could do at my size." He always managed to keep a job even in relatively bad times, but never developed any skill except as a truckdriver. Work always involved just plain "back work." He always had a good work attendance record and expressed great pride in that fact. Except for his injuries, he "hardly ever missed a day."

When Mr. McCoy reached 22, he married the girl he courted for three years. As he spoke of her, tears came to his eyes and he had to wait a bit before he could speak again. He described what had apparently been a very close marriage. Although they never "had it easy" they managed to buy a small house, give all of their children a good education, and to lead a happy life. (One son graduated from college, one trained at a technical school, a daughter graduated from a two-year business college, and the youngest boy was about to graduate from high school, after which he expected to go into military service.) All his adult life had centered around working and doing things with his family. "We used to have a lot of fun together. The boys and I played ball together, fished, and went to see various sports events." When his wife became ill with a fatal malignancy, he and the children nursed her and cared for her until her terminal hospital admission (again tears, when he spoke of this).

Since Mr. McCoy appeared depressed throughout the interview, his reaction to his wife's death was explored in some depth. Although it had been six years since she died, he had clearly never recovered from it. Apparently, she gave him much of the warmth and affection he missed during his own childhood, and he greatly relied on her to help him decide things and to carry out various family projects. Her death opened a gap in his life, which had not been filled by anyone or anything. He had bent his energies "to raising the kids the way she would have wanted," but this did not satisfy his own needs for care and affection. He lost considerable weight since then, has had trouble sleeping, and occasionally "wonder(s) whether life is worth living anymore. If it wasn't for the kids, I don't know what I'd do." Quite clearly, this man has remained deeply depressed since his wife's death. This led me to inquire about the circumstances of the accident, for I was considering the possibility of some unconscious effort to inflict self-injury. However, the accident seemed to be a clearly unforeseeable rear-end collision, in which he played only a passive and helpless role. He has had frequent and repetitive dreams about the accident ever since it happened.

I also learned that Mr. McCoy had two accidents of exactly the same kind, both in the line of work duty! (As you know, the nature of his job puts him in jeopardy for this kind of accident.) During the course of the interview (which lasted a total of two and one-half hours) he mentioned at one point that "after the last accident I realized I had had it." I asked him what he meant and he said, "I've never been afraid of anything in my life. In fact the men on the job always call me 'Tiger.' But after having that happen three times I figured my number would be up the next time anything happened to me." I inquired how he got the nickname of Tiger and he told me, with great pleasure, how on several occasions "much bigger guys had tried to push me around. Before they knew what hit them I sailed into them and that was the last time they tried anything with me." He obviously took great pride in this ability to take care of himself, even when the odds were against him.

I fully explored the events subsequent to his accident and hospitalization. While he received a supremely thorough physical examination ("It seemed like they did every test there was on me two or three times"), apparently no adequate psychiatric examination was performed, or at least none sufficient to discover what was bothering Mr. McCoy. ("They did send a head-shrinker in one day, but it seemed to me all those guys wanted to prove was that I didn't have no pain. It's *my* back and I know when I've got pain. They only wanted to get me back on that job and save the company dough. They didn't give a damn about me.") Apparently Mr. McCoy did go back to work and attempted to drive his truck. He suffered "terrible pain in the bottom of my back, and I just couldn't take it." His foreman, who seemed sympathetic to him, tried to find alternative jobs. However, having no other skills, Mr. McCoy had to do menial tasks with lower job status than truck driving. "I really tried to do them jobs, Doc, but I just couldn't do it. My back nearly killed me." He made many trips to the clinic, each less satisfactory than its predecessor. He felt more and more oppressed by the doctors who he felt didn't care at all about him. (During this period, he became increasingly more depressed.)

To summarize these observations and to formulate the psychiatric status of Mr. McCoy for you, I would say the following. Mr. McCoy experienced a very deprived childhood, during which he received little of the warmth and concern that children need. However, he learned to cope with this by developing what must be called "pseudo independence." He learned to take care of himself extremely well, but at the cost of his inner sense of well-being. Although he was able to give a great deal to his family, he slowly and progressively accrued a larger deficit balance vis-à-vis his own needs. It was as if his strong and competent exterior was being covertly hollowed out, like a great tree under assault by fungus. One day, the apparently strong one is struck down by stress or by wind, which earlier would have been weathered with great ease. (Recall that on the occasion of Mr. McCoy's second accident, he was seriously injured, suffering from several fractures, cerebral concussion, and some nasty lacerations.) He could even take on tasks (and men!) where others would hesitate. The "courage" he exhibited was an essential part of the psychological defense armor he used to keep himself unaware of his inner dread and anxiety about vulnerability. Always, defense expenditures were themselves sapping his strength, even as they carried him into situations which imposed even higher demands on his weakening capacities. Thus, when he arrived at the point in time of the last accident when the truck suddenly struck him from the rear, his whole ability to deal with life stresses was decimated. His defenses were over-run. The only thing which could have helped him then would have been to rebuild them to the degree possible within his resources, or some therapeutic augmentation, which will be mentioned later. In effect, the accident proved once and for all that "the Tiger" was not invincible. The forthcoming departure of his son and the loss of work status also cut deeply into his sense of well-being. He could not drive anymore because he was afraid to, but a tiger admits no fear. Neither could he acknowledge that he cared about such a thing as status. And to acknowledge that he would be terribly lonesome when his son left, would be downright "unmanly."

Now to the specific questions raised about Mr. McCoy. (1) In my opinion, it cannot be said that the present back pain was "attributable" to the accident, since he has been building up to this vulnerability throughout his whole life. On the other hand, one must say that the accident triggered the collapse of Mr. McCoy's defenses so the acute symptoms were brought on by the injury. Without the occurrence of the accident, he certainly would not have developed the symptoms. He might possibly have been able to sustain his son's departure by throwing himself more fully into work, as he would have done in the past. Now the psychological dilemma described above precludes that possibility. (2) In my opinion, it is highly unlikely that Mr.

McCoy can be rehabilitated so far as his old work place is concerned. He is too deeply entrenched in the use of his back symptoms, and he has cut too many bridges to former means of coping. Perhaps, if he can develop more acceptance of his basic human needs for love, affection, and care, as well as acknowledge some of his underlying anger and frustration about being left alone by those who loved him, and whom he loved, there is a remote possibility that, with intensive psychotherapy, he might be able to find some productive niche into which he can fit. I believe this can only take place after all of the legal issues are settled so that Mr. McCoy knows precisely where he stands in relation to them. Let me emphasize that I do not feel that he is malingering or consciously attempting to gain anything through his illness, beyond the unconscious psychological purposes it serves to preserve his self-esteem. For this reason, it is crucial to his future health that all of the legal issues be settled as promptly as possible so that he may work out some new adaptive means. (3) As noted above, it must be said that none of the *symptoms* existed before the accident. However, the condition which made him vulnerable to the psychic assault of the third accident was progressively developing during the previous 20 or 30 years. Each of the prior accidents, and especially the death of his wife, brought him ever closer to the point where his defenses would collapse as they did with the accident. (4) The prognosis is poor for any basic change in Mr. McCoy's psychic status. Because he has not found it easy in the past to relate to people outside his family in ways which could provide him with sources of psychic gratification, and because his own family is progressively moving away from him through death and their own growing up, he will be in short supply of these needs. Hopefully, if he gains some insight into *why* he had his back pain, he might be able, at this relatively late date, to develop some new abilities. However, this is not to be relied upon. The "Tiger" has been brought to bay.

I hope my observations and comments have adequately answered your questions. If not, I trust that you will get in touch with me so that I might clarify them further if I am able to do so. Thank you for referring this interesting patient to me.

Sincerely yours,
/s/ John F. Kirkbride, M.D.

Now that you are in possession of this report and know that your opposing counsel will also have it, you will no doubt initially gnash your teeth. It appears that you will have to face the claim for at least some of the future loss of work capacity. You may wish to argue that there should be some change in the law's current policy that a defendant has to take the victim "as he finds him." (Such a policy linked with the kind of analysis made of Mr. McCoy, tends to broaden greatly the pool of potentially vulnerable claimants. Or should the law go in the other direction and not permit liability for the "triggering effect" when it is so commonplace?) At any rate, in this case it would appear that you will ultimately have to pay the claim. You may next consider how to carry this out most efficaciously. Probably, you will hope to settle the matter, since your report has been so "helpful" to your opponent.

Following the opinion of the report (and assuming that you are persuaded of its soundness), you should make some kind of lump-sum settlement with this man. To do otherwise—for example to make payments to Mr. McCoy until he recovers—may only prolong recovery and not be good for either you or him. It therefore seems best for all concerned to calculate an appropriate settlement sum based on the assumption that he will work no more. Then he and you may proceed to make all necessary adjustments to your separate purposes.

1. In Browne v. Brooke, Wacker & Jenkins (236 F.2d. 686), a *caveat* was filed as to the admission into evidence of psychiatric testimony, obtained in a psychiatric examination instituted by a bank, and relative to the question of the validity of a will. The matter hinged on ". . . whether the doctor's testimony was privileged and therefore inadmissible unless the privilege was waived."

In this jurisdiction (D.C.), privilege extends only "to information the physician acquires 'in attending a patient in a professional capacity.'" The majority opinion stated: "We assume that the person examined, if capable of forming a judgment on the subject, must understand that the physician is not attending or treating him. If not capable of forming such a judgment, the question of the physician's status must be determined objectively."

The jury found that the deceased "was not of sound and disposing mind and capable of executing a valid deed or contract." This was affirmed by the Court of Appeals, after it found that the trial judge had satisfactorily settled the issues above, before admitting the psychiatric testimony. In his dissenting opinion, Bazelon writes:

> Here the psychiatrist's purpose was unquestionably testimonial, but it does not appear that the decedent was aware of that fact. Her normal assumption would have been that the doctor who was examining her was doing so qua doctor, not qua bank investigator. To admit the doctor's testimony in these circumstances would make the patient's rights dependent on the doctor's intentions. The statute, however, is designed for the patient's protection. Her frame of mind, therefore, rather than the doctor's, would determine whether the statute applies. Unless it appears that she submitted to examination with knowledge that the doctor might broadcast his findings, her confidences should be respected. To make the testimony competent, it must be found from the record not only that the purpose of the examination was testimonial, but also that such purpose was clearly announced to the person examined or her legal representative. No such finding being possible here, the testimony should have been excluded.

(a) Since the court above accepted the jury's verdict that decedent was not of sound mind, and the doctor had testified likewise, presumably the court used its "objective determination" to settle the question of privilege. How is this done?

(b) When a person is adjudicated to be of unsound mind, where does this status begin? For example, can an incompetent person engage counsel?

(c) Is there some point at which the community, through the court, should intervene on behalf of the incompetent? If so, at what point? What should set such a procedure in motion?

2. Many aging persons develop psychoses due to vascular changes in the brain. These persons *could* readily be adjudicated as incompetent, or they *could* be formally committed to an institution. In many cases, the family of such a person will elect to place him in a private nursing home, often against the will of the patient.

(a) If, as an attorney, you were approached by the family of such a person, how would you advise them to proceed?

(b) If you were contacted by the (psychotic) patient himself, who complained of being wrongfully imprisoned, how would you proceed?

(c) What would you consider to be an optimal law and an optimal procedure for dealing with this very common problem, which would protect the rights of all concerned, as well as meet the social problem?

4. There appears to be a wide variation in the laws of commitment, and most certainly in commitment standards.

(a) What are some of the problems you feel to be present in commitment laws?

(b) How do you think an ideal commitment law should be framed?

(c) How should *habeas corpus* petitions be handled in regard to the mentally ill who have been committed?

REFERENCES

1. Ackerman, N., *Psychodynamics of Family Life*. New York: Basic Books, 1958.
2. Alexander, F., *Our Age of Unreason*. Philadelphia: J. P. Lippincott, 1951, pp. 232-341.
3. Archbishop of Canterbury's Committee, *Putting Asunder*. London: S.P.C.K., 1966.
4. Benedek, T., Parenthood as a Developmental Phase. *J. Amer. Psychoanal. Assn.*, 7:389-417, 1959.

5. Beres, D., Communication in Psychoanalysis and in the Creative Process. *J. Amer. Psychoanal. Assn.*, 5:408-423, 1957.
6. Bernard, J. S., *Remarriage: A Study of Marriage.* New York: Dryden Press, 1956.
7. Camus, A., *The Plague.* New York: Alfred A. Knopf, 1948.
8. Deutsch, H., *The Psychology of Women*, Vol. I. New York: Grune & Stratton, 1945, pp. 456-487.
9. Dublin, L., *The Facts of Life: From Birth to Death.* New York: Macmillan, 1951, p. 63.
10. *Ibid.*, p. 64.
11. Eidelberg, L., Neurotic Choice of a Mate. In: *Neurotic Interaction in Marriage*, Ed. V. Eisenstein. New York: Basic Books, 1956.
12. English, O. S., A Brighter Future for Older People. *Geriat.*, 4:217, 1949.
13. English, O. S., How Family Forces Affect the Individual. *Bull. Menninger Clin.*, 14:66-74, 1950.
14. English, O. S. & Finch, S. M., *Introduction to Psychiatry.* New York: Norton, 1954, pp. 396-399.
15. English, O. S. & Foster, C. J., *Fathers Are Parents Too.* New York: G. P. Putnam, 1951.
16. English, O. S. & Pearson, G. L., *Emotional Problems of Living.* New York: Norton, 1955, pp. 435-437.
17. Erikson, E. H., *Childhood and Society.* New York: Norton, 1950, pp. 230-231.
18. *Ibid.*, p. 231.
19. *Ibid.*, pp. 229-231.
20. *Ibid.*, p. 230.
21. *Ibid.*, p. 229.
22. *Ibid.*, p. 233.
23. Erikson, E. H., Growth and Crises of the Healthy Personality. In: *Personality in Nature, Society and Culture*, Ed. C. Kluckhohn & H. Murray. New York: Alfred A. Knopf, 1953, p. 223.
24. Filer, R. N. & O'Connell, D. D., Motivation of Aging Persons. *J. Gerontol.*, 19:15-22, 1964.
25. Fromm, E., *Psychoanalysis and Religion.* New Haven: Yale University Press, 1950, pp. 21-64.
26. Fromm, E., *The Art of Loving.* New York: Harper Bros., 1956, pp. 9-17.
27. *Ibid.*, p. 18.
28. Freeman, H., *Legal Interviewing and Counseling.* St. Paul, Minn.: West Publishing Co., 1964.
29. Gitelson, M., The Emotional Problems of Elderly People. *Geriat.* 3:138-139, 1948.
30. *Ibid.*, pp. 147-148.
31. *Ibid.*, p. 142.
32. Goode, W. J., *After Divorce.* Glencoe, Ill.: The Free Press, 1956.
33. Goodenough, E. R., *Toward a Mature Faith.* New York: Prentice-Hall, 1955.
34. Group for the Advancement of Psychiatry, Report No. 14: *The Problem of the Aged Patient in the Public Psychiatric Hospital.* Topeka: G.A.P., 1950, p. 1.

35. Group for the Advancement of Psychiatry, Report No. 24: *Integration and Conflict in Family Behavior*. Topeka: G.A.P., 1954.
36. Guttmacher, M., The Homosexual in Court. *Amer. J. Psychiat.*, 112:591, 1956.
37. Guttmacher, M. & Weihofen, H., Sex Offenders. *J. Crim. Law, Criminol. & Police Sci.*, 43:157, 1952.
38. Kerckhoff, A. C., Husband-Wife Expectations and Reactions to Retirement. *J. Gerontol.*, 19:510-516, 1964.
39. Kubie, L. S., Psychoanalysis and Marriage. In: *Neurotic Interaction in Marriage*, Ed. V. Eisenstein. New York: Basic Books, 1956.
40. Lawrence, D. H., *Lady Chatterley's Lover*. New York: New American Library, 1954.
41. Le Shan, L., Dynamics in Accident-Prone Behavior. *Psychiat.*, 15:73, 1952.
42. Levy, J. & Monroe, R., *The Happy Family*. New York: Alfred A. Knopf, 1950.
43. Linden, M. & Courtney, D., The Human Life Cycle and Its Interruptions —A Psychological Hypothesis. In: *Mental Health and Mental Disease*, Ed. A. M. Rose. New York: Norton, 1955, p. 363.
44. McGregor, O. R., *Divorce in England*. London: Heinemann, 1957, pp. 1-34.
45. *Ibid.*, p. 127.
46. Mead, M., *Male and Female*. New York: W. Morrow, 1949.
47. Menninger, K. A., Purposive Accidents as an Expression of Self-destructive Tendencies. *Internat. J. Psychoanal.*, 17:6-16, 1936.
48. Needles, W., A Note on Orgastic Loss of Consciousness. *Psychoanal. Quart.*, 22:512-518, 1953.
49. Noyes, A. P., *Modern Clinical Psychiatry*. Philadelphia: W. B. Saunders, 1953, pp. 321-323.
50. Parsons, T., Age and Sex in the Social Structure of the United States. In: *Personality in Nature, Society and Culture*, Ed. C. Kluckhohn & H. Murray. New York: Alfred A. Knopf, 1953, pp. 368-372.
51. *Ibid.*, pp. 374-375.
52. Randall, G. C., Ewalt, J. R. & Blair, H., Psychiatric Reaction to Amputation. In: *Military Neuropsychiatry*. Baltimore: Williams & Wilkins, 1946, pp. 94-115.
53. Rasmussen, K., *The Netsilik Eskimos Social Life and Spiritual Culture*. Copenhagen: Nordisk Forlag, 1931, p. 507.
54. Resko, J., *Reprieve: The Treatment of John Resko*. New York: Doubleday, 1956.
55. Riesman, D., *The Lonely Crowd*. New Haven: Yale University Press, 1950.
56. Rosenbaum, S. & Alger, I. *Psychoanalysis and Marriage*. New York: Basic Books.
57. Saul, L. J. & Lyons, J. W., Acute Neurotic Reactions. In: *Dynamic Psychiatry*, Ed. F. Alexander & H. Ross. Chicago: University of Chicago Press, 1952, pp. 140-164.
58. Schroeder, W. W. & Beegle, A. J., Suicide: An Instance of High Rural Rates. In: *Mental Health and Mental Disease*, Ed. A. M. Rose. New York: Norton, 1955, pp. 418-419.

59. Smith, H. W. & Cobb, S., Relations of Emotions to Injury and Disease: Legal Liability for Psychic Stimuli. *Va. Law Rev.*, 30:285-291, 1944.
60. Smith, H. W. & Solomon, H. C., Traumatic Neuroses in Court. *Va. Law Rev.*, 30:87, 1943.
61. Smith, M. E. & Hall, C., An Investigation of Regression in a Long Series of Dreams. *J. Gerontol.*, 19:66-71, 1964.
62. U. S. Dept. of Health, Education & Welfare, *Looking Forward to the Later Years.* Public Health Service Pub. #116, 1953.
63. Watson, A. S., The Conjoint Psychotherapy of Marriage Partners. *Amer. J. Orthopsychiat.*, 33:912-913, 1963.
64. Watson, A. S., The Fear of Faith. *Pastoral Psychol.*, 1:18-26, 1963.
65. Watson, A. S., The Lawyer as Counselor. *J. Family Law*, 5:7-20, 1965.
66. Watson, A. S., Psychoanalysis and Divorce. In: *The Marriage Relationship*, Ed. S. Rosenbaum & I. Alger. New York: Basic Books, 1968.
67. Webster, *Collegiate Dictionary.* Springfield, Mass.: G. & C. Merriam (5th Ed.), 1948, p. 1074.

XI

Mental Illness and the Law

To leave this subject until last in a book used by lawyers, will appear to many as placing the horse behind the cart. Certainly, in terms of the psychiatrist's traditional participation in the legal process, there is some justification for this observation. However, to improve psychiatry's usefulness to the law, there must first be a better understanding by lawyers of the kind of dynamic psychiatric theory we have described.

In the second chapter, we discussed the concept of etiology—the cause-effect relationships between the various elements in a disease *process*. We mentioned that this approach to psychiatric illness is to be distinguished from the "descriptive" approach where mental illness is diagnosed according to the *presence or absence of certain symptoms* (elements of which the patient himself is aware of and can describe), and *signs* (which the physician himself may find "objectively" during his examination). If the required number of elements are present *and* satisfy the arbitrary demands of the classification system, the patient "has the disease." As we might expect, this approach characterized all early efforts by psychiatrists to conceptualize mental illness. Today, psychiatric research is concerned mainly with efforts to explore and clarify the process or processes which produce mental illness. We may see that this work relates to etiology, and not merely to description.

Before discussing the subject of mental illness, let us first note that it may be divided into *organic* and *functional* disorders. Those illnesses classified as organic have clearly demonstrable physical causes, such as infection, alteration of blood supply to the brain due to aging or other pathological processes, effects of trauma, and various toxic agents. Originally it was believed that the symptoms and signs of organic disease were solely the result of the organic cause. However, recent studies show that, even here, signs and symptoms are due, to a considerable extent, to psychological defense maneuvers directed toward re-establishing a psychological sense of body integrity (3, 34).

Functional mental illnesses (which will be our principal interest here) are, at least for the present, of "unknown" physical etiology. We should re-emphasize that, in the ultimate analysis, these reactions must be of a physiological nature. However, they produce changes which are so subtle that, at present, we have no way of describing them specifically. Recent research has shed additional light on the physiology of the central nervous system, but we still have to resort to abstract conceptualizations in order to describe and account for the functional mental disorders (12, 13, 29).

Needless to say, pathological processes which are difficult to define and substantiate with objective evidence, make the problem of classification difficult. This problem notwithstanding, psychiatrists, almost universally, have adopted a "standard" nomenclature. This is revised constantly as new knowledge is added and as changes in general acceptability of concepts occur. Such a system does not satisfy any single group of psychiatrists *in toto*. It represents deliberate compromise and is the least common denominator which is "acceptable" to all. All physicians utilize this nomenclature in an effort to simplify the process of communication within the medical profession. The shortcomings of the system are well-known by all within the profession, and further changes must await improvement in our ability to define objectively and to quantify some of the elements of the psychopathological process. The system is descriptive in character, and each disease syndrome is defined by the presence of certain signs and symptoms. The judgment of which label to apply to a given patient is indeed a difficult one. There very often will be considerable disagreement between psychiatrists in the choice of labels, even though all may tend to agree on the clinical findings they observe and which lead to the labeling. This is a factor of extreme importance when evaluating the "battle of the experts." The "battle" often has more to do with the decision of labeling than it does with the observation and description of the elements which lead to the label choice (8, 17, 19, 22, 50). Very often, nonpsychiatrists tend to exaggerate the nature of this conflict, and read into it implications of confused theory and variations in observation which are not present.[1]

We may ask why the process of diagnosis and the system of nomenclature has not been improved and refined when the deficiencies of the system appear to be so well-known. The answer is quite simple. The problem of collecting sufficiently large data samples and analyzing them in the manner necessary to arrive at solid, statistically valid conclusions would be a formidable task costing an enormous amount of money (32, 45). There are problems of separating out cultural factors, differences in the judgments of clinicians, problems of communication, plus all the standard difficulties arising in any research situation. These render the problem almost insurmountable, at least for the immediate future.

After painting this gloomy picture, many may be ready to accept the view, often put forward by lawyers, that the "science" of psychiatry is in no adequate condition to be embraced more than tentatively by the law. However, this is hardly an accurate assay of the situation. After depreciating the process of labeling, what remains of use to the lawyer? Here the value of an etiological and dynamic psychiatry comes to the fore. Here is an approach to mental illness which views human behavior as a spectrum ranging from extremes of abnormality to complete "normality." Let us now explore the concept of mental illness within this frame of reference.

Those who have followed the discussion above, by now must have the restless sensation that the concept of abnormality, or mental illness, is predicated upon certain assumptions about the nature of "mental health." Indeed, their deduction is correct, and here lies the challenge. What is mental health? What is normality? To say that mental health is the absence of abnormality, or the absence of mental illness is a circular escape. And yet a study of the literature on this subject readily reveals the immense difficulty in pinning this question down in a way which permits its study. However, since we

---

[1] Official psychiatric nomenclature is detailed in *Diagnostic and Statistical Manual: Mental Disorders,* published by the American Psychiatric Association (Washington, D.C., 1952), and prepared by its Committee on Nomenclature and Statistics. In the foreword to this volume, there is a brief summary of the history of its preparation, starting in 1927. The first trial edition was published in 1932, and the current edition represents the third major revision.

are committed to this course, we begin by describing what is meant by mental health. Although we find nearly as many definitions as there are authors, there are many common denominators among them. We end up with a definition which implies that, to be designated *normal*, an individual *at least* must have certain characteristics. These characteristics must be present in sufficient degree to enable efficient functioning in relation to life problems, and be associated generally with a sense of psychic comfort. Often, the psychiatrist equates mental health with maturity. This, however, does not escape a complex definition, with a listing of criteria. English and Pearson, in *The Emotional Problems of Living*, state that:

The mature individual should:

1. Be able to work a reasonable amount each day at his job without undue fatigue or strain, and feel that his work is serving a useful purpose.
2. Be able to like, and accept many lasting friendships; be able to love and be tender and affectionate with a few close friends.
3. Have such confidence in himself that he is not harassed by guilt, doubt, or indecision. He should have enough confidence in himself to be able to oppose impositions upon himself and his family.
4. Be as free of prejudice as possible and treat all men and women with appropriate respect.
5. Be able to give and receive love with joy in a conventional heterosexual way, free of guilt or inhibition.
6. Extend his interest in an ever widening circle from self to family, friends, community, state, and nation, and seek to take a part in contributing to the general welfare of mankind.
7. Be interested in advancing his own welfare without exploitation of his fellow man.
8. Be able to alternate work with play, recreation, reading, and the enjoyment of nature, poetry, art and music.
9. Be free of undue body strain, stresses, and tensions when performing his everyday duties, as when confronted with adversity.
10. Be dependable, truthful, open-minded, and imbued with a philosophy that includes a willingness to suffer a little in order to grow, improve, and achieve wisdom.
11. Be interested in passing on his hard-won knowledge to the young.

These criteria of maturity should enable an individual to use his mind with enough efficiency to keep up his sense of well being and thereby avoid anxiety and neurotic patterns of behavior. A mature mind creates and preserves mental health as it goes through life and has a reserve of mental health for every life period including old age.[2]

When he defines mental illness, the psychiatrist merely places a negative prefix to the qualities described above as maturity. Analysis of these qualities reveals failure in one or more of the ego's functions for coping with internal and external reality or, in other words, failure in the resolution of individual life problems (20, 27, 28, 53). This means, then, that any effort to delineate the mentally ill behavior of an individual calls for a specific description in terms of his personality functioning, his capacity to cope with his life situation. To state that a person is "schizophrenic," or "irresponsible," or "insane," or "psychopathic," or to use any number of other appellations has no specific value to the lawyer (or the psychiatrist, for that matter) in his work. The degree to which a psychiatrist can describe accurately the manner in which an individual perceives, remembers, describes, reasons, and reacts to his experience, as well as the manner in which unconscious emotional pressures impinge upon those capacities, measures his usefulness to the lawyer in his task of determining such issues as responsibility, competence, or credibility. Any other approach to these issues is misleading and does not give the maximum assistance which the law may expect from psychiatry.

Before we explore the question of what psychiatrists may contribute to the law with their diagnostic skill, let us describe how they derive their data. Then we can analyze their usefulness and specify ways in which lawyers can use psychiatric information effectively. Frequently, during a trial, it is pointed out that, since the psychiatrist obtained his data from the patient only, there is serious doubt about their accuracy. This presupposes that the examiner "believes" all he is told, and takes it as fact. Nothing could be more inaccurate. During the course of the interview with the patient, the psychiatrist listens not only to what the patient says and how he says it, but also to what he does not say. He watches closely for subtle cues to emotion which the patient may not be aware of, but which are clearly revealed to a skilled interviewer. In addition to listening to the patient's "free association," he questions him directly so that he may

[2] Jahoda (24) points up the enormous complexity of research in this area. She surveys the problems encountered in any effort to explore issues of mental health or mental illness.

ascertain how his subject's ego copes with the problems incident to an interview. He examines his capacity to remember, to perceive, to put together various thoughts; he evaluates his capacity to relate to other persons, to time and place; he evaluates the emotional qualities which are revealed in the interview; he takes a detailed history of the patient's past life, especially as it relates to important figures, such as parents, siblings and other persons closely involved in his rearing.[3] Although these "facts" may be distorted and bear little resemblance to the real historical facts, they do reflect the past as the patient thinks it occurred, and therefore represent much of the motivational basis for the patient's behavior. They may be likened to the magical conceptions of primitive man who, so long as he thought there were evil spirits, acted as if they existed: Reality as we see it has little to do with such behavior.

Now let us examine the way the law utilizes psychiatric information in a criminal trial. One of the most common errors is to use psychiatric data primarily for the purpose of arriving at a diagnostic label. In the vast majority of cases, it would appear that the goal of counsel on both sides of a criminal case is to arrive at some diagnosis (i.e., a category of cases to a label), hoping thereby to resolve the issue (5, 48). The psychiatrist is first asked what his diagnostic designation is; then he is forced to prove the accuracy or inaccuracy of the diagnosis by minutely examining each element which caused him to arrive at his diagnosis. A good example of this occurred in the Hiss trial, where the psychiatric expert was relentlessly challenged on the basis of his diagnosis of Chambers (23). Without examining the pros and cons of using such testimony, its value did not turn on what diagnostic category the witness used. Rather, it related to the accuracy of his judgments about a behavioral capacity—that of truth-telling. That judgment needed other data.

The purpose of psychiatric testimony has been excellently described and analyzed in a District of Columbia case, *Carter* v. *U.S.* (252 F.2d 608, 617), in which the court said:

> . . . to make a reasonable inference concerning the relationship between a disease and a certain act, the trier of the facts must be informed with

[3] For a thorough summary of the manner in which psychiatrists approach psychiatric examinations, see Menninger (30). An excellent description of the manner in which a psychoanalyst approaches case evaluation is to be found in "The Psychoanalytic Diagnostic Interview" by Saul (39).

some particularity. This must be done by testimony. Unexplained medical labels—schizophrenia, paranoia, psychosis, neurosis, psychopathy— are not enough. Description and explanation of the origin, development and manifestations of the alleged disease are the chief functions of the expert witness. The chief value of an expert's testimony in this field, as in all other fields, rests upon the material from which his opinion is fashioned and the reasoning by which he progresses from his material to his conclusion; in the explanation of the disease and its dynamics, that is, how it occurred, developed and affected the mental and emotional processes of the defendant; it does not lie in his mere expression of a conclusion. The ultimate inferences, *vel non* of relationships, of cause and effect, are for the trier of the facts.

We should remember that, in criminal cases, the psychiatrist is testifying on the relationship between some piece of past behavior and the psychological functioning of the defendant. In questions of competency, again his contribution is to relate some activity in the past, such as writing a will, to the witness's mental health at that time—could he perceive, think, judge, remember, act independently, etc.? Diagnostic labels, at best, give only indirect, inferential information on such matters. How then should the psychiatrist present his testimony?

In a criminal trial, what the triers of the facts desire to know is: (1) What was the nature of the mental functioning of the defendant at a specific time in the past? (2) How did that mental functioning relate to the crime committed in terms of his mental processes? A psychiatrist has no special competency for deciding whether or not the person should be punished, for this is purely a moral judgment. Any trial procedure which forces him to make such a judgment not only compromises his position as a medical expert, but also unjustifiably elevates his opinion on morality above that of the community (38). What he may be able to do is to shed light on the behavior of the accused in regard to some specific time, place, or action which will help the finders of the facts perform their function. All too often, psychiatrists, not understanding the nature of their role in the criminal trial (or the civil one either, for that matter), appropriate the function of the judge and adjust testimony in relation to legal problems, so that they arrive at some dispositional conclusion which fits their judgment about what should be done. This greatly confuses the issue, begs principal trial questions, and diminishes the possibility for arriving at a rational presentation of the scientific evidence. This is well illustrated in the case of *Briscoe* v. *U.S.* (248 F.2d 640) where psychiatrists and psychologists alike abdicated their appropriate functions and gave what amounted to judicial conclusions. For example, the psychologist stated that petitioner "is not suffering from mental defect of sufficient severity to render him mentally incompetent," while the psychiatrist stated that the petitioner was "of sound mind." Both of these conclusions are obviously judicial and do not coincide with either medical or psychological concepts (26).

Many psychiatrists feel they should not participate at all in the criminal trial, since it forces them into the position of making this sort of judgment (46). However, it would appear that, if he fully recognizes his function, the psychiatric expert may resist the pressure and render his medical opinion on the nature of the accused's behavior as it relates to the crime. Without discussing the pros and cons of the various rules regarding responsibility, a well-thought-out psychiatric opinion in relation to any case will greatly help the triers of the facts to arrive at a verdict commensurate with the rational, scientific data as well as with their own unconscious and conscious moral attitudes regarding the accused and his act (15). The psychiatrist can do little about the emotional reaction of the community in relation to any particular crime. However, if he presents his evidence clearly, he at least can help the jury find its verdict under circumstances most likely to result in a rational consideration of the issue of responsibility (6).

Another important question raised in relation to psychiatric expert testimony concerns the accuracy of diagnoses and formulations. It seems clear that the accurate use of diagnostic labels is highly questionable, since each person using the label probably interprets it somewhat differently and therefore inconsistently with other experts using the same set of labels (42). However, as noted above, this has little to do with determining the objective data needed in the case. We should recall that "objective" in this context relates also to the subjective data about the patient. The psychiatrist listening to the patient objectively analyzes subjective data. For this type of observation, there are few studies regarding its accuracy, although there is a widely held clinical impression that multiple observations will arrive readily at the same set of observed data.[4] This has led to the suggestion by many psychiatrists that the experts on both sides of a case should examine the patient simultaneously in order to determine which observations can be mutually agreed upon (35, 51, 52). These would then be presented to the fact triers without the frequent distortion resulting from adversary procedure. It would be similar to the pretrial conference in which parties concerned arrive at as many stipulated facts as possible, in order not to have to present them and prove them during the trial itself. This is an excellent suggestion. Put into practice, it would lessen considerably what appears as controversy, but what is in fact more related to the trial process than to basic differences in observation by the experts (54). We may say, then, that while observation and description of behavior can be agreed upon widely, to employ diagnostic labels which, by their very nature, are vague and controversial results in much difference of opinion. The further one moves away from the highly disturbed psychotic states toward the "acting-out" illnesses, such as the character disorders, the greater the likelihood for discrepancy, since the latter syndromes, by their very nature, are much more difficult to define.

Another critical matter which the psychiatrist often is asked to comment upon has to do with prediction of future behavior. Here again, there is very little specific data from which to evaluate accuracy. There is no doubt that the level of accuracy does not remotely approach perfection. In fact, if one were to make an optimistic speculation, it might not exceed 75 per cent.[5] Why is this? First of all, as noted in earlier chapters regarding the concept of determinism, behavior is always in response to, and in the context of, certain very specific stimuli. The well-trained dynamic psychiatrist, if he were to know specifically what future events his patient would be subjected to, could predict with a high degree of accuracy what his patient's reactions would be. However, with the wide variety of possible life situations, all of which impinge differently on the psyche and alter its end product of action, it is very difficult to state specifically what the future behavior of an individual will be. The best

[4] For a study which casts some doubt on this assumption, see Cattell and Scheier (4).
[5] It appears that psychiatrists tend to over-predict the likelihood of future emotional difficulty. See Berliner (1), and Zilboorg (55).

possible prediction must be stated in equivocal terms: *If* a certain type of event occurs, and *if* the persons in his environment have been relating to him in a certain way, since the patient will follow his typical patterns from the past, *then* his reaction will be such-and-such. This, of course, is indefinite and leaves many ponderables. But, it limits possibilities in a substantial way. While not so accurate as we might prefer, this is probably as good a prediction as is possible at the present time.

Related to prediction of future behavior is the question of the impact of various kinds of post-trial treatment upon an individual. This is a matter in which the psychiatric expert has a great deal to contribute and, in the eyes of many, is the principal area in which he should function (46).[6] After defining and formulating the personality of the individual, a psychiatrist should be reasonably capable of deciding what the results of various forms of treatment will be upon the accused (14). This is the same as the problem posed when a patient comes to him for psychotherapy.

In regard to possible psychotherapeutic results with a given patient, we cannot say how fast progress will occur and, in some cases, even if it is possible. The answers to these questions may be clarified only after treatment has been initiated for a time, and most psychotherapists begin a new patient's therapy as well as answer these questions with a "therapeutic trial." This trial is utilized to observe the actual way in which the patient responds to the therapeutic situation. Such an observational period is warranted in all forms of correctional treatment.[7] While considerable data is accumulating, psychotherapeutic efforts with criminals have been limited in the past. More humane and therapeutically oriented methods have recently been instituted in several institutions, but they have not operated long enough as yet to know exactly what basic character alteration may be expected with such institutional treatment.

Some important questions related to the use of psychiatry in the legal process relate to how long it takes to collect sufficient data to make an accurate psychiatric diagnosis and how much it costs. In regard to cost, in large metropolitan areas, the cost of competent psy-

[6] Zilboorg (55) implies that under the current status of the law, psychiatrists should avoid testifying in criminal cases.

[7] A type of sentencing with such tentativeness built into it has been suggested by the reporters of the ALI Model Penal Code (49).

chiatric consultation is roughly from $20 to $35 per hour. Since most psychiatrists work largely on a fixed office schedule, they usually charge this amount for the lapsed time spent on the case. For example, if it is necessary for the psychiatrist to leave his office and visit a prison, he is likely to charge a considerable proportion of his hourly rate for his travel time.

Comments found in legal opinions and in the psychiatric literature about this time requisite vary from conservative, which state that a period of as long as six weeks is necessary to arrive at any substantial conclusion, to others which present the view that two or three hours of skillful interviewing may produce a valid diagnostic formulation (39). The answer to this question lies mainly with the nature of the person being examined, the technical skill of the examiner, and *the use to which the data will be put.* Also, it is well known that an individual's wish to cooperate is of extreme importance in determining the ease with which appropriate and significant data may be procured. Let us illustrate this with a few examples.

A patient who is so disturbed as to be completely out of contact with reality (and who the psychiatrist would call "psychotic"), obviously can give very little data about himself. This does not raise any major problem, however, since data on his illness and the nature of past interpersonal relationships would be obtained from other sources. In these cases, especially, outside corroboration and assistance are necessary (31). Individuals examined against their will can refuse to give any information. In such cases, also, diagnostic formulations have to be drawn from outside sources, as well as from the direct observation of behavioral attributes manifested during the interview. While diagnosis based on these data quite naturally has greater tentativeness, it is not without significance, and often may be useful and substantially reliable. Many individuals who would come under criminal treatment would fit in this group. It should be re-emphasized that diagnosis is a different problem from treatment. It is considerably more difficult to block psychiatric diagnosis and formulation than it is to escape therapeutic intervention.

Another problem which frequently concerns lawyers is the question of malingering or lying. It is fear of this possibility which often elicits the criticism that psychiatrists make no effort to corroborate the statements of their subjects, and therefore cannot be sure of the accuracy of their statements about the people they examine. Careful scrutiny of the data which psychiatrists deem diagnostically significant emphasizes the difficulty which a patient would have in systematically altering his reactions to fit a faked diagnosis, even if he knew a great deal about the technical aspects of psychiatry. Also, though this may appear to be a built-in rationalization for the psychiatrist, current clinical theory holds that the symptom of malingering itself merits the diagnosis of mental illness. We must assume, however, that there are some few individuals (found in the group known as "sociopaths") who may use technical knowledge to distort, thus enabling them, for a brief time, to "fool" the psychiatrist. This group provides us with the "pathological liar" who is, indeed, most difficult to examine adequately. Such patients are able to present their consciously distorted stories with such emotional conviction that many of the clues to lying which other persons offer are nearly missing. This is the one group of adult patients whose statements it is essential to corroborate. The fact that these persons present a story which is "too pat," and too free of "normal" inconsistencies, will prompt the skillful interviewer to make corroborative investigations, all of which will give him sufficient data to arrive at the diagnosis of sociopathy (2, 10). These patients obviously require a longer period of time for examination, and the general requirement of two or three hours does not hold for them. Time works against such individuals since, inevitably, they tend to slip up on the small details which are the very essence of psychiatric diagnosis. With these persons, inexperienced or relatively unskillful psychiatric interviewers may be taken in.

A recent novel, *The Anatomy of a Murder* (47), presents the exciting story of just such a case. In this novel, the author describes a prisoner who pleaded insanity in a murder case. The end of the novel makes it clear that he was, in fact, guilty, and that he had successfully deceived the psychiatrist and all others concerned with his defense. No one may deny this possibility; however, individuals who have this capacity are not so common as to make them any substantial risk. At any rate, the psychiatrist is able to detect this type of behavior at least as well as any other person, since he is trained to detect the subtle clues which betray intentions to deceive.

We remarked above that the time needed to conduct an adequate psychiatric examination is related to its intended use. If a lawyer simply wants an opinion about a psychiatric-legal issue regarding a client, a one- to two-hour examination usually permits a fairly solid and reliable judgment by the psychiatrist. However, if the psychiatric opinion is to become the basis for testimony in court, where it will have to be *demonstrated* to a fact-finder and be subjected to crossexamination, it will usually take four or five hours to get adequate data to make the psychodynamic issue visible to nonexperts. The lawyer will want to be further buttressed by his examination of all other documents and data about the client, which might shed light on his behavior. This latter data will only rarely conflict with the inferences drawn from a skillful clinical examination. It will not only fill out the details of the client's behavior, but it will also serve to corroborate the less obvious clinical inferences.

When counsel seeks such examination data he may proceed in a sequence of steps. There is no need to do as thorough a study as described above, unless it has been decided to use the information at trial. Each stage should be developed in consultation with the psychiatrist so that he understands fully the legal purposes for which his data will be used. Otherwise, there can be much wasteful exploration of *culs-de-sac*.

We may say in summary that a two- or three-hour interview by a competent, dynamically oriented interviewer will provide the sort of data necessary to arrive at the kind of psychiatric opinions needed in most legal situations. At the rates quoted above, for approximately $80 to $175 a skilled psychiatric diagnostic opinion can be obtained about most individuals. However, for accurate prognostic opinions, more time investment may be needed.

PSYCHIATRIC TESTIMONY

The perennial complaints of the psychiatric profession in regard to its function with the law tend to center around the kind of information they are asked to give in testimony for insanity pleas. Psychiatrists strenuously object to being asked for moral judgments such as whether or not the patient "knows right from wrong" (36). We have already noted that psychiatrists are no more competent to make moral judgment than other members of society (56). Their main competency is their ability to delineate and describe a person's psychological activity, and its relationship to experience and environment. The psychiatrist may comment, with some accuracy, about how these matters relate to past actions, and he may predict how they will influence future behavior. The second important area of competency involves the therapeutic skills armamentarium of the psychiatrist and relates to issues of disposition.

A. *The Diagnostic Formulation*

First, let us examine the nature of the psychiatric diagnostic formulation. As we have already made clear, most of the psychiatrist's data are drawn directly from the patient himself. There are exceptions when working with children, psychotics, and persons afflicted with some forms of character neuroses (designated as sociopaths) who are given to prevarication. Through relatively indirect questions, the psychiatrist seeks to gain a comprehensive picture of the background of the patient, the personality characteristics of the principal members of the family, the nature of the social environment and, most important of all, the emotional attitudes and adaptive techniques of the patient. As we have emphasized, the matter of factual accuracy is relatively unimportant, since the point of real diagnostic significance is *how* the patient views and evaluates his experiences. We do not expect the "facts" which are presented to be historically accurate. However, they are the *most* accurate presentation of the patient's attitudes about these facts. Since these are the forces which motivate his behavior, they must be regarded as the crucial data (40).

During the course of the interview, the psychiatrist "listens with his third ear";[8] in other words, he listens for the spoken and unspoken clues to deeper emotional attitudes which the patient holds unbeknownst to himself. In addition to emotional expressions which emerge as the patient relates his history (the anamnesis), there is ample opportunity to observe the patient's awareness of where he is, what he is doing, and to whom he is talking. For instance, involvement in a world of unreality may be revealed through such serious defensive aberrations as hallucinations and delusions. The patient's ability to place his observations into appropriate and reasonable categories, to think about them logically and to relate them more or

[8] An expression apparently coined by Theodor Reik.

less accurately with past experiences and future possibilities, and to associate the whole to ethical and philosophical considerations can be estimated and evaluated. The nature of his impulse life, the manner in which his ego copes with inner impulses and relates them to the world around him, as well as to his own moral and ethical value system, are observed and "formulated" by the examiner.

After the examination has been concluded (in fact, while it is going on), the psychiatrist formulates in his mind a dynamic concept of the total scope of his patient's psychological behavior and its genesis. After these data are derived, the psychiatrist is able to delineate the patient's character structure, and to know the nature of his specific repetition-compulsions. Once this is established, he may predict with fair accuracy how this person will relate to future situations and stresses. Here we should re-emphasize that prediction *must* be related to a multiple set of variables. We know from everyday experience that individual reactions vary according to shifting circumstances. For example, a person living within the bounds of his usual life situation will behave in one way, but if subjected to severe stress by some catastrophic circumstance, he may act like an entirely different person.[9] In our everyday estimates of people, we make intuitive rule-of-thumb judgments of their reactions to various kinds of situations. The psychiatrist does the same thing, but he carries his prediction to a greater degree of refinement, and can also describe explicitly *how* he made his judgments. He is able to describe more specifically the kinds of stresses which cause a person to alter behavior. Also, he is able to define the *cause* of particular reactions specifically in relation to varying stresses and to anticipate the manner in which they will be handled. Needless to say, at this time we cannot specify the precise degree of accuracy of these predictions.[10]

The single most significant technique which the dynamic psychiatrist has available to test and retest his hypothesis regarding his subject's behavior is the manner in which his subject relates to him in the interview setting. This relationship, which we have defined

[9] See the *Wells* case described by Diamond (7).

[10] Some efforts to quantify emotional reactivity and its direction are made in such projective tests as the Rorschach, and in such studies as those by Saul and his colleagues in which they attempt to quantify the emotional forces symbolized in dreams (25, 41).

as transference, is the source of the most accurate evaluation.[11] Using a well-structured situation, the analyst is able to watch the specific manner in which the patient reacts to him, as well as how he himself reacts and counter-reacts to the patient (37). It should be recalled that he works in a more-or-less standardized situation, with a more-or-less clearly defined concept of how his own personality impinges on others. Using this knowledge, he is able to ascertain the nature of the patient's specific reactivity to emotional stimuli.[12] During the course of the interview, he may deliberately introduce certain questions which provoke responses in the subject, and which he may measure against his clinical standard. We re-emphasize that the accuracy of this technique rests completely with the interviewer's ability to comprehend the nature of his own contribution to the interview situation. Herein lies the specific and highly refined diagnostic skill of the psychoanalyst.

Finally, we should comment on the manner in which the psychiatrist approaches a patient. The more he does this in the role of physician, the more data he will obtain. If the approach is that of a "prosecutor" whose function is to attack rather than help, problems are raised automatically which detract from the reliability of the data. A subject who knows that his revelations may be used against him will certainly not be so open as one who expects help in the form of treatment from a physician. This can raise deep conflicts for the psychiatrist, since he can be placed squarely between the Scylla of what he may conceive as his confidential relationship to a patient, and the Charybdis of his obligation as an investigator retained by a court or institution.[13] While this is an ethical matter which the psychiatrist can and must clarify for himself, it also involves the serious legal question of how and when his testimony may be utilized (32, 44). There are many problems remaining to be solved in this area, and we can expect continuing controversy over psychiatric expert testimony. So long as punishment and retribution play such important conscious and unconscious roles in decisions, psychiatrists and lawyers alike will continue to find themselves in ambiguous positions in relation to their professional roles.

[11] See Chapter I.
[12] See the example in the Problems section, Chapter IX.
[13] For a good analysis of this subject see the report on The Privileged Communication and Confidentiality of Psychiatrists by the Group for the Advancement of Psychiatry, Committee on Law (16).

B. *Diagnostic Labeling*

Diagnosis and its implications constitute one of the most highly controversial subjects in psychiatry. The concept of etiology, which rests at the foundation of any scientific approach to medicine, has been discussed previously. We assume that every disease is caused either by an alteration in the normal physiological process or by the introduction of a foreign agent which produces a secondary change in the body's functioning, even if it has not yet been isolated. We do not yet have an adequate etiologic explanation for most mental diseases. Although we assume that all mental functioning stems, ultimately, from physiological processes, due to the subtlety of these processes we are not yet, and perhaps never shall be, able to describe their particulars.[14] Therefore, most psychodiagnosis rests upon the arbitrary selection of certain behavior manifestations, which, if present in certain groupings or "syndromes," cause us to apply a certain diagnostic label. For about 200 years, psychiatrists have been attempting to arrive at a consistent diagnostic system. The mere fact that they have not been able to do so in the face of considerable scientific information demonstrates the elusiveness of the problem.

The currently accepted standard diagnostic system is contained in the manual referred to above.[15] Examination of this manual reveals a system of diagnostic classification which is meant to encompass all known psychiatric disabilities. While it is possible to place all psychiatric patients within the framework of this nomenclature, no psychiatrist is completely satisfied with it. The organically oriented psychiatrist complains that it depends too much on the "intangible, internal attitudes" which smack of the metapsychology of the psychoanalyst. The psychoanalyst, on the other hand, objects to the rigidity and "artificiality" produced when only external manifestations of behavior are utilized which imperfectly reflect personality functioning. Therefore, at best, this diagnostic system indicates the least common denominator acceptable to all groups of practicing psychiatrists. We have already mentioned the kinds of

14 For a recent study on the physiology of schizophrenia see Heath, et al. (21).
15 See this chapter, footnote 1.

research and the expenditures necessary for evolving a scientific nosology more acceptable to all concerned.[16]

Since there are many textbooks which fully present the details of diagnostic categories, no effort to explore these problems specifically will be made here. For detailed information on diagnostic classification, the reader is referred to standard works (9, 33).

Finally, I wish to caution once more that lawyers should not focus their interest on the labels a psychiatrist may apply to a patient's mental illness, but rather on how the patient's personality functioning relates to the specific issue being litigated. Labeling *per se* is of no use whatsoever, but description of functioning is. It will take considerable educative effort on the part of both lawyers and psychiatrists to erase this constant source of distortion and misunderstanding.

CONCLUSION

It is my hope that the material in this book will help law students, lawyers, and judges with their continuing effort to make the substance and practice of law better conform to the realities of human behavior. Effective counseling, more skillful advocacy, and rational legislation will all be better effectuated through incorporation of this kind of information and knowledge. Finally, it should facilitate work between behavioral scientists and those ultimate interdisciplinarians—lawyers. All of this will profit society, the most important benefactor of our two professions.

PROBLEMS

Example

One day, while you are working at your desk, your secretary informs you that there is a telephone call from a man who urgently wants to speak with you. You pick up the receiver and the man introduces himself as Mr. Midway. He says that he must see you about a friend, Mr. Samuel

---

[16] In his article, "Psychoanalysis Under Scientific Scrutiny," Scriven states that for the cost of 1.5 bombers we could scientifically answer the questions about the treatment (and therefore by necessity, the diagnosis) of mental illness. This is indeed an extravagantly optimistic estimate of cost (43).

Johnson, who is being held "in a hospital against his will." You inquire a bit further, and find that Johnson is in a private mental hospital, where he has been for the better part of a year. You ask Mr. Midway why he is calling you. He tells you that he visited his friend recently, and the man pleaded with him for help because "his family is keeping him locked up there against his will." He says that he spoke to the man's brother about it and was bluntly told "Stay out of it, and mind your own business. Sam is where he belongs and where he can get the help he needs." You ask Mr. Midway if he believes Sam needs help, and he responds that he thinks his friend is "as normal as you or me." Although you are not reassured by this, you suggest that he come in to see you at your office, and you give him an appointment.

During the intervening day before Mr. Midway sees you on behalf of his friend, you find yourself pondering several things. For example, if this man is mentally ill and "incompetent," who can proceed to engage you as his counsel, and how? Would a note from Mr. Johnson suffice to bring you into the matter on his behalf? What if the family objects to your seeing him, what will you do then? Mr. Midway himself sounded a bit odd on the phone. Should you get mixed up in this case at all? Assuming you do decide to intervene on Mr. Johnson's behalf, how will you go about finding out whether or not he is being improperly held? In regard to the latter point, you quickly ascertain that under the statutes of your state, "a person may be committed to a properly licensed mental hospital or to one of the hospitals maintained by the State Department of Mental Health if: (1) such person is certified to be mentally ill by two duly licensed physicians, and (2) is in need of treatment for said mental illness because he is dangerous to himself, others, or to property." You also find that a proper commitment is made by an order from the County Court, after the certificate is filed with the judge of that court, and he rules that it is in proper order.

When Mr. Midway arrives for his appointment, you are not terribly reassured by his appearance. Although he is properly dressed, there is a kind of "nearly coming apart" look about him. Upon questioning him, you find that he became friendly with Mr. Johnson when he was a patient at the same hospital. To your surprise, Mr. Midway presents you with a note from Johnson which gives Midway permission to act on his behalf and seek the assistance of counsel for him.

You ask Midway his opinion of why Johnson is not able to get out of the hospital if he's all right. He tells you that he doesn't know why Johnson can't leave: "He's as normal as I am and a lot better than some of those quacks they have working in that hospital." Although, again, you are not reassured by Mr. Midway's reasoning, he does describe what seems to be a more or less normally acting man, and you decide you will explore the matter further.

Hoping to be able to clear matters up some, you call up Mr. Johnson's brother from the phone number provided by Midway. After you have introduced yourself and explained the purpose of your call, instead of the help you hoped for, you are treated to a nasty blast in which you are told to "keep your damn hands off this case. My brother's as crazy as a March hare and you don't know what trouble we had with him until we got him into that place." You inquire if they are his guardians, and the answer you receive is "No, but we're taking care of him." This contact also fails to set your mind at rest, so you decide to go to the hospital to see Mr. Johnson.

When you introduce yourself to the receptionist, she hastily retreats to call the head nurse who informs you there is nothing on Mr. Johnson's "order sheet" which will permit her to let you visit him. You suggest to her that she had best get that amended immediately or you will have to take the matter up with the court, and you suggest to her that it is illegal to keep a lawyer from seeing his client. Does she "wish to take that responsibility?" It does not take her long to find a way to "permit" you to see Johnson, and you do.

Although you have little experience with mental patients, you gain the impression that Johnson appears quite normal. While you do not succeed in getting a very clear picture from him of the events which led to his hospitalization, you wonder whether or not you should attribute that lapse to his explanation that "they had me all doped up when they brought me here or I never would have come in." You sense that there is, at least, a very long history of tension if not open fighting between Mr. Johnson and his brother George, with whom you spoke earlier. Both are the sons and heirs presumptive of a very flourishing family business in which they both work (or did until Samuel was hospitalized). By now you are becoming a bit concerned, so you decide to press further with your exploration of the matter on Mr. Johnson's behalf, and you tell him so. You say you will call on him in about a week, after you have had a chance to gain a better understanding of the situation.

By the time you leave the hospital, you wonder if you might not have come upon a case of "railroading" (even though you accept that such things are quite rare). You decide that you will get a complete report from Mr. Johnson's doctor, and find out the details of the commitment procedure. You call the doctor on the telephone, and while he has some of the same questions you encountered at the front desk of his hospital, he is more tactful and suggests that he is "only trying to protect my patient's interests." You agree with him that such is a good line to follow, and you join with him fully in that concern. He promises to have his report in your hands within the week.

When you get a copy of the commitment order, you discover it to be couched in many expressions of conclusion, such as, "Mr. Johnson is suffering from acute schizophrenia, which makes him need hospital care. He has delusions and hallucinations, . . . etc." You can see at once that on the basis of the case law you looked up, there would be no trouble at all in getting Mr. Johnson released on a writ of habeas corpus, because of an improper commitment procedure. Now you find yourself with the interesting question of whether or not you should do that now. Because you wish to act in the best interests of your client, you should find out if he *needs* to be in the hospital for treatment.

By the time you arrive at this concern, you have received Dr. Altivez's report on Mr. Johnson. To your dismay (and satisfaction?) you find it filled with the same jargon which appeared in the commital form, although he had nothing to do with that procedure. "Mr. Johnson is suffering from a chronic form of schizophrenia which leaves him with a well organized system of delusions in which he thinks he is being persecuted by his brother. He is somewhat unrealistic in his thinking (for example he believes he should be released from the hospital because he is well— which he is not), he is deeply depressed and still suicidal, and probably he is unable to take care of himself adequately in relation to his family and his work." The report goes on, but does nothing more to enlighten you about Mr. Johnson's actual capacities, and it is totally devoid of the kind of evidence which would permit you to test whether such conclusions are true or not.

You dictate a letter to Dr. Altivez, telling him of your legal problem, and you set forth the *test* of commitability with an explanation of what these questions mean. You tell him that you would like to have him tell you in complete detail *why* he has arrived at the conclusion that Mr. Johnson is not well enough to take care of himself, and how he knows that Mr. Johnson is a suicide risk. Since you have an impression from your talk with Dr. Altivez that he may not fully understand what you are concerned with, you telephone and tactfully explain to him what is needed. In order to give him added motivation, you mention the inadequacy of the commitment form and suggest that there will have to be better evidence than you have seen so far, or surely Mr. Johnson will have to be released. The doctor's own anxiety becomes clearly palpable with your last remark, and he says somewhat testily that he does not "understand what you lawyers expect. I stated as plain as day what the facts are. Mr. Johnson is a sick man and needs help."

By now you are skeptical about receiving the kind of data you need to make a good decision from Dr. Altivez. Although you are on the verge of simply proceeding to file a petition for a writ of habeas corpus, something keeps you from doing so. While you *thought* Mr. Johnson appeared normal when you saw him, you have come to be more receptive to your feeling responses to people. You recall that you *felt* there was "something funny" about him, which you never could quite put your finger on. It had "something to do with the way he looked" at you, but you never could decide exactly what it was. For this reason, you proceed with a psychiatric examination by a consultant with whom you have had several satisfactory contacts in the past and with whom you now communicate rather freely (both you and he have learned something of each others' language). You call Dr. Peterson, make arrangements at the hospital for his visit, and await his report.

In the meantime, you have a second talk with Mr. Johnson. He has been waiting for you impatiently, and asks you as soon as you enter his room, "How come I'm not out of here yet?" This time you can recognize a little more of what made you restless about him on the last visit. It is the more palpable anger he now exhibits, and you note it to be sufficiently strong to make you experience a ripple which you can only think of as fear. You have learned not to be cowed in these circumstances (a *very* appropriate attitude to take with those who threaten, no matter what their mental state may be), and you promptly confront him with the fact that, "You sound pretty mad. Why?" You notice that the minute you press back at him this way, although he looks at you quizzically for a moment, he withdraws psychologically and looks very down in the mouth (depressed?). You explain to him that you don't blame him for being impatient, but you must make sure that you do the right thing for him. You tell him about your decision to have another examination done, and that Dr. Peterson will be in to see him shortly. You tell him that the minute you receive his report, you will come out and tell him what you think should be done.

Three days later, you get a telephone call from Dr. Peterson, who says that he thought that you would like to get the results of his examination before the written report arrives. He suggests that you will "probably want to tell Mr. Johnson about it as soon as possible so he doesn't have a lot of time to get it all wrapped up in the complications of his imagination." In essence, Dr. Peterson tells you the following about Johnson.

Johnson, being the older of two boys, was always the one who took most of the pressure from his parents to come up to their standard of performance. He had always done well in fact, but progressively and with the passage of time, he felt his parents favored his younger brother. "He always got things easily, they would never let me do." By the time Samuel and George were both graduated from college and started to work for their father, the old rivalry between them had broken out into the open. This became worse when Samuel's wife divorced him because of "mental cruelty." She complained that she could not stand her husband's withdrawn and often morose nature, and she just had to leave the marriage.

After that Johnson began to make "outrageous" accusations that his brother was trying to steal the business and that he and the father were always plotting against him. He threatened ominously that one of these days he would take matters in his own hands and he would "fix them" so they would not bother him any more. (These matters had been corroborated by Dr. Peterson through interviews with Samuel's father and brother George. He felt from his interviews that there was no indication whatsoever of such attitudes or intentions on their parts).

On other occasions, Mr. Johnson would go into the depths of despair and threaten to kill himself. At first, his threats were loud and coercive, but just before his hospitalization, he had become terribly moody. At those times it was feared that he might, in fact, follow out his threat. Dr. Peterson informs you that there is no doubt in his mind at all that Mr. Johnson is a very disturbed person, who has many deep convictions that his family are "against him." This belief came from the many imagined reasons he defensively deduced during his childhood. As a result of those inner images, he has built up more and more murderous feeling toward them in recent years (Dr. Peterson details a whole series of examples). Because he also has a very strict belief that a "nice person" doesn't even entertain such thoughts, he just as often, turns his fury back upon himself and becomes dangerously suicidal. According to Dr. Peterson there is no question but that Mr. Johnson should stay under hospital control until such time as he comes to understand his own impulses in better perspective and with insight into their origins as well as their current reality. Until that point in time, he might well kill his brother, or himself, or both. He also suggests that in the present hospital setting, while he is getting adequate control, he is not getting any kind of treatment which will enable him to develop the controls, insight, and understanding which can help him test out and resolve his psychological dilemma. Perhaps some other treatment facility would be more effective for achieving these goals.

Now counsel has a new set of problems. Clearly Mr. Johnson could get a release on a writ of habeas corpus because of procedural defects in the commitment.[17] However, if he did so, it might have tragic consequences.[18] Counsel goes to see Mr. Johnson and tells him that the results of the exploration reveal that he *is* still sick and in need of hospitalization. "I cannot even think of helping you get a release when you might get into serious trouble." Because Mr. Johnson does not have anyone looking out for his interests now, it might be a good idea to have the court appoint a guardian *ad litem* for him. This would assure that neither his family nor anyone else, could do anything which would be against his interests.

If he presses to get a petition filed, counsel would urge Doctor Altivez or the family to move for a new commitment, properly filed, coupled with the appointment of a guardian *ad litem*. (I would not consider this likely if he is dealt with honestly and openly. After all he "knows" that he is disturbed. This is an assumption one can always make with the mentally ill. But issues must be put to them openly and honestly, or they will believe nothing which is said. One is discredited.)

Counsel would urge the family to seek some other kind of treatment facility in which Dr. Peterson's recommendations could be carried out. (Here Dr. Peterson has an ethical problem, because he must take exception to Dr. Altivez' program. However, we also have the fact that Mr. Johnson himself has stated that he does not feel he is getting proper help at this hospital. The combined tact of counsel and the consultant should be able to solve this problem.)

We should observe here that, although the commitment form was defective, there were, in fact, serious grounds for commitment. This is not an unusual case. Nearly always, by the time a person is hospitalized he has used up all of the available family and community resources for his care. Commitment is a last resort. As we saw here, the right thing is often done for the wrong reasons. Lawyers should always explore the whole issue, not just the legal procedure. If this is done, then counsel will surely be acting in his client's best interests, which is *one* of the ethical obligations he owes by virtue of his professional role. Such a course, followed in this case, will assure the optimal opportunities for Mr. Johnson to return home and will protect society, thus also fulfilling counsel's obligations to the bar.

[17] The vast majority of civil commitments are subject to these defects and could be overturned if tested in court.

[18] This raises an interesting ethical problem for the lawyer. Should he get his client out of the hospital? Would that be in his client's best interest? Is it "the lawyer's role" to do so? Or should he take a broader view and make sure that he can't get out, in order to keep him out of trouble? The course of action I lay out, is the solution I would think proper for counsel to follow.

1. The Court of Appeals for the District of Columbia, when setting forth its test for responsibility said, "It is simply that an accused is not criminally responsible if the unlawful act was the product of mental disease or mental defect." (*Durham v. United States*, 214 F.2d 862, 874-875). Many of the learned commentators on this rule have said that it is anything but "simple," and they feel this will lead to testimony going to the jury which leaves them "groping their way through a blizzard of scientific terminology and conflicting theories, without any guide to their objective. . . . How could there be any certainty at all of their reaching the objective of the rule of law?" (18).

    (a) Using the information about mental illness and its evaluation found in this chapter, argue both the negative and affirmative sides of this contention.

    (b) Argue the same issues for the M'Naghten test of "knowing the difference between right and wrong" and "knowing the nature and quality of the act."

2. A man has been held on an indictment for armed robbery. You are sitting as a judge in the criminal court, and counsel for defendant petitions you to find his client incompetent to stand trial because of mental illness. In your jurisdiction, you will have an investigation of competency by a commission of physicians.

    (a) What information would you direct such a commission to supply for you? Frame a specific request, so its members will have no doubt as to what information you wish from them.

    (b) How will the nature of the information you wish to obtain influence the type of doctors you appoint to the commission?

    (c) What are the pros and cons of appointing nonpsychiatrists to this sort of commission?

3. Under the current commitment laws in many states, persons may be permanently committed to a mental hospital upon examination of any two licensed physicians. This kind of statute obviously raises many serious questions.

    (a) What do you think of the medical validity of such laws?

    (b) What do you think the standards for involuntary hospitalization should be, and what kind of information do you think should be presented by the doctors in support of their contention?

    (c) In the light of the irregular geographic distribution of qualified psychiatrists, how would you set up an optimal arrangement so that the best medical evaluations are available for involuntary hospitalizations, commensurate with the full protection of a patient's civil liberties?

5. Psychiatrists are often called upon by courts to testify in cases involving the custody of children. This is based on the assumption that they possess the means to determine what is in the best psychological interests of the child, as well as for the parents or parent surrogates.

(a) What kind of evidence do you think they should be required to present in cases where they recommend that the child be removed from its natural parents?

(b) In what form do you think this information should be presented? How would you frame a statement to the psychiatrist so that he would conduct his examination appropriately, as well as present you with the kind of information which you think necessary for this purpose?

REFERENCES

1. Berliner, I., The Psychiatric Aspects of Military Manpower Conservation. *Amer. J. Psychiat.*, 111:91, 1954.
2. Biach, R., The Psychiatric Aspects of Malingering. In: *Handbook of Correctional Psychology*. New York: Philosophical Library, 1947, pp. 321-332.
3. Brosin, H., Contributions of Psychoanalysis to the Study of Organic Cerebral Disorders. In: *Dynamic Psychiatry*, Ed. F. Alexander & H. Ross. Chicago: University of Chicago Press, 1952, pp. 211-254.
4. Cattell, R. & Scheier, I., Clinical Validities by Analyzing the Psychiatrist Exemplified in Relation to Anxiety Diagnosis. *Amer. J. Orthopsychiat.*, 28:699-713, 1958.
5. Diamond, B., With Malice Aforethought. *Arch. Crim. Psychodynam.*, 2:10, 1957.
6. *Ibid.*, p. 11.
7. *Ibid.*, pp. 17-21.
8. Douglas, W. O., *Law and Psychiatry*. Presented Jan. 1956, W. Alanson White Institute of Psychiatry, Psychoanalysis, and Psychology.
9. English, O. S. & Finch, S. M., *Introduction to Psychiatry*. New York: Norton, 1954.
10. *Ibid.*, p. 183.
11. English, O. S. & Pearson, G. H. J., *Emotional Problems of Living*. New York: Norton, 1955, pp. 420-421.
12. French, J. D., The Reticular Formation. *Sci. Amer.*, 196:54-60, May, 1960.
13. George, F. H., Machines and the Brain. *Science*, 127:1269-1274, 1958.
14. Goldstein, J. & Katz, J., Dangerousness and Mental Illness—Some Observations on the Decision to Release Persons Acquitted by Reasons of Insanity. *Yale Law J.*, 70:225-239, 1960.
15. Goldstein, J. & Katz, J., Abolish the "Insanity Defense"—Why Not? *Yale Law J.*, 72:853-876, 1963.

16. Group for the Advancement of Psychiatry, *Confidentiality and Privileged Communication in the Practice of Psychiatry*. New York: G. A. P., Report #45, 1960.
17. Guttmacher, M. S., The Psychiatrist as an Expert Witness. *U. Chicago Law Rev.*, 22:325-330, 1955.
18. Hall, J., Psychiatry and Criminal Responsibility. *Yale Law J.*, 65:779, 1956.
19. Hall, J., Responsibility and the Law: In Defense of the McNaughton Rules. *Amer. Bar Assn. J.*, 42:918-919, 1956.
20. Hartmann, H., Psychoanalysis and the Concept of Health. *Internat. J. Psychoanal.*, 20:308-321, 1939.
21. Heath, R., Martens, S., Leach, F., Cohen, M. & Fergley, C., Behavioral Changes in Non-psychotic Volunteers Following the Administration of Taraxein, the Substance Obtained from Serum of Schizophrenic Patients. *Amer. J. Psychiat.*, 114:917-920, 1958.
22. Hill, W. P., The Use and Abuse of Cross-examination in Relation to Expert Testimony: The Second Alger Hiss Trial. *Ohio State Law J.*, 15:458-468, 1954.
23. *Ibid.*, p. 461.
24. Jahoda, M., Toward a Social Psychology of Mental Health. In: *Mental Health and Mental Disorder*, Ed. A. Rose. New York: Norton, 1955, pp. 556-577.
25. Klopfer, B., & Kelly, D. M., *The Rorschach Technique*. New York: World Book Co., 1942.
26. Krash, A., The Durham Rule and Judicial Administration of the Insanity Defense in the District of Columbia. *Yale Law J.*, 70:905-952, 1961.
27. Kubie, L. S., The Fundamental Nature of the Distinction Between Normality and Neurosis. *Psychoanal. Quart.*, 22:182-185, 1954.
28. Lewis, A., Health as a Social Concept. *Brit. J. Sociol.*, 4:109, 1953.
29. Marrazzi, A. S., Messengers of the Nervous System. *Sci. Amer.*, 196:87-94, Feb. 1957.
30. Menninger, K. A., *A Manual for Psychiatric Case Study*. New York: Grune & Stratton, 1952.
31. *Ibid.*, pp. 45-50.
32. Menninger, K., Ellenberger, H., Pruyser, P. & Mayman, M., The Unitary Concept of Mental Illness. *Bull. Menninger Clin.*, 22:4-12, 1958.
33. Noyes, A. & Kolb, L., *Modern Clinical Psychiatry*. Philadelphia: W. B. Saunders, 1958.
34. Ostow, M., The Illusory Reduplication of Body Parts in Cerebral Disease. *Psychoanal. Quart.*, 27:98-100, 1958.
35. Overholser, W., *The Psychiatrist and the Law*. New York: Harcourt, Brace, 1953, p. 117.
36. Platt, A. & Diamond, B. L., The Origins of the "Right and Wrong" Test of Criminal Responsibility and Its Subsequent Development in the United States: An Historical Survey. *Calif. Law Rev.*, 54:1227-1260, 1966.
37. Racker, H., Meanings and Uses of the Countertransference. *Psychoanal. Quart.*, 26:354-356, 1957.
38. Roche, P. Q., *The Criminal Mind*. New York: Farrar, Straus & Cudahy, 1958, Chapts. 1 & 2.

39. Saul, L. J., The Psychiatric Diagnostic Interview. *Psychoanal. Quart.*, 26:76-90, 1957.
40. Saul, L. J., *Technic and Practice of Psychoanalysis.* Philadelphia: J. B. Lippincott, 1958, pp. 47-62.
41. Saul, L. J. & Sheppard, E., An Attempt to Quantify Emotional Forces Using Manifest Dreams. *J. Amer. Psychoanal. Assn.*, 4:486-502, 1956.
42. Schmidt, H. O. & Fonda, C. P., The Reliability of Psychiatric Diagnosis: A New Look. *J. Abnorm. & Soc. Psychol.*, 52:262-267, 1956.
43. Scriven, M., Psychoanalysis Under Scientific Scrutiny. *Swarthmore Coll. Bull*, 3:5-9, 1958.
44. Silving, H., Testing the Unconscious in Criminal Cases. *Harvard Law Rev.*, 69:683-705, 1956.
45. Szasz, T., The Problem of Psychiatric Nosology: A Contribution to a Situation Analysis of Psychiatric Operations. *Amer. J. Psychiat.*, 114:405-413, 1957.
46. Szasz, T. S., Psychiatry, Ethics, and the Criminal Law. *Columbia Law Rev.*, 58:183-198, 1958.
47. Traver, R., *Anatomy of a Murder.* New York: St Martin's Press, 1958.
48. Watson, A. S., Durham Plus Five Years: Development of the Law of Criminal Responsibility in the District of Columbia. *Amer. J. Psychiat.*, 117:289-297, 1959.
49. Wechsler, H., The American Law Institute: Some Observations on Its Model Penal Code. In: *Crime and Insanity,* ed. R. W. Nice. New York: Philosophical Library, 1958, pp. 224-228.
50. Weihofen, H., Eliminating the Battle of Experts in Criminal Insanity Cases. *Mich. Law Rev.*, 48:961-982, 1950.
51. Weihofen, H., *Mental Disorder as a Criminal Defense.* Buffalo: Dennis, 1954, pp. 347-349.
52. Weihofen, H., *The Urge to Punish.* New York: Farrar, Straus & Cudahy, 1956, pp. 106-112.
53. Whitehorn, J. C., Stress and Emotional Health. *Amer. J. Psychiat.*, 112:781, 1956.
54. Zilboorg, G., Misconceptions of Legal Insanity. *Amer. J. Orthopsychiat.*, 9:86-94, 1939.
55. Zilboorg, G., *The Psychology of the Criminal Act and Punishment.* New York: Harcourt, Brace, 1954, pp. 122-128.
56. *Ibid.*, pp. 109-113.

Index

Object love, 190, 195
Obscenity, 210
Oedipal conflict, 76, 141, 190, 208, 251
Omnipotence, 73
Orality, 141, 142
Orgasm, 245, 248, 272
Overdetermination, 71

Pain-pleasure principle, 69, 77, 94
Paranoia, 122, 180
Parapraxes, 90
Parsons, T., 5, 11, 13, 18
Paulsen, M., 256
Pavlov, I., 71, 142
Pearson, G. H. J., 296
"Peeping Tom," 249, see also Voyeurism
Penfield, W., 62
Peptic ulcer, 81
Perception, 61, 145, 170, 178
Persecution, 122
Personality development, 139
Perversions, 158, 210, 272
Petty, M., 200
Phobia, 113
  school, 225
Pimp, 211
Pinel, P., 42
Pornography, 210, 246
Preconscious, 91
Prediction, 161, 301
Premeditation, 103
Privacy, see Confidentiality
Privileged communication, 308
Probation, 87
Professionalism, nature of, 11, 18, 20, 308
Projection, 4, 95, 99, 120, 174
Projective testing, 39
Promiscuity, 201, 211, 244
Prostitution, 201, 211, 244
Psychiatric theory, validity of, 56, 66, 300
Psychiatry, definition of, 36
Psychiatrist, training of, 36
Psychoanalysis
  definition of, 37
  history of, 45
Psychodynamics, definition of, 38, 295

Psychology, definition of, 38
Psychophysiologic disease, 81, 123, 131, 280
Psychosis, 122, 131, 172, 210, 301, 306
Psychosomatic illness, see Psychophysiologic disease
Psychotherapy, process of, 8, 48, 132, 231, 286, 302
Puberty, see Adolescence
Punishment, 80, 126
Putnam, J. J., 49

Rado, S., 38
Rank, O., 142
Rape, 201
Rationalization, 86, 128
Reaction formation, 125, 210, 270
Reality principle, 69, 78
Reality testing, 64, 75, 93, 120, 173, 232
Reconciliation, see Marriage counseling
Redl, F., 61, 209
Reflex, 143
Regression, 127, 272, 282
Rehabilitation, 67, 87, 244, 277
Reich, W., 60, 229
Reik, T., 306
Religious concepts, 84, 195
Repetition-compulsion, 71, 101
Repression, 94, 116, 118, 170, 210, 226
Responsibility, 85, 178, 297
  diminished, 177
Retribution, 67, 87, 119, 122, 174, 308
Reynolds, Q., 186
Ribble, M., 140
Robbery, 186
Role diffusion, 258
"Rooming in," 151
Russell, B., 38

Sacher-Masoch, L., 171
Sadism, 172, 175, 180
Satyriasis, 210
Saul, L. J., 38, 195, 248, 307
Scheier, I., 301
Schizophrenia, 157, 297, 309